# THE NATURAL HISTORY
# OF NORTH-CAROLINA

*SERIES IN AMERICAN STUDIES*

*Editor-in-Chief:* Joseph J. Kwiat

PROGRAM IN AMERICAN STUDIES

UNIVERSITY OF MINNESOTA

# THE NATURAL HISTORY
# OF NORTH-CAROLINA

### By

## JOHN BRICKELL

With a New Introduction by
### CAROL URNESS
ASSISTANT CURATOR
JAMES FORD BELL LIBRARY
UNIVERSITY OF MINNESOTA

## Johnson Reprint Corporation

New York and London

1969

Library of Congress Catalog Card Number: 70-79654

Printed in the U. S. A.

# INTRODUCTION

Travelers can hardly be blamed for emphasizing the exciting
and the wonderful in reporting their journeys. This author is no
different. And his combination of imaginative and factual reporting
on the Carolina colony as he saw it makes interesting reading.
Brickell asserts that he often watched butterflies chasing humming-
birds away from flowers; that he met a planter who was cured of a
serious disease by drinking an Indian herbal potion and then wrapping a rattlesnake (fortunately defanged) around his waist for a
night. Perhaps. On the other hand he presents an observant and
impartial description of the Carolina colony and its development.
Here, then, is a curious mixture of folklore and truth, presented
in a book which has always been rare and controversial.

Brickell devotes the first section of his work, over fifty pages, to
a general description of North Carolina. Included in this section are
comments on the geography, history, climate, and crops of the
colony. Freedom of religion and good government in the colony
are stressed, and the author notes that, "There are abundance of
Attorneys in this Province . . . yet all Law-Suits are quickly decided
in Carolina, to prevent the Planters ruining each other. . . ." Much
detailed information of value to prospective colonists is contained
here. The daily life, amusements, houses and furniture, clothes,
food and liquor, languages, diseases, and livestock of the colonists
are described. The writer explains the currency, and notes the sad
addiction of many of the colonists to gambling. Imports and ex-
ports of the colony are listed, and the author cites those goods
which the colonist should bring with him from Europe. "There is
a scarcity of sufficient Hands to cultivate this noble and fertile
Soil," writes Brickell, and promises that a successful living is
assured to those who are willing to work.

From the description of the colony and its prospects Brickell
turns his attention to the animals and plants that live there. This
second section of his book, containing some two hundred pages, is
divided into four sections which list the "vegetables," "beasts,"
birds, and fish of North Carolina. Commentary on these plants and

animals usually suggests the medical use to which they can be put. He notes, for example, that lice are "eaten by Rusticks for the Jaundice, and Consumption. . . ." and that the fat of carp "cures diseases of the Nerves." The inclusion of these many cures adds a historical sidelight, occasionally horrifying to be sure, on the state of medicine in Brickell's day. In spite of much that is fantasy, this section of Brickell's work has been recognized as a valuable contribution to the history of natural history in this country.

Following this nature section is a second section of general information on the colony. In these twenty-five pages the author reiterates his arguments that Carolina is an outstanding place for new colonists. Added to this, and not found in the first section, is a description of slavery in the colony. The life, training, and punishments of slaves are described, with the author's observation that the planters "prevent all Opportunities they might lay hold of to make themselves formidable."

The final section of the book, more than one hundred and twenty-five pages, is given to an account of the Indians of North Carolina. Their languages, appearance, clothing, homes, and skill in hunting are all described, together with their money, manner of trade, and wars. Brickell notes the painting of their faces, when "you may be sure they are about some mischief or other." Indian feasts and dancing are also depicted. Much as he was intrigued by the way the Indians lived, the writer seems even more impressed by their attitudes and values. He reports that "They are for the most part very gentle, loving and faithful, void of Guile or Treachery (except they are highly injured) and live after the manner of the Golden Age. . . ." Their disregard for worldly possessions surprises him, and he approves of their evaluation of their neighbors on what they could do rather than on what they owned. That the Indian women never scolded was refreshing, and it appeared to him that Indian men were masters of their tempers and passions. The Indian attitude toward marriage was strange, but almost seems to bring the author's envy, for "they do not bind themselves for as long time as they shall live, but for as long only as they shall agree together and love each other." The Indians never interrupt when another is speaking, notes Brickell, and they are free from fears of the night. They are not free of all superstitions, writes Brickell, for they will not kill snakes, believing that the relatives of that snake would revenge themselves on the killer's family and friends. Concluding this section is a description of Indian doctors and medicines, and Indian burial ceremonies.

No consideration of this book can avoid the fact that because of it John Brickell is charged with the most serious of literary sins. The catalog card for this book, as supplied by the Library of Congress, includes a note declaring it "An almost verbal transcript of Lawson's History of Carolina." Reference is then made to an article in the *North American Review*, volume XXIII for 1826, pages 288–289. In this article Jared Sparks writes that ". . . as a whole, a more daring piece of plagiarism was never executed." Not all of Brickell's commentators have been so harsh. A milder, though scarcely less damning notice is given in the historical introduction to *Birds of North Carolina* (Raleigh, 1942) by T. G. Pearson, C.S. and H. H. Brimley. Brickell's list of birds is considered by these authors, who report that, "the text in many instances strongly suggests the idea that he frequently bordered on plagiarism." Elsa Allen writes of this section of Brickell's book in her *History of American Ornithology before Audubon* (Trans. of the American Philosophical Society, n.s. volume 41, part 3, 1951, p. 463) in a different tone. "For some reason he is supposed to have based his descriptions, even to the point of plagiarism, upon John Lawson's work of 1709," she states, and then gives her opinion that "Brickell apparently used Lawson as a suggestive guide. . . ." Before further consideration of this charge of plagiarism, which is indeed a grave one, it will be useful to note something of Brickell's life and experiences in North Carolina, which in many ways parallel those of John Lawson.

Very little (not even the date or place of his birth) is known of John Brickell's life before his arrival in North Carolina. Surely he must have been Irish, for in speaking of American plants and animals he compares them with those of Ireland. Then too, he later returned to Ireland, where this book was published. John Brickell came to Carolina with his brother, the Reverend Matthias Brickell, probably under the sponsorship of Governor Burrington. He was educated as a doctor, and for a number of years practiced medicine in Edenton, North Carolina. While there, he was selected as a member of an expedition sent in 1730–31 to the western part of Carolina and probably into Tennessee, to promote friendly relations with the Cherokee Indians. Some of his experiences of this journey are contained in this book, which appeared in reprints of 1739 and 1743 as well as the first edition of 1737. Though the writer does admit some of the disadvantages of North Carolina it seems that his book was, in part at least, meant to be a promotion piece for the colony. Brickell's only other book was the *Catalogue of American Trees and Plants which will bear the Climate of England*, published in London, 1739.

The very similar experiences of John Lawson in Carolina might well have encouraged Brickell to use Lawson's book as a "guide" in writing his own account of his travels. John Lawson went to Carolina in 1700, apparently for the sake of adventure. He was obviously well educated, perhaps with some training in science. Lawson traveled extensively while in Carolina, and he also was involved with Indian tribes. After eight years he left Carolina and returned to his native England. The first separate publication of Lawson's book was dated 1709 in London and was titled *A New Voyage to Carolina*. The same account was included in John Stevens' *A New Collection of Voyages and Travels* in editions of 1708–11 and 1711. A German translation of Lawson's book appeared in Hamburg dated 1712. Later English editions of it, under the title *The History of Carolina*, were issued in 1714 and 1718.

Quite possibly John Lawson's book describing his experiences in Carolina was scarce soon after its publication. Its worth, however, was recognized and it seems that with three English editions, a German translation, and its inclusion in a collection of voyages it could not have been entirely unknown to many readers. John Brickell's *The Natural History of North Carolina* was published less than twenty years after the last English edition of Lawson's book. Certainly Brickell must have known that persons interested in his account of Carolina might well be familiar with the Lawson book. That Brickell did not expect to gain financially from his work is assumed because he published it himself and includes a list of more than 200 subscribers to the book. In his preface Brickell states that his aim is to present "a compendious Collection, of most things yet known in that part of the world." Writers of his time were not footnote conscious, and Brickell was no exception. That he did not acknowledge his debt to Lawson is not praiseworthy, but the fact remains that the Brickell book has real merit as an early commentary on Carolina — even when, and sometimes even because, the information added by Brickell is incorrect.

What did Brickell take from Lawson? Nothing from the first part of Lawson's book which describes his travels. The second part of Lawson's account, which is the general description of the geography and climate of Carolina, is utilized as the beginning of Brickell's narrative, and the sentences and paragraphs present a painful similarity. Brickell has taken lists of plants and animals from Lawson, has added his own commentary, and for almost all of them suggests medical uses. In the section describing Indians, Brickell has stolen from Lawson but has added much that is his own. The Brickell book is almost twice as long as that of Lawson.

The University of North Carolina Press has recently published a reprint of John Lawson's *A New Voyage to Carolina*, edited by Hugh Talmadge Lefler. It is a pleasure to have John Brickell's controversial book again available to the public here.

*Carol Urness*

# BIBLIOGRAPHY

Brickell, John. *The Natural History of North Carolina.* Dublin, Printed by James Carson, for the Author, 1737. Later editions, 1739 and 1743.

Lawson, John. *History of North Carolina.* London, Printed for W. Taylor and F. Baker, 1714.

Allen, Elsa Guerdrum. *The History of American Ornithology before Audubon,* in *Transactions of the American Philosophical Society,* n.s. vol. 41, part 3. Philadelphia, 1951. Pp. 461–464.

Grimes, J. Bryan. Note in the reprint of Brickell's *Natural History of North Carolina.* Raleigh, 1911. 3 pp.

Harriss, Frances Latham, ed. Biography of John Lawson in reprint of Lawson's *History of North Carolina.* Richmond, 1951. Pp. xii–xvii.

*National Cyclopaedia of American Biography.* New York, 1893–1944. Vol. 7, p. 278. John Brickell.

*North American Review,* XXIII (n.s. XIV; 1826), 288–289.

Pearson, Thomas G., Clement S. and Herbert H. Brimley. *Birds of North Carolina.* Raleigh, 1942. Pp. xxi–xxiv.

Smallwood, William M., and Mabel C. Smallwood. *Natural History and the American Mind.* New York, 1941. Pp. 23–24.

Weeks, Stephen B. *Libraries and Literature in North Carolina in the Eighteenth Century,* in *Annual Report of the American Historical Association for 1895.* Washington, 1896. Pp. 224–235.

# NOTE.

THE NATURAL HISTORY OF NORTH CAROLINA, written by John Brickell, a physician who lived and practiced medicine in Edenton, N. C., about 1731, is the most interesting of the early histories of the State. Copies of this book are now very rare and difficult to obtain. Within the past few months a student of the State's history considered himself fortunate in securing one from abroad, at a cost of more than $40.

As the growing interest in the State's history in the past few years makes it desirable to place this book within the reach of readers, the trustees of the State Library have authorized its republication.

Dr. Brickell's history is the best description we have of the natural, social, and economic conditions in the Colony of North Carolina, but its merits have been obscured and its value largely depreciated by careless and unjust reviewers.

Jared Sparks and others charged him with plagiarizing Lawson. Of this, Dr. Stephen B. Weeks says:

"These statements are only partially correct, and do grave injustice to Brickell. He acknowledges in his preface that his work is 'a compendious collection of most things yet known in that part of the world.' But it is a good deal more than a mere slavish reprint of Lawson. It is further increased almost one-half in bulk. The reprint of Lawson made in 1860 contains 390 pages, with about 270 words to the page. Of this space, 106 pages are taken up with his 'Journal of a Thousand Miles Travel.' This part is not used by Brickell. The edition of his work published in 1737 contains 408 pages, about 340 words to the page.

"Brickell took the book of Lawson, reworked it in his own fashion, extended or curtailed, and brought it to his time. The effect of his professional training is seen everywhere,

# Note.

for there is hardly a description of a plant or animal which does not have some medical use attached to it. His work is fuller, more systematic, and seems more like that of a student; Lawson's work seems more like that of a traveler and observer. There is, besides, much more relating to the social condition of the Colony in Brickell, who has a section on 'The religion, houses, raiment, diet, liquors, firing, diversions, commodities, languages, diseases, curiosities, cattle, etc.,' while Lawson sticks close to the natural, economic, and Indian history of the Province."

Of Dr. Brickell little is known. Major John W. Moore says that Dr. John Brickell, "the naturalist, physician, and historian," and his brother, the Rev. Matthias Brickell, came with Governor Burrington to Carolina. Dr. Brickell remained at Edenton, while his brother became the first rector of St. Johns in Bertie County, "which for years was the only house of worship west of the Chowan River."[1]

Dr. Brickell appears as a member of the grand jury of the whole Province, in 1731, and signed a congratulatory address[2] to the King upon the purchase of the Colony by the Crown from the Lords Proprietors.

While in North Carolina, Dr. Brickell probably rendered the Colony some service in a friendly mission to the Cherokee Indians, and penetrated far into the territory now included in the State of Tennessee. His description of this journey is most interesting, and though overdrawn, is a distinct contribution to our history of the habits of the North Carolina Indians. We have no record of Dr. Brickell's career after he left North Carolina.

The Rev. Matthias Brickell is said to have been a man of power and influence in the Colony, and his son, Col. Matthias Brickell, was a soldier in the Revolution.

---

[1] Moore's History of N. C., Vol. I, page 49.
[2] Col. Rec., Vol. III, pp. 134–135.

## Note.

Several of the family have been members of the General Assembly, and though the name is now extinct, numerous descendants still live in the State.

In reprinting Brickell's Natural History of North Carolina, the original text is followed as closely as possible. The original editions do not contain an index, but a copy in the possession of the writer has been carefully indexed in such a painstaking, accurate hand, as to appear almost like copperplate, and that index is added to this reprint.

J. Bryan Grimes.

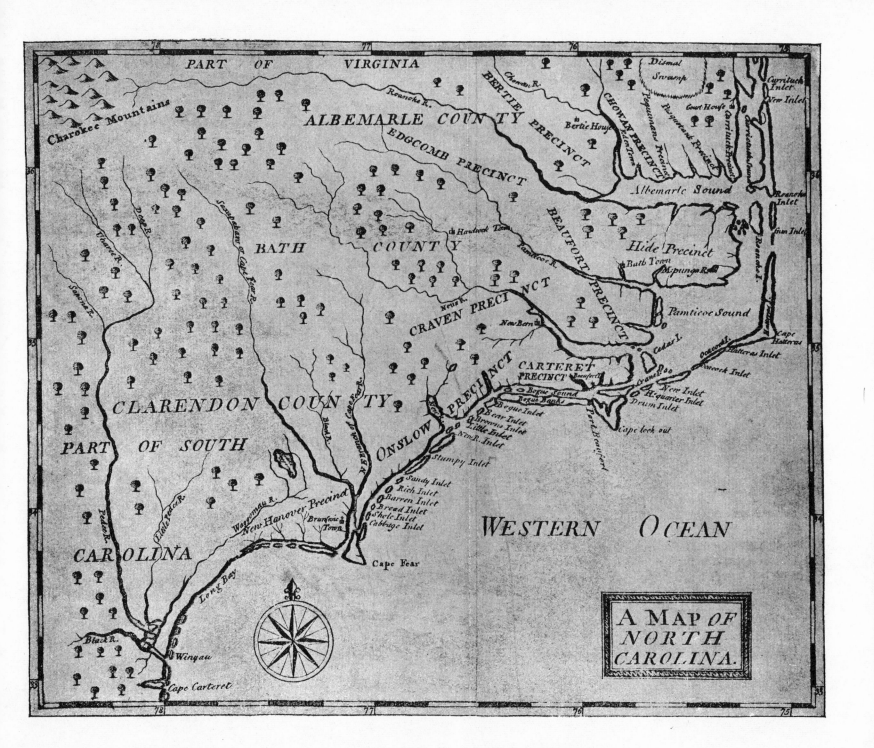

# The NATURAL

# HISTORY

## OF

## *North - Carolina.*

### WITH AN

# ACCOUNT

## OF THE

Trade, Manners, and Customs of the
CHRISTIAN and INDIAN Inhabitants. Il-
lustrated with *Copper - Plates*, whereon are
curiously Engraved the *Map* of the Country,
several strange *Beasts, Birds, Fishes, Snakes,
Insects, Trees,* and *Plants,* &c.

## *By* JOHN BRICKELL, M. D.

*Nostra nos in urbe peregrinamur.*     CIC.

### *DUBLIN:*

Printed by JAMES CARSON, in *Coghill's-Court, Dame-*
*street,* opposite to the *Castle-Market.* For the AUTHOR,
1737.

# THE PREFACE.

 *T will not be to my purpose to enquire whether America was known to the Antients, there being various Opinions about it, yet with more Curiosity than certainty, whence this* New World *was Peopled; some assigning that the* Hesperides (*so called from* HESPERUS *King of* Spain) *and the Continent of* America *were Peopled by the* Spaniards. *Others affirm that the* Americans *are the Race of* Jews *carried into captivity by* Salamanazer *and placed in Countrys till then not Inhabited, after a progress of 18 Months. Many believe they were People carried by Storm, being* Chinesses *sailing on the* Pacifick South Sea, *or other* Northern People *(allowing the possibility of each Opinion)*

*I will*

*I will not pretend to take upon me to decide the Controversy, being altogether a stranger to the certainty of the Fact.*

*The Writings of many Learned Men may be seen on this Head, who after having search'd all the Records of Antiquity, shew much Erudiction, but nothing of certainty, concerning the Antient Affairs of* America. *I know the Memory of a Deluge is preserved amongst these People, but whether it is to be understood of the universal Flood, or the Inundation of some particular Provinces, I leave it to others to discourse upon, for I am willing to lay aside all manner of Conjectures of this Nature, having enough of Truth to treat of.*

*The several Climates of the World have influenced the People with Natures very different from each other, and even their different Speeches bear some proportion of Analogie with their Natures, as is to be seen amongst the* Whites, Indians, *and* Blacks, *that are to be met with in this part of the World.*

*But waveing these Discourses, we here present the World with a* Natural-History *of* North-Carolina, *it being a compendious Collection, of most things yet known in that part of the World; wherein I have laid down every thing with Impartiality and Truth, in the most plain and easie Terms, which indeed is the Duty of every Writer, and preferable to a more eloquent Stile, accompanied with many Falsities.*

*I have therefore endeavour'd in the following Sheets to give as faithful and exact Account of* Carolina, *as discoveries*

*yet*

*yet made will Authorize, and if any take offence at what is said about the* Indians *and their wanton and lascivious manner of living, I hope they will Judge of every Passage with due deference to good Authority of the most knowing and substantial Planters in those Parts. And consider that the nature of the Work required my being somewhat particular, in order to shew the good and bad Qualities of these poor Creatures, who at present have no light or benefit of the* Gospel.

*And had we been as careful as the* Spaniards *and* French, *in sending over proper* Missionaries *to Instruct these miserable People, we shou'd never have had occasion to give this Relation of them. Besides if these Methods had been put in practice, we undoubtedly had been better informed and acquainted with the many hidden Secrets in this part of the World, which these People are well aquainted with, and which they never will make known to us till they are Instructed in the* Christian *Faith, and have intirely abolished the many Idolatrous Customs and Practices still prevailing amongst them.*

*I have viewed not only most part of the Lands Inhabited by the* Christians, *but likewise vast spacious Tracts lying between them and the Mountains, from whence our noblest Rivers have their rise, running for several hundreds of Miles towards the Ocean, while they water and adorn as pleasant and fertil a Country as any in* Europe, *the greatest part whereof is only inhabited by* Savage Indians, *who covet a*

Christian

Christian *Neighbourhood for the advantage of Trade. But not to amuse the Reader any longer with Encomiums on* Carolina, *I refer them to my Description of that Country, and it's Inhabitants, which they will find in the following* Natural History, *in which I have been very exact; and for Methods sake, have ranged each Species of* Animals, Vegetables, *etc. under distinct and proper Heads.*

*A Collection of the Natural Curiosities of this spacious part of the World, will, I hope, not only give Satisfaction and Pleasure to each Reader, but likewise Profit, to all that are inclined to live in those Parts.*

*If these my Endeavours meet with this good success, I am thoroughly satisfied, having nothing more at Heart than to be in any Degree serviseable to the Publick; this being the principal Motive that induced me to undertake any Work of this Nature, (the Task being not only* Laborious *but* Difficult) *and not out of any Praise I expected from it.*

*To conclude, Whatever Defects may be found in this Undertaking, we hope in time they will be supplied by the Labours and Industry of such as shall come after; and this we are made to expect chiefly from those of our own Nation; and that their laudable Attempts may meet with just Encouragement, shall be my constant Wish and Desire.*

# SUBSCRIBERS.

## A.

THE Honourable Capt. Richard Allen.
Stephen Allen, M. D.
Mr. Pat. Archbold.
Mr. John Archbold.
Mr. Richard Armstrong.

## B.

EDward Bond, *Esq;*
Worsopp Bush, *Esq;*
Edmond Barry, M. D.
Mr. Michael Barry, Attorney.
Mr. Peter Brandon.
Mr. James Brickell.
Mr. George Brickell.
Mr. William Brickell.
Mr. Robert Bijar.
Mr. Jos. Burry, Attorney.
Mr. Thomas Brennan.
Mr. Stearne Brock, Bookseller.

Mr. Alexander Brown.
Mr. David Bush, of *Philadelphia, Merchant.*
Mr. Henry Barton, *Apothecary;*
Mr. John Brenan,
Mr. Richard Baxter.
Mr. Benjamin Brickenden.
Mr. Martin Bourke.
Mr. Arthur Brerton.
Mr. Benjamin Bardon, *Apothecary.*

## C.

THE Honourable Thomas Coote, *Esq;*
The Revd. Charles Carthy, A. M.
William Clements, A. M. F. T. C. D.
Edmond Castello, *Esq;*
John Curry. M. D.
Mr. John Clinch.
Mr. Patrick Connor.
Mr. James Connor.
Mr. Patrick Cassidy, Attorney.
Mr. Call. McCarty.
Mr. Patrick Carrick.
Mr. John Carson, of *Rathmullin.*
Mr. Nathanial Carson, of *Killough.*
Mr. William Connor.
Mr. Samuel Card.
Mr. William Carlile.
Mr. John Common.
Mr. Edmond Cumerford.
Mr. Samuel Cleapem, Chirurgion.
Mr. Robert Calderwood.
Mr. Thomas Coote.

## D.

THE Revd. Patrick Delany, D. D.
  Henry Davis, *Esq;*
Chap. Dawson, *Esq;*
Mr. Walter Davey.
Sam Davey.
Joseph Davey, *Esq;*
Mr. Moses Darling.
Mr. James Dove.
Mr. Oliver Delahoide.
Mr. Henry Delamain.
Mr. James Doyle.
Mr. James Dobbin.
Mrs. Judith Doran.
Mr. George Dogherty.
Mr. Walter Durham.
Mr. William Dane.

## E.

MR. Valentine Egan.
  Mr. James English.
Mr. William Edwards, Apothecary.
Mr. James Easdell, Saddler.

## F.

SIR William Fowns, Bart.
  Lewis Falliott, *Esq;*
John Fitch, *Esq;*
John Fergus, M. D.
Captain Samuel Farra.
Captain Matthew Fitzgerald.
Mr. Charles Franck.

Mr. William Floyd.
Mr. Peter Fitch.
Mr. Richard Fitzsimons.
Mr. Robert Finlay.
Mr. Francis Fitzgerald.

### G.

**M**R. James Glasco.
    Miss Sophia Gordon.
Mr. Thomas Gilbert, Architect.
Mr. Andrew Gore, Jun.
Mr. Matthias Gower.

### H.

**M**R. Obadiah Hill.
    Mr. Samuel Hill.
Mr. Thomas Hall.
Mr. Jos. Harper, Chirurgion.
Mr. Richard Harford.
Mr. William Hamilton.
Mr. John Hill.
Mr. William Heatly, *Bookseller.*
Mr. Phil. Hughes, A. B. T. C.
Mr. Anthony Hay.
Mr. Nicholas Hadfer, Chirurgion.
Mr. John Hamilton.
Mr. Hans Hamilton.
Mr. James Hamilton.
Mr. Kane O'Hara.
Mr. Thomas Holt, Attorney.
Mr. Thomas Hartwell.
Mr. Richard Harney.
Mr. John Hitman.

### I.

MR. William Jackson.
 Mr. John Johnston.
Mr. William Johnson.
Mr. Samuel Johnson.

### K.

THE Rt. Revd. Dr. Charles Cobbe, Bishop of Kildare.
 Mr. William Keating, Chirurgion.
Mr. Charles Kelly.
Mr. Martin Killikelly.
Mr. Nathaniel McKinlie.
Mr. Charles Kelly.
Mr. Gilbert Kelly.
Mr. Nich. King.
Mr. James Keating.

### L.

THE Revd. Edward Ledwich, A. M.
 Mr. Joseph Lamb.
Mr. Richard Lincoln.
Mr. Thomas Lynch.
Mr. William Lamb.
Mr. James Lee.
Mr. William Leary.
Mr. Edward Lynch.
Mr. Patrick Leary.

### M.

PATRICK Mitchell, *Esq;*
 Topham Mitchell, *Esq;*
Thomas Morse, *Esq;*
The Revd. John Maxwell, A. M.

The Revd. John Magill, A. M.
The Revd. John Moore, A. M.
Mr. Sam Monsell.
Mr. Patrick Murray.
Mr. Thomas Murphy.
Mr. Matthews, Attorney.
Mr. Bernard Messink.

### N.

JOSEPH Nelson, A. M.
    Mr. William Neale.
Mr. Thomas Noble.

### P.

COLONEL Thomas Pollocxsen.
    Gervas Parker, *Esq;*
Captain John Petry.
Mr. Samuel Parks, Chirurgion.
Mr. Matthew Pendergast.
Mr. Ur. Pepys.
Mr. Richard Pateson.
Mr. George Parker.
Mr. Robert Patten.
Coleman Pierson, *Esq;*
Mr. Abraham Panel, Apothecary.
Mr. William Philips.

### Q.

MR. Jeremiah Quill.
    Mr. John Quin.
Mr. Francis Quire.

### R.

SIR John Rowdon, *Bart.*
   Francis Richardson, *Esq;*
Mr. John Stanton, Chirurgion.
Mr. Richard Richardson.
Mr. Edward Richardson.
Mr. Thomas Reading.
Mr. Garret Ronan.
Mr. Christopher Russel, Chirurgion.
Mrs. Dorothea Rowdon.
Mr. Matthias Reily, Attorney.
Mr. James Reily.

### S.

JOHN Smith, Esq;
   Mr. Frank Smith, T, C. D.
Mr. Matthew Slater.
Mr. Stephen Stretch.
Mr. John Shaw.
Mr. Hugh Shaw, Apothecary.
Mr. Robert Sisson.
Mr. Charles Seaton.
Mr. James Simon, Merchant.
Mr. Samuel Smith.
Mr. Matthew Swiny, Attorney.
Mr. John Smith.
Mr. Edward Smith, Chirurgion.
Mr. Edwards Sands.
Mr. Hugh Stafford.
Mr. Philip Swettenham.
Mr. Elias Shee.
Mr. Randal Stretch.

## T.

RICHARD Talbot, *Esq;*
    John Taaffe, M. D.
Miss Margaret Tenison.
Mr. Joseph Taylor.
Mr. John Thornton.
Mr. Denis Tinan.
Mr. Thomas Tallon.
Mr. James Todderick.
Mr. Thomas Todderick.
Mr. James Thompson.
Mr. Matthew Templeton.
Mr. Daniel Tracy.
Mr. William Terrill.

## U.

Mr. Thomas Vincent.

## W.

CHAMBERLEN Walker, M. D.
    Mr. Samuel White.
Mr. Thomas Wren.
Mr. Thomas Wilkinson of Kilkenny.
Mr. Isaac Wills.
Mr. Thomas Wetherlt.
Mr. Laurence Whyte.
Mr. James Wall.
Mr. Robert Whitehall.
Mr. Thomas Woods.
Mr. John Warham.
Mr. Cornelius Wunne.
Mr. Jacob West.
Mr. Michael Waldron.

# THE
# NATURAL HISTORY
### OF
# NORTH CAROLINA.

 HE Province of *North Carolina* is separated from *Virginia* by a due West Line from *Currituck* Inlet, in 36 Degrees and 30 Minutes of *Northern* Latitude, extending Indefinitely Westward, and from thence to the Southward, including *South Carolina,* as far as 29 Degrees North.

The Eastern Parts of this Country are hemmed in with a great number of Islands and Sand Banks, which defend it from the violence of the *Atlantick* Ocean; by which Barrier, a vast Sound is formed, and inclosed, which fronts the Mouths of the most pleasant and navigable Rivers, in this spacious and delightful Country. There are vast numbers of Creeks on the sides of these Rivers, and most of them Navigable for small Crofts, and abundance for Vessels of larger Burthen.

A                                                    Between

Between these Islands and Sand Banks, are Inlets of several depths of Water, some admitting only of Sloops, Scooners, Brigantines, and Vessels of small Burthen, and such are *Currituck* Inlet, *New* Inlet, *Roanoke, Gun* Inlet, *Hatteras, New* Inlet, *Huntington-quarter* Inlet, *Drum* Inlet, *Bogue* Inlet, *Bear* Inlet, *Brown's* Inlet, *Little* Inlet, *New River* Inlet, *Stumpy* Inlet, *Sandy* Inlet, *Rich* Inlet, *Barren* Inlet, *Broad* Inlet, *Shole* Inlet, *Cabbage* Inlet, *Wachestau* Inlet, *Wahacau* Inlet, and *North* Inlet: many of these being only Navigable for Periaugers and small Crofts, by reason of their many Shoals which are continually shifting by the violence of Storms, and particularly, North East Winds, to which they are mostly exposed. Others are large and deep, and receive Ships of Burthen, such are *Ocacok, Beaufort,* or *Topsail* Inlet, and *Cape Fear.*

I will here give an Account of the most considerable Inlets and Havens of this Country. And first, *Currituck* Inlet, it being the Northermost of this Province, it lyes in the Latitude of 36 Degrees and 30 Minutes, and the Course over it is S. W. by W. having not above seven or eight Foot Water on the Barr, though a good Harbour when you are over, where you may ride safe and deep enough. But this part of the Sound is so full of Shoals, continually shifting, and Oyster Banks, as not to suffer any thing except Periaugers to Trade through it to Vessels that ride near the Inlet, it not being Navigable or safe for any Croft that draws above four or five Foot at most, to pass through it, which renders it very incommodious for Trade.

*Roanoke* Inlet, lyes in the Latitude of 35 Degrees and 50 Minutes, and has about ten Foot and a half Water upon the Barr; the Course over it is almost West, which brings you through the best of the Channel. This Barr, as well

*Currituck*

*Currituck,* often shifts by the violence of the N. E. Storms; both these Inlets lying exposed to the said Winds. Notwithstanding a considerable Trade is carried on by the Assistance of Pilots, this part of the Country being very Fertile, and the Planters Rich.

*Hatteras* Inlet lyes in the Latitude of 35 Degrees and 20 Minutes, it lyes to the Westward of the Cape, round which is an excellent Harbour, when the Wind blows hard a N. or N. E. If you keep a small League from the Cape Point, you will have three, four, or five Fathom Water, the outermost Shoals lying about seven or eight Leagues from the Shoar. As you come into the Inlet, keep close to the South Breakers, till you are over, whereon you may have two Fathom at low Water. You may come to an Anchor at two Fathom and a half; when you are over, then steer close aboard the North Shoar, where is four Fathom close to a Point of Marsh; then steer up the Sound a long League, till you bring the North Cape of the Inlet to S. S. E. half E. then steer W. N. W. the last Point of the Bluff Land at *Hutteras,* bearing E. N. E. the Southermost large *Hamock,* towards *Ocacock,* bearing S. S. W. half S. then you are in the Sound, over the Barr of Sand, whereon is but six Foot Water, then your Course to *Pamticoe* is almost West.

It flows on these three Barrs S. E. by E. ¾ E. about Eight of the Clock, unless there is a very hard Gale of Wind at N. E. which will make it flow two Hours longer, but as soon as the Winds are down, the Tides will have their natural Course. A hard Gale at N. N. W. will make the Waters Ebb sometimes 24 Hours, but still the Tides will Ebb and Flow, though not seen by the turning thereof, but may be observ'd by the rising of the Waters, and falling of the same at the Shoars.

*Ocacock* Inlet lyes in the Latitude of 35 Degrees 8 Minutes. It is one of the best Inlets in this Country, having thirteen Foot at low Water upon the Barr. There are two Channels, One is but narrow, and lyes close aboard the South Cape; the Other in the middle, *viz.* Between the middle Ground and the South Shoar, and is above half a Mile wide. The Barr itself is but half a Cables length over; then you are in 7 or 8 Fathom Water, and an excellent good Harbour. The Course into the Sound is N. N. W. at High Water, and Neip Tides here is 18 Foot Water. It lies S. W. from *Hatteras* Inlet.

*Port Beaufort,* or *Topsail* Inlet, lyes in the latitude 34 Degrees and 44 Minutes, and is above two Leagues to the Westward of Cape *Look-out,* where you have a fair Channel over the Barr, and two Fathom Water thereon, and a good Harbour, in five or six Fathom, to come to an Anchor. Your Course over this Barr is almost N. W.

*Cape Fear* Inlet lyes in the Latitude of 33 Degrees 53 Minutes; it is the best in all *North Carolina,* where you have 7 Fathom Water at the Barr. You have likewise a fine Harbour, and can come with safety to an Anchor 5 or 6 Leagues up the River.

And notwithstanding it is so commodious for Navigation, yet few or no Planters settled here till within these few Years, but now in all Appearance, it seems to be the most rising Part of all this Province; there being now many Substantial Planters settled there, and are become very Rich within the space of Nine or Ten Years, it being little frequented or inhabited before that Time, *viz.* in the Year 1723.

Most of the other Inlets that I have already mentioned, are so very incommodious for Trade, that they are little fre-

quented

quented or resorted to, except it be by small Crofts and Peri-augers. I shall therefore omit giving any further Account of them.

*North Carolina* has some considerable Promontories or Capes in it: That Cape called *Hatteras,* is the most Northern of this Province, it lyes in the Latitude of 35 Degrees and 20 Minutes, Longitude 75. *Cape Look-out,* is the largest in this Province, extending a great way into the Main Ocean, and is about two Leagues to the Northward or Mouth of *Top-sail* Inlet, in the Latitude of 34 Degrees and 46 Minutes, Longitude 75, 50. *Cape Fear* lyes at the Mouth of the Inlet in the Latitude of 33 Degrees and 53 Minutes, Longitude 77, 20. *Cape Carterett* is part of *South Carolina,* and is the Northermost Promontorie in that Province, lying to the Southward of *Santee* River in Latitude 32 of Degrees, and 50 Minutes, Longitude 77, 55. Within these Capes is a very large Sound, with abundance of Islands of several Sizes, abounding with various kinds of Timber Trees, many whereof are fine Cedar, with variety of Wild Beasts, especially Deer, and great Quantities of Birds, according to the Seasons of the Year, but there are scarce any of them inhabited by Christian Planters at present.

I shall in the next Place proceed to give an Account of the Rivers that are to be met with in this Province; many whereof are very considerable and large, running for several hundred Miles, and taking their Rise for the most part in or near the Mountains, others are but small in comparison with the former, as may be seen by the Map.

I shall therefore begin with the most Northerly, and so proceed to the most Southerly. And first, *Black-Water,* or *North River,* which falls into *Currituck* Sound, *North River, Pas-*
quotanck

*quotanck River, Little River, Pequimans River,* and *Yaupin River,* all these Water and Adorn the Southern Parts of Virginia, and Northern Parts of this Province, which are very Fertile. Most of these Rivers being Navigable for Sloops, Brigantines, and other Vessels of Burthen.

*Chowan* River likewise Waters the North Parts of this Province, and part of *Virginia,* and is very considerable in these Parts; the Inhabitants on its Banks are very Rich by its Fertility, and being so commodious for Trade, it is the fifth large and considerable River in this Province; it falls into *Albemarle* Sound.

*Keja* River is likewise to the Northward of this Province, but is not very Considerable.

*Roanoke* River is the largest in this Province, taking its noble Rise from the *Charokee* or *Appelapean* Mountains, and Watering several Parts of *Virginia,* as it crosses the due West Line that separates it from *Virginia,* it is very commodious for Trade, being Navigable for a vast way up the Country, most of the former Rivers empty themselves into this *Albemarle* or *Currituck* Sound.

*Maca Punga* River, is a North Branch of *Pamticoe* River, and admits of Sloops, Brigantines, and other Vessels of Burthen.

*Pamticoe* River is the fourth considerable River in these Parts, taking its Rise near or from the Mountains, and falls into *Pamticoe* Sound, with a very large Mouth, several Miles in Breadth, and is not inferior to any of the other large Rivers, for the goodness of its Navigation, as is manifest by the many Rich Inhabitants dwelling upon its delightful and fertile Banks.

*Bay River* is not very considerable, being small, yet its Trade is not despisable.

*Neus*

*Neus River* is the Third large River in this Province, but is not so good as *Pamticoe,* for Navigation, notwithstanding its Rise is near the Mountains.

*Trent* River is a South Branch of *Neus* River, which falls into *Pamticoe* Sound.

*North* River lyes to the Southward of *Neus,* and empties itself into *Cour* Sound; as do likewise *Newport* River, *Weetock* River, and *New* River; but are not very considerable, being only Navigable for Sloops and small Crofts.

*Black,* or *Swampy* River, is but small, and lyes to the Northward of *Cape Fear* River.

*Cape Fear* River is the Second considerable and large River, and is one of the best for Navigation in these Parts: There is a large River which is the Northeast Branch of *Cape Fear* River, but is distinguished or called by no proper Name that I know of at present.

*Waggomau* River is a Northeast Branch of *Pedee* River, and is large, taking its Rise from a great Lake to the Northward of the said River.

*Little Pedee* River is a North Branch of the following, and is not large.

*Pedee* River is the Third large and considerable River in *North Carolina.*

*Black* River, and *Santee* River are the two Southermost in those Parts, being part of *South Carolina.*

One thing worthy of Observation is, That the Current of all the Rivers in this large Country, are scarce to be perceived, 'till you travel several Hundred Miles, or near their Heads, which is chiefly owing to their being so large, and the Country so very level.

In many of these noble and spacious Rivers, are abundance of Creeks, several whereof are very commodious for Trade, being Navigable for several Miles; there are likewise

many

many considerable Islands in these Rivers, abounding with several sorts of Trees, Wild Beasts, especially Deer, and various kinds of Fowl; they are Inhabited by few or no Christians at present. In several parts of these Rivers are likewise to be seen great number of decayed Cypress and other large Trees, standing at a great distance in the Water, the Earth being entirely washed away from them in the series of many Ages.

The next thing to be considered, is the Towns and their beautiful Situation. And first, *Edentown* is the largest, consisting of about Sixty Houses, and has been the Seat of the Governors for many Years, and is pleasantly seated on a Creek on the North-side of *Roanocke* River; where you have a delightful Prospect of the said River.

*Bath Town,* is the Second considerable Town in this Province, and is most delightfully seated on a Creek on the North-side of *Pamticoe* River, with the same beautiful Advantages of the former: It's Navigation is much better, being the most considerable and commodious for Trade in this Province, except *Cape Fear.*

*Newbern* is situated on the South-side of *Neus* River, with a pleasant Prospect of that River: This Town has but a few Houses or Inhabitants in it at present.

*Handcock* Town is seated on a North West Branch of *Neus* River, being above two Hundred Miles from the Mouth of that River, and is scarce worth taking Notice of, only for its being formerly an *Indian* Town, and where they had a Fort in time of War.

*Beaufort* Town stands on the North-side of *Newport* River, it's prospect being as pleasant as any of the former: It is small, and thinly inhabited.

*Brunswick* Town is most delightfully seated, on the South-side of that Noble River *Cape Fear;* and no doubt but it will be very considerable in a short time, by it's great Trade, the

Number

Number of Merchants, and rich Planters, that are settled upon it's Banks, within these few Years.

The Streets in these Towns are as level as a Bowling-Green, there being no manner of Pavement to be met with over all this Province.

The first Settlement of this Country was made in Queen *Elizabeth's* time, by Sir *Walter Raleigh* and others, at *Roanoke,* in *Albemarle* County; but continued not long, either by Sickness or other Misfortunes, or by the Barbarity of the *Indians,* who were very numerous and powerful in those Days, but are now very few, being for the most part destroyed by their continual Wars with each other, and *European Distempers,* brought in amongst them, and especially the *Small-Pox,* which prov'd fatal to most of the *Indians* that were seized with it.   This Distemper, and many others unknown to these Savages, before the arrival of the Christians amongst them in those Parts.   I hope it will not be unpleasing to the Reader to insert here a pleasant Story which still prevails amongst them; and is attested by the most substantial and credible Planters of this Place, which is, "That the Ship that brought "the first Colonies, does often appear to them (in *Albemarle* "Sound near *Roanoke*) under Sail, in a most gallant posture." Which they call Sir *Walter Raleigh's* Ship.

The second Settlement was made in King *Charles* the Seconds Time, chiefly in *Chowan* and *Barty* Precincts, in *Albemarl* County, by several Persons from *Virginia,* and other Northern Colonies, who finding the Soil so very good and fertile, settled here, and are become very Numerous and Rich; for the Lands here produce every thing Planted in them in great abundance; Horses, Cows, Sheep, and Swine, breeding in vast Numbers, the Winter, being very short, and that so

B                                           mild

mild, the Planters are at little or no Labour or Expence in providing Fodder for their Stocks, to what other Northerly Countries are.  For in the Winter they only fell large Trees, whereon grow long Moss, which the Horses and Cows feed upon, and makes them both fat and strong; the Cows will produce Milk, with this kind of Fodder, all the Winter Season, in great plenty.  As for Hay, I never observed any made in the Country, tho' they have such plenty of Grass, that they are obliged to burn it off the Ground every 10*th* of *March,* by vertue of a Law made in the Country for that purpose.

These Inducements encouraged them to Settle here, though but a handful of People, seated at great distance one from another, amidst such vast Numbers of Savage *Indians,* of different Nations, who were then in *Carolina* to be met withal.

The Fame of this Province soon spread itself to the Neighbouring Colonies, and in a few Years drew considerable numbers of Families, not only from them, but likewise from several Parts of *Europe,* who all found Land enough to settle themselves in, had they been many Thousands more, both for Pleasure and Profit; which makes the Planters in a great measure live after a most luxurious manner, and void of Care, to what other more Northerly Climates are obliged to, by providing Necessaries for the Winter.  So that it may properly be said, that Nature produces every thing here for the Pleasure and Profit of the Inhabitants.

Most of the Plantations naturally have a very noble and beautiful Prospect of large and spacious Rivers or Creeks, abounding with variety of Fish and Wildfowl; as also, pleasant and delightful *Savannas* or *Meddows,* with their Green Liveries, interwoven with various kinds of beautiful and most

glorious

glorious Colours, and fragrant Odours, which the several Seasons afford, and fenced in with pleasant Groves of the fine Tulip Tree, Laurel and Bays, equalizing the Oak in bigness and growth, likewise the Myrtle, Jessamine, Wood-bines, Honeysuckles, and several other odoriferous Plants, the most beautiful Vines and Ever-greens, shadow and interwave themselves with the most lofty Timber, yielding a very pleasant and delightful Prospect, to those that travel through the Woods of *Carolina;* that, turn your Eyes, which way you will, you have nothing but pleasing and diverting Objects, and the more to be admired, being the Work of Nature, and not of Art.

The Lands being thus richly adorn'd, and the Planters enjoying all these Blessings, are as hospitable People as any in the World, to all that come to visit them, there being few House-keepers, but what live decently, and give away more Provisions to Coasters and Guests, that come to see them, than they expend amongst their own Families.

The Lands in *Carolina* lie indifferently low and level, no Rocks, or even small Stones are to be found, till you come near the Mountains, and the Heads of the great Rivers, where the best Lands are generally to be met with, abounding with all sorts of Clover, in great Plenty, but is at present only inhabited by Savage *Indians,* of different Nations, or the Habitation of Wild Beasts; and is more healthful to live in, than where the Plantations are already established.

Here are in several Places large *Savannas,* beautiful to behold, which at certain Seasons, appear at a distance like so many Pleasure Gardens, being intermixt with variety of Spontaneous Flowers of various Colours, such as the Tulip, Trumpet-flower, Princess-feather, and several others, with great quantities of Grass on them, but of a coarser and stronger Nature than up the Rivers, where there is mostly Clover to be met with, notwithstanding Horses, and other Cattle feed very well on the former, and are fat, strong, and fit for Labour, most Seasons of the Year.

There are likewise *Perkosons* and *Swamps,* which are good Pasturage for Cattle; so that by the richness of the Soil, and the many other Advantages and Blessings that attend the Planters, they live after a lazy and indolent Manner, to what those in *New England* do, and other Northerly Countries are, by providing Necessaries for Winter.

Lands are so very Cheap, that (after you have taken out your Patten for *Six Hundred and forty Acres,* which will cost three or four Pounds *Sterl.* or the Value in *Carolina* Money) you pay at the dearest, for the said Number of Acres, *Six Shillings and Six pence Sterl.* Yearly, and at the lowest *three Shillings and three Pence,* free from all Taxes at present: So that with moderate Industry may be acquired all manner of Necessarys for the Support of a Family, though never so Numerous, nothing being wanting there but a sufficient Number of Hands, and Industry, to make it as fine a Country as any in the World.

They Plant or Sow all their Corn by one Plough, or the Hoe, and several Plantations have produced *Indian* Corn, or some other Grain every Year, since the Settlement of the Christians in those Parts, without any Manure, and yet seems not to be the least Impoverished, producing continually a good Crop, unless a bad Season prevents, which seldome happens in *Carolina.*

And, I am satisfied, that there cannot be one greater Argument in the World, to prove the goodness and fertiltie of the

Lands

Lands than this, which is one of the greatest Blessings that can attend a Country where there are so few Hands to Manufacture the Lands after that laborious Manner, which is customary with us, which every Farmer in *Ireland* is well acquainted with, who is at continual Expence for Servants, Horses, and many other Necessaries to improve his Lands to the best Advantage.

The Lands of *Carolina* consist of different Sorts of compost, in several Places, some Stiff, others Light, some Marle, others a rich Black Mold, some Sandy, one Part Pieny, another large Timber Trees, others Savannas, with variety of beautiful Flowers and long Grass, a rich black Earth, where scarce any Tree will grow, yet produces the best Wheat and Rice of any Land in these Parts, as has been experienced by the Planters.

I have seen several of these Savannas some Miles in length and breadth, but are little regarded or made use of by the Planters, by reason that they are at some distance from their Plantations, some being two, three, or four Miles from the Water side, and are only Pasturage for Cattle. The Reader must understand, that all the Inland in this Province lyes waste at present.

Other Lands in this Province are *Perkosons,* where large *Cypress* Trees grow, others Swamps, where hollow Canes, Myrtle Trees and several sorts of Vines grow, and produce good Pasturage for Cattle, but are generally the Habitation of wild Beasts; both these being very wet and low Lands, and so full of Canes and Underwood, that there is no passing through them, many of which are several Miles in length. The *Indians* in their Hunting Matches set these Places on Fire at certain Seasons of the Year, by which Means they drive out the Game, and kill vast Numbers of them.

The

The Planters for the most part live by the Water side, few or none living in the In-land parts of the Country at present, though the Lands are as good and fertile as any that are yet inhabited; but not so commodious for Carriage as by the Water, for most part of the Plantations run but a Mile backward into the Woods, so that betwixt every River you shall see vast Tracts of Land lying waste, or inhabited only by wild Beasts: What is worthy of Observation is, That almost every Planter may have a convenient Dock upon his Plantation, and a sufficient Quantity of good Timber to build Ships and Boats withal.

## OF THE CORN OF

# NORTH CAROLINA.

THE *Wheat* of this Province is very good and fair, the Flour very White, but the Grain is not altogether so large as ours, yet it seldom yields less than thirty Measures for one sown; not but that there has been Sixty Increase for one sown in Piney Land, which is accounted the worst Soil in the Country, and I have been credibly inform'd, that the Wheat which was Planted in the Savannas, and such like rich Soil, has produced a Hundred for one Measure Sown. These considerable Increases prevent the Planters to make strict and nice Observations of the Nature and Goodness of the Soil; for I never saw one Acre of Land managed as it ought to be, and were they as Negligent in their Husbandry in *Europe,* as they are in *North Carolina,* their Land would produce

nothing

nothing but Weeds. And I must confess, when some of the Planters enquired of me how we managed the Land in *Ireland,* and what Labour and Expence we were at in ordering them to the best Advantage, it seemed very surprising to them how we could live, and especially when I told him, that we paid from three Shillings to four or five Pounds *per* Acre (besides many heavy Taxes) which Relation they could by no means give Credit to, but looked upon what I said as meer Romances or Tales, to impose upon their Credulity.

The *Rye* thrives very well here, but they having such Plenty of Maiz, in this Province, they little regard or value it, and especially by Reason of the Blackness of the Bread it makes.

The *Barley* does much better here than may reasonable be expected from their Management of it, that Grain requiring the Ground to be well Wrought, with repeated Plowings to make it Mellow, which their general Way of breaking with *Hoes* will never perform; though I have seen extraordinary *Barley* produced in *North Carolina,* after that manner, or with one Plowing only.

*Oats* does well here, but the vast Plenty of other Grain prevents their propagating of it in many Places, so that it is not common in these Parts of *America* at present.

The *Rice,* whereof there are several Sorts, some Bearded, others not, beside the White and the Red, but the White is best. The *Rice* of *Carolina* is esteemed as good as any brought to *Europe*, and is of a prodigious Increase, yielding from eight Hundred to a Thousand for one Measure that is sown. It grows best in their Wet and wild Land, that hath not been cultivated or broken up before. The *Indian-Corn* or Maize is most commonly Planted with the *Hoe,* and proves

the

the most useful Grain in these Parts, being in great Plenty all over this Province; it is very nourishing in Bread Sodden or otherwise, as appears by those that continually feed upon it, making them strong, able, and fit for hard Labour.   It grows in all manner of Ground except Barren Sands; but when Planted in good Ground, produces for one Measure, Seven or eight Hundred, at the lowest Computation that can be made.   Pigs and Poultery fed with this Grain, eat the sweetest of all others.

The *Millet* does very well here, especially in light and loose Ground, they sow it in *April* and *May,* and prospers best in moist and rainey Weather: The Plenty of other Grain, prevents the Planters from sowing much of it, being only made Use of in *Carolina* to fatten their Poultry with.

There are two Crops of Corn in the Year, *viz.* the *European* Wheat is generally cut down first, and in their Barns the beginning of *June,* then they immediately Plow, Sow, or Plant the same Ground with *Buck-Wheat,* or *Indian Corn,* which wonderfully increases, and is ready to be brought home in *September, October,* or *November,* with which they generally feed their Horses, Hogs, and Poultry.

The *Guinea* Wheat thrives likewise very well here, and serves for the Uses of the former.

There are several sorts of Pulse in this Province; and first, the *Bushel Bean,* so called from producing a Bushel of Beans or more from one that is Planted; they are a Spontanious product in *Carolina,* and are Set in the Spring round Arbours, or near long Poles set in the Ground for that purpose, where they make a good Shade to sit under in the extreamity of hot Weather; they continue Budding, Flowing, and Ripening all the Summer, until the approach of Frost, which pre-

vents

vents their farther Growth, and so dye; they climb prodigious high, and their Stalk is about the thickness of a Man's Thumb, the Pod grows like the *Kidney Bean,* but the Bean is flat, white, or mottled, with a purple Colour: They are extraordinary good, and well relished Pulse, either by themselves or with Meat.

The *Indian Rouncival,* or *Miraculous Pea,* so called from their long Pods and great Increase. These are a late Pea, and require a pretty long Summer to ripen and bring them to Perfection, they are a good Pulse, and in great plenty all over this Province with *Christians* and *Indians.*

The *Bonavis* is another kind of *Pulse,* and yields a great Increase, it doth not require so long a Summer to ripen as the former, they grow like *Kidney-Beans,* and are very plenty in this Province.

The *Calivances* are another kind of *Pulse,* resembling the former, but are not so flat, they are in great plenty in most of the Plantations amongst the Indian Corn. These and the *Bonavis,* afford two Crops in the Year, and are generally ripe and in full perfection in six Weeks time.

The *Nanticoacks* are another kind of *Pulse,* and resemble the *Calivances,* and are in great plenty all over this Province.

There are several other kinds of *Pulse* in this Province that we have no Name for, which are well known amongst the *Indians,* and are excellent Food.

The *Kidney-Bean,* is likewise here in great plenty, growing for the most part in every Corn-Field. The *Indians* had these four Sorts of *pulse, viz.* the *Bonavis, Calivances, Nanticoacks,* and *Kidney-Beans,* and several other sorts, long before the Arrival of the *Europeans* amongst them; which Report I have had affirmed several times, not only from the *Christians,* but likewise from the *Indians* in these Parts.

2            C            The

The large *European-Bean,* will in two or three Years degenerate into a dwarfish Kind, if not prevented by a new Supply of Foreign Seed, as I have experienced during my stay in those Parts; yet these Dwarfish sort become sweeter, and better relish'd, than any Bean of the same Sort in *Europe;* but these kind of Beans are very little regarded or made use of, and therefore seldom Planted, by reason the other *Pulse* are in such Plenty all over this Province.

I have observed several sorts of *European-Pease* in this Province come to as great Perfection, as in most Parts of *Europe,* particularly the white and gray *Rouncival,* the *Hot-Spur,* the *Dwarf,* the *Field* and the *Sickle-Pease;* and there is no doubt but that all other kinds of *European-Pease* would thrive well here had any tryal been made.

The Garden Roots that thrive here are *Parsnips, Carrots, Skirrets, Turnips,* Ground-*Artichoakes,* Garden-*Radishes,* Horse-*Radishes, Potatoes* of several sorts, and very large, some whereof weigh four Pounds; *Leeks, Onions* in great plenty, and excellent good *Shallots, Cives, Garlick,* and wild *Onions, Beets,* and most other Roots that are to be met with in *Europe.*

The *Sallads* are the curl'd *Cabbage, Savoy, Lettice,* round prickly *Spinage,* the sweet and common *Fennel, Endive, Succory, Mint,* the *Dock* or *Wild Rhubarb, Cresses* of several sorts, as *Winter, Garden, Indian, Sciatica, Water-Cresses,* and many more; *French* and *English* Sorrel, *Purslain* two sorts, *viz.* the Tame and the Wild; which are so plenty, that they are common Weeds in their Gardens, the Leaf is not as large as the Tame, but as good; the Planters boil it with their Salt Meat for Greens, this is never to be met with in the *Indian* Plantations; and is supposed to be produced from the Cow-Dung, which Beast the *Indians* keep not amongst them.

*Samphire,*

*Samphire,* is in very great Plenty along the Marshes near the Sea and Salt Water, and is very good.

*Mushrooms,* good and in great Plenty all over the Fields.

*Asparagus,* thrives in this Province to a miracle, without the assistance or benefit of Hot-Beds, Dung, or other Manure, being only produced from the natural goodness of the Soil, and it is found in Plenty in most Gardens in this Province, and as good as any in *Europe.* As likewise *Selery* and *Clary.*

*Parsley,* two Sorts, the White-Cabbage, from *European* Seeds thrive well here, but the planters seldom or never take Care or Pains to preserve good Seed of their own; so that by their Negligence, it is not so common as otherwise it might. The *Colly-Flower* does not thrive well here, by what tryals I have seen made during my abode in those Parts; but the plain and curled *Coleworth,* flourisheth.

The *Artichoak* I have observed but in two Places in this Province, which is tollerable good, here are likewise great quantities of excellent good *Water-Mellons* of several sorts, *Musk-Mellons,* very good and of several sorts, as the Golden, Green, Guinea, and Orange. *Cucumbers,* long, short, and prickly, and all produced from the natural Ground with great Increase, without any help of Dung, or reflection from Glasses.

*Pompions,* yellow and very large *Burmillions, Cashaws,* which is an excellent Fruit when boyl'd, *Squashes, Symnals, Horns* and *Gourds,* besides variety of other Speces of less value, such as the *Poke,* which is a kind of *Mechoacan,* and grows in every Field, the tender Tops whereof may be boiled and made use of as other Greens with all the safety immaginable, and are very good and nourishing, but the Roots (which are as thick as a Man's Leg) are not to be medled

with,

with, being in their Nature violent Purgers, and occasion
those that eat of them to be frantick for some time, though
I have never heard of any farther Mischief done by them.
*Lambs-Quarter,* and various kinds of Salleting, too tedious
to mention.

The Pot-Herbs, and others which are useful in Physick
are common here, and are as follows, *Angelica,* two sorts,
*viz.* the Wild and the Tame, *Balm, Bugloss, Borrage, Bur-
net, Marygold, Pennyroyal, Rue, Marjoram,* two sorts, *Summer* and *Winter Savory, Thyme, Rosemary, Lavender, Hys-
sop,* which grows very large, *Sweet Bazil, Groundsel, Derg,*
red and white, *Nep* or *Cat-mint, Mallows* several sorts, *Tan-
say, Columbine, Dandelion, Wormwood, Southernwood, Bastard Saffron;* and several sorts of *Mustard.*

The more *Physical* Plants are *Anis, Asarabacca,* growing
in most Places in the Woods; *Cardus, Benedictus, Caraway,
Cummin, Coriander, Scurvy-Grass,* two sorts; the one from
*Europe,* and the other Spontaneous.

In these Parts *Tobacco* of many sorts, *Dill,* all the *Euro-
pean* sorts of *Plantain,* and two Spontaneous, *Elecampain,
Archangel,* or *Dead-Nettle,* the *Stinging-Nettle,* the Seed
being brought from *Europe,* there being none found growing
Spontaneous in *North Carolina—Comfery, Monks-Rhubarb,
Burdock, Featherfew, Wormfeed, Garden-Poppies,* none yet
being discover'd growing Wild in this Province.   *Ground-
Ivy* is Spontaneous, but much smaller than the *European;
Perewinkle* growing in great plenty in most parts of the
Woods; *Golden-Rod,* several sorts of *Horehound, Melilot,
Bastard-Lovage.* The *Rattle-Snake*-Root, whereof there are
three sorts, and is so called, because it alone cures the Bite
of the *Rattle-Snake;* it is very plenty in all the Savannas
and Woods.   *Snake-Root,* four sorts in *Carolina; Purging
Bindweed* or *Scamony,* growing in most parts of this Prov-
ince.

The

The *Ipecacuana* grows likewise in great Plenty in this Province, which I frequently made Use of during my stay in that Country, with as good Success as any I have ever met with in *Europe.* This Herb bringeth forth one or more Stalks, which are Quadrangular, about a Foot high, whereon grow Leaves confusedly set at certain distance one from the other, unless at the Top, where they grow one opposite to the other, something like *Purslain,* but more sharp, and of a dark green colour, with a red circle about the Edges, and divided with Threads or Sinews in the middle, which perish in Winter. I am not certain whether it beareth Flowers or Seed; the Root is so well known in every Apothecary's Shop, that it would be needless to trouble the Reader with a farther Description about it. This and the *Scamony* grow in high Sandy Ground, in many Places in *Carolina.* Oak of *Jerusalem, Indian-purger, Swallow-wort, Palma-Christi,* several sorts of *Mint, Red-Dock, Jamestown-Weed,* so called from its being so very plenty in *Virginia,* especially on both sides of *James's River:* The Seed it bears is exactly like that of an *Onion,* but it's Leaves are very coarse and large, and indented about the Edges; it is excellent good in asswaging all manner of Inflammations, and curing Burns, by applying it outwardly, with which the *Indians* are well acquainted, but if it be taken Inwardly, it immediately occasions a Giddiness and Madness, so that you shall see those that take it (which most commonly happens to Children) run up and down the Fields in a most distracted manner, during its Operation, but does no further Mischief.

There is another Weed, vulgarly called the *Swamp-Lillie,* which grows in the Marshes and low Grounds, and is something like our *Dock* in its Leaves, and hath the same Effect,

and

and possesses the Party with Fear and Watchings; though few have had the Tryal, or felt the Effects of these intoxicating Plants, except Boys and Children; it is likewise used with good Success in Inflammations and Burns, as the former.

*Camomil* thrives well here, but it must be Planted under a Shade, otherwise it comes to little or no Perfection.

The *Red-Root,* the Leaves whereof are like those of *Spearmint,* is used with good Success for Thrushes, and sore Mouths.

*Vervine* is very common here, being Spontaneous. *House Leek,* being first brought from *Europe.* *Night-shade* of several kinds, *Yarrow* and *Mullein,* in plenty, both being Spontaneous. *Harts-Tongue, Polypodium of the Oak*; the greater *Centaury,* in great plenty; but I never observed any of the Lesser growing in this Province. *Prickly Bind-Weed, Larks-Spur, Hops, Flax* and *Hemp,* the best and finest in the known World groweth in *North Carolina.*

*Tisinaw,* or *Bastard China-Root,* these grow in great Clusters, together, and have a stalk like a *Brier,* whereon grow small *Black-Berries,* the *Indians* boil these Roots and eat them, and sometimes make them into Bread.

*Sarsaparilla, White Hellebor,* several sorts of *Thistles, Fern, Male* and *Female, Liquorice, Oris, Water-lillies, Peony, Male* and *Female, Solomons-Seal, Agarick, Coloquintida, Guinea-Pepper, Water-Flag, Flower de Luce, Betony, Shepherds-Purse, Chervil; Coffee,* whereof they begin to plant much, within these few Years; *Jessamine, Pellitory* of *Spain, Cloud Herb,* by the *Indians* call'd *Yaughtli.* *Strawberries* are in such Plenty in the Season, that they are Feeding for Hogs; *Narcissus, Daffodil, Snow-Drops, Wall-Flowers, Bloodwort,* the white and red *Lillie, Stargrass,* which is used with good Success in most Fevers in this Country; *Rushes* of several sorts; the Herb *Mastick, Indian-all-*

*heal,*

*heal, Cinquefoil,* or five leav'd Grass, *Rib-wort,* which is a kind of Plantain; *Pellitory* of the Wall, this Herb grows very plentiful on the Ground, there being no Rocks or Stone Walls for it to grow upon; *Shepherds-Needle, Rosa-Solis,* or *Sun-dew;* several sorts of *Sage* being first brought from *Europe; Misseltoe* of the *Oak,* in great Plenty all over this Province, whereof good *Birdlime* is made.

There are several sorts of Beautiful *Tulips* growing Spontaneous in this Province: The *Trumpet-Flower,* so call'd from its resembling the Form of that Instrument, and is of a beautiful *Orange* colour.

The *May-Apple,* so call'd from its having Apples in the Month of *May;* it grows upon one Stalk like the *Wood-Sorrel,* about half a Foot high, and has Leaves like it, but very near as large as a Man's Hand, underneath which grow one Apple on each Stalk, about the bigness of a Musket Ball: This Plant is of a very strong Purging nature, and is frequently made use of in these Parts for several Disorders with good Success.

The *Sun-Flower,* the *Indian-Figg,* or *Prickly-Pear,* the Fruit of this Vegetable is frequently eaten, and is very sweet and luscious, but occasions such a high Tincture in the Urine, that it seems like pure Blood; by which means several Persons that have been unacquainted with its Effects, have been so surprized, that they expected nothing but immediate Death; yet it does no manner of harm, and as soon as its Operation is over, which is in less than twenty-four Hours, the Urine resumes its natural Colour, and the Patient, tho' almost out of his Senses, becomes easy and well. There are various Kinds of Physical Plants growing in their Gardens, the Seed being brought from *Europe* and other Parts.

Thus have I given an Account of some of the Plants growing in this Country, yet not of the hundredth Part of what

remains;

remains; a Catalogue of which, would be a Work of many Years, and more than the Age of one Man to perfect, or bring into a regular Classes, this Country being so very large, and different in its Situation and Soil; so that what one Place plentifully produces, another is altogether a Stranger to: Yet it is generally to be observed, that the greatest Variety is to be found in the low Grounds and Savannas.

The Pleasure Gardens of *North Carolina,* are not yet arrived to any great Perfection, or Adorned with many beautiful fragrant Flowers; there being only some few *Rose-Trees, Bead-Trees, Orange-Trees, Clove Gilly-Flower, Pinks* of several sorts, *Sweet-William, Cowslips, Lavender-Spike,* and *Lavender-Cotton, Violets, Princess-Feather, Tres-Colores,* and such like: But their Kitchen Gardens are very good, abounding with most sorts of Necessaries for that Use.

I will give an Account of the Climate, and so proceed to the *Present State of North Carolina.*

This Climate is very Healthful, and is not so Hot in the Summer as other Countries to the Eastward, in the same Parallels of Latitude; neither is the Country subject to Earthquakes, as *Italy,* and many other Hot Countries are: The Sky is generally very serene and clear, and the Air very thin and pure; and though we have but little Rain, yet the constant Dews that fall in the Night, sufficiently refresh the Ground, and supply the Plants with Moisture.

The North West Winds in the Winter, occasion very sharp and piercing Weather, the North East Winds blowing in the Winter, bring with them thick Weather, and in Spring some times Blight the Corn and Fruits of the Earth, but they very seldom continue long, being carried off by Westerly Winds, which are the most pleasant and healthful we have in these Parts of the World. And though these Northerly

Winds

Winds cool the Air in Summer and are very pearcing in the Winter, yet they are of no Continuance.

Southerly Winds cause very hot and unwholsom Weather, and often occasion Fevers, and other Disorders in these Parts. The Spring and Fall are the most delightful and pleasant Seasons of the Year, being neither too Hot or too Cold; and though these Seasons are very pearcing, yet the Cold is of no Duration, and are in a great Measure owing to˙ the Winds shifting from one Point to the other; for Southerly Winds will occasion it to be warm in the midst of Winter, as with us in *April,* and the North East Winds will on the contrary, make it cool in the midst of Summer.

The Weather is generally pretty moderate till after Christmas; then the Winter comes on apace, and continues variable 'till the midle of *February,* according to the Winds, sometimes warm and pleasant, at other times Rain, Snow, or Frost, but the Ice is seldom so strong as to bear a Man's weight.

In the Year 1730, we had the most agreeable and pleasant Summer that has been known for many Years, and the Winter most severe.

In the Months of *August* and *September* we frequently have very great Storms and Squals of Wind, and it is remarkable for two or three Days before they break forth, that the Clouds seem to hang down very thick and pressing towards the Earth, and scarce a breath of Wind to be perceived for the said time; they are sometimes so very violent, that they make Lanes through the Woods by tearing up Trees by the roots.

These Storms are generally attended with most violent Claps of Thunder and Lightning, and pouring with Rain all the time they continue, which are very dreadful whilst they

D                                                    last;

last; and I have seen old decay'd Trees, and especially the *Pitch-Pine,* frequently set on Fire by these violent claps of Thunder and Lightning, and sometime Trees in their Bloom tore and split in Pieces, yet I have seldom known or heard of any farther Dammage.

There are prodigious *Water-Spouts* to be seen in this Country, which are the forerunners and certain Signs of Storms and bad Weather, which quickly follow after them: These Water-spouts are vast exhalations of Water running out of the Clouds like little Rivers, and are generally to be met with at Sea and near the Shores, but seldom or never at Land; and are to be seen at a great distance, resembling all the colours in the Rainbow; it is said they are dangerous to be met with at Sea, for fear of falling upon their Vessels, for which reason when they espie them near at Hand, they frequently fire their great Guns to break them in the Air, before they come near the surface of the Water, as I have been credibly informed by several Masters of Ships; for I have never seen them otherwise than at a great distance. There are no regular Tides in *Carolina,* but what are occasioned for the most part by the Winds shifting from one Point to another.

THE

# THE PRESENT STATE

OF

# NORTH CAROLINA.

T HIS Province, and South *Carolina,* were granted by King *Charles* II. *March* the 24*th* in the Fifteenth Year of his Reign, and Confirmed by Letters Patents bearing Date, *June* the 13th. in the 17*th*. Year of his said Majesty's Reign, to the following Lords Proprietors, (*viz.*) *Edward,* Earl of *Clarendon; George,* Duke of *Albemarl; William,* Earl of *Craven; John,* Lord *Berkeley; Anthony,* Lord *Ashley;* Sir *George Carterett,* Knight, and Baronet; Sir *John Colleton,* Knight, and Baronet; and Sir *William Berkeley;* who possessed them until the Year 1729: At which time King *George* II. Purchased them from all the said Proprietors, excepting the Lord *Carterett,* who still retains his Eighth Part. Whilst it remained in the Hands of the Proprietors,

D 2                                      they

they had a Governor who acted for them until the Year 1731, at which Time his Majesty sent over Governor *Burrington,* who was the first Governor after the King had made the Purchase, and with him came most of the Superior Officers; such as Secretary of the Province, Chief Justice, Attorney General, Provost-Marshal, and Naval Officers, the rest were at his arrival in the Country, but Nominated by the King, such as Surveyor General, Judge of the Admiralty, Comptrollers and Collectors.

They have two Houses, which resemble the two Houses of Parliament with us. The first or *Upper-House* consists of twelve Members and the Governor; in this House are heard all Chancery Suits, and other Causes that cannot be decided in the Inferior Courts; from whence there can be no Appeal, except to *England.*

The *Lower-House* consists of thirty five Members, being the most knowing, discreet and substantial Planters, chose out of each Precinct and Borough. In this and the *Upper-House,* are made all manner of Laws for the Safety and better Government of this Province. But whatever Laws are here made must be conformable to the Laws of *England,* and in no wise repugnant thereto. And such Laws as are made in these two Houses by the Governor, Council and Burgesses, are all recorded, and are as authentick and binding there, as our Acts of Parliament are with us.

There are likewise two other Courts in this Province, *viz.* the *Precinct-Court,* which is held in every Precinct of this Province, being much of the same Nature of our *Court-Leets,* or *Court-Barons.* The other is called the *General-Court,* which is held twice every Year, as the former is four times. This is much the same as our *Assizes,* where all

Causes

Causes relating to Life and Death are heard, where the Chief Justice sits as Judge, and determines all Causes within the Jurisdiction of this Court. In the *Precinct-Court,* the Justices of the Peace sit on the Bench, and decide all Controversies brought before them. This Court upon any Grievance can Appeal to the General Court for Justice, and the General to *Chancery.* The Governor by the Power invested in him, Commissions all Justices of the Peace, and all Officers in the Militia, who upon any Occasion may call his Council, to advise with them, upon any Emergency that is necessary, or expedient, for the good and safety of the Country.

There are abundance of Attorneys in this Province, who are Licenced by the Governor, yet all Law-Suits are quickly decided in *Carolina,* to prevent the Planters ruining each other, as is too frequent to be met with amongst us.

These, and many other good Laws, that are to be met with in this Province, make it one of the best and mildest Governments to live under in all *America.* Whoever consider the Latitude and convenient Situation of *Carolina,* may easily inform themselves, that it is a most delightful and fertil Country, being placed in the same Latitude or part of the World which produces Wine, Oil, Fruit, Grain and Silk, with many other rich Commodities, besides a sweet moderate and healthful Climate to live in with all manner of Plenty, which are as great blessings as can attend any People upon Earth, which the Planters of *Carolina* at this Day enjoy, being subject to no vexatious Taxes, or Racking Landlords, to give them the least uneasiness or discontent.

The

The Planters by the richness of the Soil, live after the most easie and pleasant Manner of any People I have ever met with; for you shall seldom hear them Repine at any Misfortunes in life, except the loss of Friends, there being plenty of all Necessaries convenient for Life: Poverty being an entire Stranger here, and the Planters the most hospitable People that are to be met with, not only to Strangers but likewise to those who by any Misfortune have lost the use of their Limbs or are incapable to Work, and have no visible way to support themselves; to such Objects as these, the Country allows *Fifty Pounds per Annum* for their Support. So there are no Beggars or Vagabonds to be met with Strowling from place to place as is too common amongst us.

The Country in general is adorned with large and Beautiful Rivers and Creeks, and the Woods with lofty Timber, which afford most delightful and pleasant Seats to the Planters, and the Lands very convenient and easie to be fenced in, to secure their Stocks of Cattle to more strict Bounderies, whereby with small trouble of Fencing, almost every Man may enjoy to himself an intire Plantation.

These with many other Advantages, such as the cheapness and fertility of the Lands, plenty of Fish, Wild-fowl, Venison, and other necessaries that this Country naturally produces, has induced a great many Families to leave the more Northerly Plantations, and come and settle in one of the mildest Governments in the World, in a Country that with moderate Industry may be acquir'd all Necessaries convenient for life; so that Yearly we have abundance of Strangers that come amongst us from *Europe, New-England, Pensilvania, Maryland,* and from many of the Islands, such as

*Antegua,*

*Antegua, Barbados,* and many others, to settle here; many of whom with small Beginnings, are become very Rich in a few Years.

The *Europians,* or *Christians* of *North-Carolina,* are a streight, tall, well-limb'd and active People; their Children being seldom or never troubled with Rickets, and many other Distempers that the *Europians* are afflicted with, and you shall seldom see any of them deformed in Body.

The Men who frequent the Woods, and labour out of Doors, or use the Waters, the vicinity of the Sun makes Impressions on them; but as for the Women that do not expose themselves to Weather, they are often very fair, and well featur'd, as you shall meet with any where, and have very Brisk and Charming Eyes; and as well and finely shaped, as any Women in the World. And I have seldom observ'd any Red-hair'd Women, or Men, born in this Country.

They marry generally very young, some at Thirteen or Fourteen; and she that continues unmarried, until Twenty, is reckoned a stale Maid, which is a very indifferent Character in that Country. These Marriages for want of an Orthodox Clergyman, is performed by the Governor, or the next Justice of the Peace; who reads the Matrimonial Ceremony, which is as binding there as if done by the best divine in *Europe.* The Women are very fruitful, most Houses being full of Little Ones, and many Women from other Places who have been long Married and without Children, have remov'd to *Carolina,* and become joyful Mothers, as has been often observ'd. It very seldom happens they miscarry, and they have very easie Travail in their Child-bearing.

The Children at nine Months old are able to walk and run about the House, and are very Docile and apt to learn

any

any thing, as any Children in *Europe;* and those that have
the advantage to be Educated, Write good Hands, and prove
good Accomptants, which is very much coveted, and most
necessary in these parts. The young Men are generally of
a bashful, sober Behaviour, few proving Prodigals, to spend
what the Parents with Care and Industry have left them,
but commonly Improve it.

The Girls are most commonly handsome and well Featur'd, but have pale or swarthy Complexions, and are generally more forward than the Boys, notwithstanding the Women
are very Shy, in their Discourses, till they are acquainted.
The Girls are not only bred to the Needle and Spinning, but
to the Dairy and domestick Affairs, which many of them
manage with a great deal of prudence and conduct, though
they are very young.

Both Sexes are very dexterous in paddling and managing
their Canoes, both Men, Women, Boys, and Girls, being bred
to it from their Infancy. The Women are the most Industrious in these Parts, and many of them by their good Housewifery make a great deal of Cloath of their own Cotton,
Wool, and Flax, and some of them weave their own Cloath
with which they decently Apparel their whole Family though
large. Others are so Ingenious that they make up all the
wearing Apparel both for Husband, Sons and Daughters.
Others are very ready to help and assist their Husbands in
any Servile Work, as planting when the Season of the Year
requires expedition: Pride seldom banishing Housewifery.
Both sexes are most commonly spare of Body and not Chol-
erick, nor easily cast down at Disapointments and Losses,

and

and seldome immoderately grieving at Misfortunes in Life, excepting it be the loss of their nearest Relations.

By the Fruitfulness of the Women in *North Carolina,* and the great Numbers of Men, Women, and Children, that are daily Transported from *Europe,* they are now become so powerful, in this and most of the other Provinces in the Hands of the *English,* that they are able to resist for the future any attempts the *Indians* may make on them. Add to this, the several *Indian* Kings that at present are in the Christian Interest, who pay some small Tribute as an Acknowledgment of their Subjection, and are ready upon all occasions to assist them when ever they are required so to do; therefore they live at present without any dread or fear of those Savages to what they formerly did.

The Men are very ingenious in several Handycraft Businesses, and in building their Canoes and Houses; though by the richness of the Soil, they live for the most part after an indolent and luxurious Manner; yet some are laborious, and equalize with the *Negro's* in hard Labour, and others quite the Reverse; for I have frequently seen them come to the Towns, and there remain Drinking Rum, Punch, and other Liquors for Eight or Ten Days successively, and after they have committed this Excess, will not drink any Spirituous Liquor, 'till such time as they take *the next Frolick,* as they call it, which is generally in two or three Months. These Excesses are the occasions of many Diseases amongst them. But amongst the better Sort, or those of good OEconomy, it is quite otherwise, who seldom frequent the Taverns, having plenty of Wine, Rum, and other Liquors at their own Houses, which they generously make use of amongst their Friends and Acquaintance, after a most decent and discreet Manner, and are not so subject to Disorders as those who Debauch themselves in such a Beastly Manner. The former sometimes bring their Wives with them to be pertakers of these Frolicks, which very often is not commendable or decent to behold.

OF

## OF THE
### Religion, Houses, Raiment, Diet, Liquors, Firing, Diversions, Commodities, Language, Diseases, Curiosities, Cattle, &c. of
## NORTH CAROLINA.

THE Religion by Law established, is the *Protestant,* as it is professed in *England;* and tho' they seldom have Orthodox Clergymen among them, yet there are not only Glebe Lands laid out for that Use, commodious to each Town, but likewise convenient for building Churches. The want of these Protestant Clergy, is generally supply'd by some School-Masters, who read the Lithurgy, and then a Sermon out of Doctor *Tillitson,* or some good practical Divine, every Sunday. These are the most numerous, and are dispersed through the whole Province.

I shall treat of the other Religions as they are to be regarded according to their Numbers; and first of the *Quakers*: These People enjoy the same Privileges as with us in *Ireland,* and live for the most part in *Albemarle* County, wherein they have a decent Meeting-House.

The *Presbyterians* succeed next, and have had a Minister of their own Order for many Years past; they are chiefly settled in and about the River *Neus.*

*Roman-Catholicks* are the next considerable, and are settled in many Parts of the Country, but mostly in and about *Bath-Town,* they have likewise a Clergyman of their own Order among them at present.

Next succeed the *Anabaptists,* who live mostly in *Albemarle* County.

There are likewise many Sectaries in *Carolina,* who have little or no appearance of Religion, except some few Forms of Prayers.  This I take to be intirely owing to our want of Orthodox Divines, to instruct them in the true Notions of God, and right method of Worshiping, according to the tenor of revealed Religion.  It is common to see here numbers of Men, Women, and Children, Baptized all together, when a Clergyman arrives in those Parts, and I have actually seen the Grandfather, his Son, and Grandson, receive this Sacrament at one time.  There are numbers who never require Baptism, and consequently never covet to be made Christians, yet use some few Forms of Prayer.

By what I have already urged, my Readers will naturally observe, that there is Liberty of Conscience allowed in the whole Province; however, the Planters live in the greatest Harmony imaginable, no Disputes or Controversies are ever observed to arrise among them about their Religious Principles.  They always treat each other with Friendship and Hospitality, and never dispute over their Liquor, which is a Custom too frequent and too much indulged with us, and from whence dangerous Consequences have arisen:  By this Unity of Affection, the Prosperity of the Province has increased from its first rise, to this Day.  But though they are

thus

thus remarkable for their Friendship, Harmony and Hospitality, yet in regard to Morals, they have their share of the Corruptions of the Age, for as they live in the greatest Ease and Plenty, Luxury of Consequence predominates, which is never without its attendant Vices. Can it be admired, that the generality of them live after a loose and lacivious Manner, when according to my former Observation, they have no Clergy to instruct them, and recommend the Duties necessary belonging to a Christian; and is it not natural to believe that Impiety and Imorality, when a People are void of those Benefits, must sway the major part of them. I would not be understood here, as if I designed to advance these imputations of Vice against the whole Body of the People: No, there are certainly Persons of both Sexes Temperate, Frugal, Good Oeconemists, remarkably kind to Strangers, and those in Distress, and zealous in the practice of Christanity.

Their Houses are built after two different Ways; *viz.* the most substantial Planters generally use Brick, and Lime, which is made of Oyster-shells, for there are no Stones to be found proper for that purpose, but near the Mountains; the meaner Sort erect with Timber, the outside with Clap-Boards, the Roofs of both Sorts of Houses are made with Shingles, and they generally have Sash Windows, and affect large and decent Rooms with good Closets, as they do a most beautiful Prospect by some noble River or Creek.

Their Furniture, as with us, consists of Pewter, Brass, Tables, Chairs, which are imported here commonly from *England:* The better sort have tollerable Quantities of Plate, with other convenient, ornamental, and valuable Furniture.

The

The Cloathings used by the Men are *English* Cloaths, Druggets, Durois, Green Linnen, &c. The Women have their Silks, Calicoes, Stamp-Linen, Calimanchoes and all kind of Stuffs, some whereof are Manufactured in the Province. They make few Hats, tho' they have the best Furrs in plenty, but with this Article, they are commonly supplied from *New-England,* and sometimes from *Europe.*

Their Diet consists chiefly of Beef, Mutton, Pork, Venison in Abundance, Wild and Tame Fowl, Fish of several delicate Sorts; Roots, Fruit, several kinds of Sallads, good Bread, Butter, Milk, Cheese, Rice, *Indian* Corn, both which they concoct like a *Hasty-Pudding:* But as I shall treat more particularly of the Productions of the Country in the succeeding Pages, I shall now proceed to their *Liquors.*

The *Liquors* that are common in *Carolina* at present, and chiefly made use of, are, Rum, Brandy, Mault Drink; these they import. The following are made in Country, *viz.* Cyder, Persimon-Beer, made of the Fruit of that Tree, Ceder-Beer, made of Ceder-Berries; they also make Beer of the green Stalks of *Indian-Corn,* which they bruise and boyle: They likewise make Beer of Mollosses, or common Treacle, in the following manner, they take a Gallon of Mollosses, a Peck of Wheaten Bran, a Pound of Hops, and a Barrel of Fountain Water, all which they boile together, and work up with Yest, as we do our Malt Liquors; this is their common Small-Beer, and seems to me to be the pleasantest Drink, I ever tasted, either in the *Indies* or *Europe,* and I am satisfied more wholsom. This is made stronger in proportion, as People fancy.

It is necessary to observe that though there is plenty of Barly and Oats in this Province, yet there is no Malt Drink

made,

made, notwithstanding all kind of Malt Liquors bear a good Price, nor have any of the Planters ever yet attempted it.

*Chocolate, Teas,* and *Coffee,* are as common in *Carolina* as with us in *Ireland,* particularly the last, which of late Years they have industriously raised, and is now very cheap: These are sober Liquors, and take off the better Sort from Drinking what are hot and spirituous, who are not so addicted to Rum and Brandy as the inferior Sort, *Caslena* or *Yaupan,* an *Indian Tea,* which grows here in Abundance is indifferently used by Planters and *Indians.*

The *Fireing* they use is Wood, and especially Hickery, though we discovered Pit-Coal in our Journies towards the Mountains, yet it is not worth their while to be at the expence of bringing it, Timber being so plenty.

The chiefest Diversions here are Fishing, Fowling; and Hunting, Wild Beasts, such as Deer, Bears, Racoons, Hares, Wild Turkies, with several other sorts, needless to treat of here, 'till we come to describe each particular Specie.

*Horse-Racing* they are fond of, for which they have Race-Paths, near each Town, and in many parts of the Country. Those Paths, seldom exceed a Quarter of a Mile in length, and only two Horses start at a time, each Horse has his peculiar Path, which if he quits, and runs into the other, looses the Race. This is agreed on to avoid Jockying. These Courses being so very short, they use no manner of Art, but push on with all the speed imaginable; many of these Horses are very fleet.

It is common for People to come and go from this Province to *Virginia,* to these publick Diversions.

They are much addicted to *Gaming,* especially at Cards and Dice, Hazard and All-fours, being the common Games they use; at which they play very high, nay to such a pitch,

that

that I have seen several hundred Pounds won and lost in a short time.

*Cock-Fighting* they greatly admire, which Birds they endeavor to procure from *England* and *Ireland,* and to that intent, employ Masters of Ships, and other Trading Persons to supply them.

*Wrestling, Leaping,* and such Activities are much used by them; yet I never observed any Foot Races.

*Dancing* they are all fond of, especially when they can get a Fiddle, or Bag-pipe; at this they will continue Hours together, nay, so attach'd are they to this darling Amusement, that if they can't procure Musick, they will sing for themselves.   Musick, and Musical Instruments being very scarce in *Carolina.*

These are the most material Observations I have made in respect of their usual Diversions.

But they have a particular Season, which is only at their *Wheat-Harvest,* not to be omitted; this they celebrate with great Solemnity, it is in the beginning of *June,* at which time the Planters notify to each other, that they design to reap the aforesaid Grain, on a certain Day, some send their *Negroes* to assist, others only go to partake of the great Feasts, *&c.*   Some will frequently come twenty, nay thirty Miles on this Occasion, the Entertainments are great, and the whole Scene pleasant and diverting; but if they can get Musick to indulge this Mirth, it greatly adds to the Pleasure of the Feast.   It must be confest, that this annual Revelling is very expensive to the Planters, but as its customary, few omit it, nor have they ever those publick Diversions at the reaping any other Grain but the *European Wheat.*

I am sensible that many Persons, who by their Misbehaviour in this Country, were obliged to quit it, have ma-

liciously

liciously endeavoured to represent, not only the Province, but its Inhabitants, in a wrong Light; but as they intirely take the Opportunity to talk either before those who were never there, or before Persons incapable of judging, it is to be hoped, that the scandalous reports of such, will not be regarded. Several of those trifling Nusances have to my knowledge, scarcely been out of the Town or Port where they first arrived, during their Residence there: How therefore cou'd they be acquainted with the Fertilty of the Country, the Constitution, and Temper of the Inhabitants; before the learn'd, by whom they can be convicted, they dare not appear? And if the credulous and ignorant will be amused, all the Arguments Man can produce will not avail.

The People live to as great Ages as most *Europeans,* they are entire Strangers to Consumptions, a Distemper fatal to us; but they are much addicted to aguish Disorders, which is incident to all Strangers, for they generally have their Seasonings at their first Arrival, or soon after, though it seldom proves mortal, and is easily carried off by *Emeticks,* and other Medicines properly given.

This Colony boasts more Advantages than several others on this Continent, both for Pleasure, Ease, and Profit: Were the Inhabitants as industrious as the Soil is bountiful, they might supply themselves with all the Necessaries of Life. With little Industry they may have Wines, Oil, Silk, Fruits, and many sorts of Drugs, Dyes, &c. Here the Curious may have a large Field to satisfie and divert their Curiosity; here they may collect strange Beasts, Birds, Fishes, Insects, Reptiles, Shells, Mines, Herbs, Flowers, Plants, Shrubs, Trees, Gums, Tears, Rosin, Stones, and several other things that

F                                                            yield

yield both Profit and Satisfaction: If the plenty and cheapness of Provisions, and the low rate of Lands, may tempt People to this delightful Country, sure those who have but small Beginnings, with moderate industry, may here live more comfortably, and provide for their Families better than in any place I have yet seen in *Europe*.

The Rivers are very beautiful, pleasant, profitable, large and Navigable for several Leagues up the Country: They rise for the most part in or near the Mountains, and abound not only with great Quantities of delicate Fish, but likewise with Wild-Fowl of different kinds. In many of these Rivers are to be seen large and delightful Islands, where is excellent Pasturage and some of them afford large Stocks of Cattle and Deer, but scarce any Wild Beasts, and few Beasts of Prey. In these Islands frequently grow vast quantities of Cedar with several other kinds of valuable Timber Trees, as I have already mentioned.

The civilized *Indians* are very serviceable to the Planters in many Cases, particularly in making Weares to catch Fish; this they do for a small consideration, and it proves very advantagious to large Families, because they not only take great Quantities of different Sorts, but moreover what are very good and nourishing; these Weares are made after a method peculiar to the *Indians* only. Others Hunt and Fowl for them at very reasonable rates, this Country being as plentifully provided with all sorts of Game as any in *America;* the *Indians* sometimes assist the poorer sort of Planters in planting their Corn for small Triffles, when expedition is required.

The Mountains that are the most considerable are the *Charokee,* or *Appelapean* Mountains, they take their rise

from

from the North-west part of South *Carolina,* and so continue in one Ridge to the Northward for several hundred Miles, being in most places five or six hundred Miles from the Sea; they are vastly high, and abound with Trees, various kinds of Plants, and Stones of several different Natures. Beyond these Mountains you have a prospect only of large Woods, Savannas, dismal Swamps and Forrests, being as is supposed, the Habitation of Savage *Indians,* and wild Beasts of various kinds.

The Commodities convenient to bring to this Province from *Europe,* are as follows; Guns, Powder, Ball, Shot, Flints, Linnens of all Sorts, but chiefly Blues; Brown and Stampt Linnens, Oznabrigs, Men and Women's Apparel ready made up; some few Broad-Cloaths, Blew and Red Stuffs, Callimancoes, Druggets, Kersies, Camblets, all light Stuffs for Men and Women's Summer Wear, Habberdashers Wares, Stockings of all sorts, some few Gloves, thin Wigs, Linnen Caps, Silk-thread, common Thread of all Sorts, Needles, Pins, Tobacco Pipes, Glass for Sashwindows, Looking Glasses, all sorts of hard Ware, such as Knives, Forks, Sizers, Saws, Hatchets, Chisels, Bills, Hoes, Spades, Shovels, Grubing Hoes, Wedges, Nails, and all manner of Tools for Carpenters, Shoemakers, Coopers Shave Locks, Locks for Doors, Traps of all Sorts, and especially for Beavers, what we commonly call Fox-Traps, Grindle-Stones, all manner of Whet-Stones, Paper, Ink, Saddles, Bridles, Fish-hooks of all Sorts, several Toys, as Fans, Necklaces, Beads, Ribbons, Tape, Thimbles, Shoe-buckles, and the like; Tradesmen of all sorts, Honest Servants and Negroes.

The produce of this Country for Exportation to *Europe* and the Islands, are Beef, Porke, Tallow, Hides, Deer-Skins, Furs, Wheat, *Indian-Corn,* Pease, Potatoes, Rice, Honey,

Bees-wax,

Bees-wax, Myrtle-wax, Tobacco, Snake-root, Turpentine, Tar, Pitch, Masts for Ships, Staves, Planks and Boards of most sorts of Timber, Cotton, and several sorts of Gums, Tears, with some medicinal Drugs; Bricks and Tiles are made here, likewise several useful Earths, such as Bole, Fullers-Earth, Tobacco Pipe Clay, and Oaker, in great Plenty, excellent good Earth for the Potters Trade, and fine Sand for the Glassmakers. They export abundance of Horses to the Islands of *Antegua, Barbadoes, &c.*

Lead, Copper, Sulphure and Antimony, have been found here, but for want of good Encouragement, few or no endeavours have been made to discover these subterraneous Productions; here is likewise found in great Plenty the true *Blood-Stone,* near the Mountains, as also a very fine Earth, the same with Bruxels Sand, which the Goldsmiths use to cast with, which bears a good Price in several parts of *Europe.* We have likewise *Chalibeat Waters,* of several Tastes, and different Qualities, some Purging and others working by the *Emunctories;* there are several Waters also amongst the Inhabitants that outwardly cure Ulcers, Tettars, and Sores (disorders they are very subject to in this Country) by washing themselves in it; neither do they want very good Springs of fresh Water; as for Pump-water, 'tis to be had in most places in this Province.

We have an Account from the *Indians,* that there are hot Baths near the Hilly Country, where a great likelihood appears of making Salt-petere, because the Earth in many places is strongly mixed and impregnated with a Nitrous Salt, which is much coveted by the Beasts of this Country, who come at certain Seasons of the Year in great Numbers, and by their licking this Earth, make great Holes in those

Banks,

Banks, which sometimes lye at the Heads of great Precipices, where they often tumble down and are dash'd in pieces.

It is very certain that the most Sweet and healthful Part of this Country is inhabited only by the Savage *Indians* at present; and a great deal thereof has no other Inhabitants but the wild Beasts. For the *Indians* are not inclinable to settle in the richest Lands, because the Timbers are too large for them to cut down to make Plantations of: A farther confirmation of the healthfulness of the Hilly parts of this Country, is very apparent, in the large Stature and gray Heads so common to be met with amongst the Savages that dwell near the Mountains.

The Christians or Planters of *North Carolina,* Barter the Commodities that are produced in the Country for Rum, Sugar, Mollosses, Negroes, and the like.

The current Coin of this Country is at present only made of Paper Bills, which pass throughout all this Province; not but that the Gold and Silver Coin of all Nations pass here, according to their Weight or intrinsick Value, which the Planters carefully preserve to buy Negroes with in the Islands and other Places. The Contents of the Bills in this Province are as follows, *viz. This Bill of ten Pounds shall be current in all Payments in* North Carolina, *according to an Act of Assembly made* November *9th.* 1729. This is the greatest Bill, and twelve Pence the smallest, which is wrote after the same manner of the former. The Assembly nominate five of their Members, who sign all these Bills with different Ink; all these Bills are numbered in figures at the top, in the nature of Bank-Bills, and Seals fixt to each of them; there is about thirty or forty thousand Pounds of this kind of Money in *North Carolina.*

There is a Treasury Office kept wherein all the Bills are changed, and new ones given for those that are old and

torn;

torn; yet notwithstanding all the Care that is taken, these Bills are counterfeited, and the publick very often imposed upon. The Money of *North Carolina* is in value five Shillings for one Sterling; and in *South Carolina,* the difference is Seven to One Sterling; with these Bills they purchase Lands, and all Necessaries.

It is admirable to observe the Prosperity of several Adventurers to *Carolina,* in the memory of Man; and how many from the most despicable beginnings in a short time, by Gods blessing and their own industry, are arrived to as splendid Fortunes, as any have in other *British* Provinces on this Continent. All manner of Game is here very plenty, neither are there any Laws here to bind their Priviledges, as it is with us in *Ireland,* for the meanest Planter may, with as much Freedom, destroy all manner of Game, as he that is the most Wealthy, or highest in Dignity. So that the poorest Planter has as much Right to the delicaceies of this Country, as the richest; nay the very Labourer is intituled to the same Priviledge.

The Language principally made use of in this Province is the *English;* notwithstanding there are Planters settled here from *France, Germany, Holland,* and many other parts of *Europe,* who have all learn'd and speak the *English* Tongue, many of the *Indians* also use it, and especially the three civilized Kings, and those that Trade and Converse with the *English;* there are many of the Planters that understand and speak the *Indian* Language well.

The Diseases that are most common in *Carolina* are, *Agues,* or intermittent *Fevers, Cachexia, Diarrhœa, Dysenteria,* the *Clap* and *French Pox,* the *Yaws, Chollicks, Cholera-Morbus, Convulsions, Hooping-Cough, Cutaneous Disorders,* such as *Tetters, Ring-worms, Rashes, prickley-Heats,* and the *Itch.*

The

The *Agues* or *intermittent Fevers,* do generally admit of
the same method of Cure as with us in *Ireland,* so that it
would be needless to repeat it here, which almost every old
Woman pretends to have an infalible Cure for.

The *Cachexy,* or ill habit of Body, is a very common Distemper in these Parts; 'tis very stubborn in its Nature, and
tedious and difficult to be cured. In this disorder, the Face
is very pale and discolor'd, and the Body big and swoln; this
Distemper is principally owing to their eating great quantities
of Fruit that this Country produces, and to a sedentary way
of living, and their eating Clay and Dirt, which the Children,
both Whites and Blacks, and some of the old People are very
subject to; by which means the whole Humours of the Body
are corrupted and vitiated to that degree (through surfeits
and ill digestion) that they will hardly admit of a Cure.
Steel'd Wines, and other Preparations of filings and rust of
Iron, strong Purgers, and Exercises, are the only Methods to
perfect the Cure of this Distemper.

The *Cholera-Morbus,* is a vehement Perturbation of the
whole Body and Bowels, from a deprav'd Motion of the
Ventricle and Guts, whereby bilious, sharp, or corrupt Humours, are plentifully and violently discharged upwards and
downwards. This disorder is happily carried off by giving
proper Doses of the *Ipecauacana,* that grows plentifully in
*Carolina,* which I have already made mention of.

The *Cramp* or *Convulsions,* is a Motion whereby the Muscles or Membranes are contracted and remitted, without the
Will. This Disorder is common in these Parts, and especially amongst the *Negroes* or *Blacks,* whereof many die,
either for want, or before proper Medicines can be administer'd; it admits of the same method of Cure as with us in
*Europe.*

The

The *White* and *Bloody-Flux* are common Distempers in *Carolina*, and so are the *Clap* and *French Pox;* these are cured after the same manner as with us.

The *Yaws,* are a Disorder not well known in *Europe,* but very common and familiar here; it is like the *Lues venerea,* having most of the Symptoms that attend the Pox, such as Nocturnal Pains, Botches, foul Erruptions, and Ulcers in several parts of the Body, and is acquired after the same manner as the *Pox* is, *viz.* by Copulation, &c. but is never attended with a *Gonorrhœa* in the beginning. This Distemper was brought hither by the *Negroes* from *Guinea,* where it is a common Distemper amongst them, and is communicated to several of the *Europeans* or Christians, by their cohabiting with the Blacks, by which means it is hereditary in many Families in *Carolina,* and by it some have lost their Palates and Noses.

This Distemper, though of a venereal kind, is seldom cured by Mercurials, as I have often experienced, for I have known some undergo the Course of three Salavations to no purpose, the virulency still continuing as bad as ever: Wherefore I judge it not amiss to set forth the most effectual method for curing it, which I have often experienc'd, and never without good success (during my residence in those parts) though the Distemper was of ever so violent a nature, or long continuance; it is as follows:

*Take four Ounces of the Bark of the* Spanish Oak, *two Ounces of the middle Bark of the* Pine Tree, *two Ounces of the Root of the* Sumack, *that bears the Berries, of these Ingredients make a strong Decoction, whereof let the Patient drink a full Pint milk-warm and half a Pint cold, this gives a strong Vomit, by which abundance of filthy Matter is dis-*

*charged,*

*charged.* This is what is to be done the first Day. *Then let the Patient drink half a Pint three times a Day,* viz. *in the Morning, at one o'Clock in the Afternoon, and at Night, for six Weeks; and if there be any outward Sores, wash them clean five or six times a-Day with part of the same Decoction, 'till they are all healed up, and the Patient becomes well.*

The Patient must abstain from all sorts of flesh Meat, and Strong Liquors during the said Course, his principal Diet must be Broth, Gruel, Penæda, and the like. They may boil the above quantity of Ingredients four times, if more, it will be too weak; this Method effectually cures the *Yaws* in the said time, and the Patient becomes as strong and healthy as ever. I have here given the true method of the Cure of this Distemper, it being little known in *Europe.*

The *Cholick,* or *Dry Belly-ach,* is another common Distemper in this Country, and is often attended with such violent Convulsions, that frequently the Limbs are so contracted (and especially the Hands) that for want of Care and good Advice, they have continued so all their life time; though I have known some of them die in these Fits, which are attended with such a violent constipation of the Bowels, that they cannot void any thing either upwards or downwards. Strong Vomits, Purges, Clysters, and Oyntments, for the contracted Limbs, are the most effectual Methods to carry off this Disorder.

*Rashes* and *Prikley-heat,* are common Disorders here; in the extremity of the hot Weather, which suddenly comes after cold, they are attended with extream Itchings all over the Body, especially the Legs, which if scratched immediately, inflame, and become inveterate Sores and Ulcers; to

4 G prevent

prevent which, Spirit of Wine and Camphir or any other Spirit, is of excellent use, by applying it to the Parts.

*Tetters* and *Ring-worms,* are common in this Province, and are easily cur'd by several Plants in this Country, and especially by the Juice of the Sheep-Sorrel, by applying it to the Part infected.

The *Hooping-Cough,* at my arrival in *Carolina,* was an universal Disorder amongst young and old, whereof several *Negroes* died. It continued in this Province for seven or eight Months successively, beginning in *September,* and ending in *June;* after Bleeding and Vomiting, I found the *Jesuite Bark* to be of excellent use in this disorder. I was assured by many in *Carolina,* that they never knew this Distemper in these Parts before that time.

The Children are much afflicted with the *Worms,* which is owing to their eating vast quantities of Fruit, this excess sometimes occasions Fevers amongst them, yet they are cured after the same manner as with us, likewise with many Plants growing here.

As for *Cutaneous* Disorders they are seldom at a loss for a speedy Cure, not only from the Plants, but likewise the Waters. Thus have I given an Account of the most common Disorders amongst the Christian Inhabitants.

The Curiosities here are, variety of strange wild Beasts, and several kinds of Birds, Fishes, Snakes, Insects, Reptiles, Herbs, Plants, Shrubs, Trees, and Fruits: many whereof are not to be met with in *Europe,* which the Reader will find inserted in their proper Places, when I come to treat on those heads. There is a large Cave on the top of the Mountains, that will hold a hundred Men and more to sit in, but whether it be natural or artificial, is not known by any that have seen

it;

it; but I am of Opinion that it is natural, the *Indians* having had no Tools to work in Wood or Stone, at the first arrival of the *Europeans,* so that it cannot be reasonably imagined that a Work of this nature could be perfected without proper Instruments for that purpose.

As all Grain and Pulse thrive here to admiration, so do the Stocks of Cattle, Horses, and Swine multiply surprizingly, there being as great numbers of each Species, as in any Province possessed by the *English* in *America.*

The *Veal* is very good and white, but they seldom kill any for the Market, being fond to preserve their Calves to a larger growth. The Planters make Penfolds adjacent to their Habitations, wherein they milk their Cows every Morning and Evening; after which, they turn them into the Woods, where they remain feeding all Day; when they return at Night, they carefully shut up their Calves with some few of the Cows, in those Penfolds, which protects them from the Wolves, or any other voracious wild Beasts: In the Mornings and Evenings the Cows return from the Woods to be milked, and are turned out as usual; the Calves are turned into the Inclosures where they remain feeding and safe all the Day, no wild Beast ever appearing near their Plantations in that space of time. I have seen one hundred Calves together in one of these Penfolds, being all the Property of one Planter. The Calves generally suck their Dams all the time they are milking, otherwise the Cows would not suffer any one to touch them. The Milk is very pleasant and rich.

Their Heifers bring forth Calves at eighteen or twenty Months old; this early production makes such a wonderful increase, that many of the Planters, from mean beginnings, are Masters now of such large Stocks of Cattle, that you may

G 2                                              buy

buy hundreds in the Season: Their method of killing, is
generally to shoot them in the Fields, or in the Penfolds;
then they cut off the Head and Feet, and take out the Intrails,
which they throw away as useless, except the Fat, (which
they carefully preserve.) After this manner they continue
killing all the Year, as they have Occasion.

If the Cattle be suffered to live to a proper Age, their
Beef proves as large and fat as any in the neighbouring
Colonies. They kill vast Quantities of Beeves in *October,*
and the other cool Months, especially when they intend them
for Salting and Exportation, for at those Seasons they are in
their prime of Flesh, and best preserved. The Exportation
of this Commodity is one of the greatest Branches of their
Trade.

It may perhaps seem very strange to some *Europeans,* how
the Planters can have such large Stocks of Cattle, where
there are such Numbers of *Wolves, Tygers, Panthers,* and
other Beasts of Prey; but I can assure them that they give
themselves no further trouble than what I have already observed, few or no wild Beasts ever daring or attempting to
kill either Calves or Foles, fearing their Dams, who vigor-
ously defend them. When a Cow hath once espied a *Wolf* or
any other voracious Beast near, she gives a Signal by bellowing and roaring, upon which all the Black Cattle within her
hearing will run to her assistance, and most resolutely defend their own Species.

There are great Numbers of those Cattle wild, which continually breed in the Woods, (so are there of Horses and
Mares) here you shall see great Droves feeding promiscously
in the *Savannas* amongst the Deer, fifty or Sixty Miles distant from any Inhabitants. This sociable Disposition
amongst Beasts of different kinds we observed in our Travel-

ing

ing up towards the Mountains, which, together with the Beauty of the Country gave us no small Satisfaction.

The Horses are well shaped, swift, and generally about thirteen or fourteen Hands high, they are durable and will travel incredible Journies. They are never shod, partly by reason of the softness of the Ground, which is covered over with Grass, without any Gravel or Stones; they have few or no distempers amongst them as in *European* Countries, such as *Spavin, Splint, Ringbones,* and the like; they are seldom or never blind, and generally live twenty Years or more, most commonly dying of old Age. If there were but good Stallions and Mares sent here from *England,* or any other Parts, we could not fail of a good Breed in a short time; the Country and Pasturage being so proper for that end.

The Planters are the worst Horse-masters I have ever met with, for few or none allow Corn to their Horses after long Journies, for they frequently tye them to a Tree for Hours together, and sometimes for a Day or two without any manner of subsistance, from whence it sometimes happens that they break loose, and take into Woods, where they remain for Weeks together, with the Saddles on their Backs, before they are found out, and had not they been such good Drudges as they are, there would be but few in this Province, with the bad usage they give them.

The Horses which they keep within the Inclosures, and some times feed with *Indian-Corn,* are rendered very durable for Journies and Hunting in the Woods. I hope it will not be improper here to give the Reader an Account how they take the Wild Horses in the Woods, which is as follows. The Planters generally, two or more hunt on Horseback in the Woods together, and as soon as they espie a wild Horse,

they

they pursue him, and their Horses are so well train'd to this way of Hunting, that they will neither hurt themselves nor the Riders against a Tree, though you ride them in full Speed, they will perform this for Hours together, 'till such time as the wild Horse stands still; then one of the Hunters alights and claps a Bridle into his Mouth, and a Saddle on his Back (tho' ten or fifteen Years old) and rides him to their own, or the next Plantation, where they feed him with *Indian-Corn* and *Salt,* which feeding, in a little time, makes him as tame and domestick, as any in their Plantation, and fit to pursue his wild Species in the Woods at the next Hunting match, or any other use they have occasion to make of him.

The *Sheep* thrive well, having two or three *Lambs* at one Yeaning; they are never suffered to ramble in the Woods (as the other Cattle are) but are kept in Inclosures in the Plantations, from whence they will come every Evening to the Planters Houses, having no Defence against the wild Beasts (and especially the *Wolves,* their mortal Enemy) at Night they are put up in their Penfolds made of Timber, which every Planter has for that Purpose to defend them from all manner of wild Beasts, but it sometimes happens, through Negligence, that if they are not Inclosed, they become a Prey to the *Wolves,* who never fail to search and watch for them at Night. The Mutton is generally exceeding Fat, and as well relish'd as any I have met with in *Europe.* Their Wool is fine, and a good Commodity here. They seldom kill any of their *Lambs* for the *Market,* but generally preserve them to a greater Age; neither are the native Planters so fond of Mutton (which is of a middling Size) as the *Europeans* generally are.

Of

Of *Goats,* they have but very few in *Carolina,* and yet they would thrive very well there; but they are so mischievous to Gardens, Orchards, and other Trees, that the Native Planters are not fond of keeping or preserving great numbers of them, though their Flesh is fat and well relish'd, as any in *Europe,* and their skins are as good.

The *Swine* are more numerous here than in any of the *English* Provinces; and the Pork exceeds any in *Europe* for Goodness. The plenty of Acorns, Nuts, and other Fruits, which the Woods naturally afford, make their Flesh of an excellent Taste, and produces great quantities of them; some Planters possess several hundreds, and vast numbers are to be met with in the Woods, which are every persons Property that can kill them; for no one claims them as his own, except they bear his own Mark or Brand, and it is so with Horses and Cows, that are wild in the Woods. The Planters export vast quantities of Pork to the Islands in the *West Indies,* such as *Barbadoes, Antegua,* and several other places where Provisions are scarce, for such Commodities as they have occasion for.

They have plenty of all manner of Domestick Fowl, such as Geese, common Ducks, *Muscovy* Ducks, Turkeys, Cocks and Hens, Pigeons, and the like, to be purchased at cheaper Rates, than in any part of *Europe.*

Notwithstanding *North Carolina* yields to no Country in point of Fertility, especially for Cattle, Venison, Fish and Flesh, yet amongst all this Plenty, there is a scarcity of sufficient Hands to cultivate this noble and fertile Soil. It is capable of producing as good Hemp and Flax, as grow in most parts of *Europe,* and Linnen might here be brought to great perfection.

This

This Country likewise produces as good Tobacco, as any to be met with in *Virginia, Maryland,* or any other Neighbouring Province in the Hands of the *English:* But the Planters having so many other valuable Commodities proper for Exportation, they little regard or improve it at present, in proportion to what they do in other Provinces.

THE

# OF THE VEGETABLES

OF

# NORTH CAROLINA.

T HE Spontaneous Shrubs of this Country are the *Larks-heel* Tree; four sorts of *Honey-suckle* Tree, or *Woodbind,* the first always grows in low moist Grounds, the other in clear dry Lands, the Flowers of which are more cut and lacerated; these grow about two or three Feet high; the third, which is of the same height, is one of the most beautiful Flowers of its Colour that is to be met with, and is found growing for the most part by the sides of Swamps, or on the Banks of the Rivers, but never near the Salt Water. The Flowers of these are of a whitish colour, but the last is the most beautiful, growing in great bunches out of one Stem, and is commonly the bigness of a large Turnip. In *April* and *May,* nothing can be more beautiful, being at that time in their greatest splendor, which affords not only a pleassant sight, but a most grateful and fragrant Smell to those that pass through the Woods. There is another *Honey-suckle* that grows in the Forrest, and is about a Foot high, bearing it's Flowers on small Stems, the main Stock being no thicker than a Wheat Straw; all these sorts differ very little from ours, only with this variation, that those here are larger.

H                                    *Princes-*

*Princes-feather,* are very large and beautiful, not only in the Gardens, but in several parts of the Woods. *Tres colores, Branched Sun-Flower, Double Poppies, Lupines* of several sorts, and all Spontaneous. The *sensible Plant,* (as I have been informed) grows near the Mountains, which I did not see during my stay in those Parts.

The *Bastard Saffron* is plenty in this Province, and I do not doubt but that the true *Saffron* of *England* would thrive well here if Planted, and the same care taken.

The *Cotton* Plant being so very profitable, I will give a Description of, which is as follows: It hath small Stalks about three Feet high, and sometimes higher, divided into several small Branches, wherein are many broad Leaves, cut for the most part into three Sections, and sometimes more, indented about the Edges, not unlike the Leaves of the common *Mallows,* but lesser, softer, and of a grayish Colour, among which come forth the Flowers, the Edges whereof are of a Yellowish Colour, and the middle part Purple; after which appears large Burs or Husks, wherein the Seed and Cotton is contained, as soon as it is ripe it opens into four Parts or Divisions, if Care be not taken, it casteth forth its Seed and Cotton upon the Ground. This Plant beareth but for one Season, and as soon as the Seeds are ripe it immediately perisheth, as many other Plants do; so that the Planters are obliged to sow the Seed every Spring, which is ripe in the Autumn, and they cut it down at that time as we do Corn. It groweth in great Plenty in several Parts of this Country, and is a beneficial Commodity to the Planters.

The *Yellow Jessamine* grows wild in several parts of the Woods, affording a most pleasant and grateful Smell.

*Ever-Greens* are to be met with all over this Province, of several curious sorts, of a very quick Growth, affording pleas-

ant

ant and refreshing Shades in the extremity of hot Weather:
And such are the lofty *Cypress* or *White Cedar,* the *Red
Cedar,* the *Pitch Pine,* the *Yellow Pine,* the *White Pine* with
long Leaves, and the smaller *Almond-Pine: Hornbeam, Holly*
two sorts, *Bay-Tree,* two sorts of *Myrtle,* two sorts of *Ever-
green Oaks, Misseltoe* of the *Oak, Gullberry-Tree, Privet,
Savine, Yaupan,* or *Cassena,* whereof the Tea is made, so
very much in request amonst both the *Indians,* and *Christians,* with many other *Ever-greens.*

I shall in the next Place treat of the Timber that this
Country produces, *viz.*

The *Chestnut Oak,* is a very lofty Tree and clear of
Boughs and Limbs, for fifty or sixty Feet high, and is commonly four or five Feet Diameter, they are the largest Oaks
we have, and yield the fairest Planks. These kind of Oaks
grow chiefly in low Land that is stiff and rich; some of them
are so high that a good Gun will hardly kill a Turkey on the
top of them, though with Swan Shot. They are called the
*Chesnut Oak* from the sweetness and largeness of the Acorns;
the Leaves and Bark of this and all the following Oaks are of
a very Binding Nature, and may successfuly be used to stop
all kind of Fluxes, the Salt is Diuretick, and the Wood of
some are of the same Uses and Virtues with *Guajacum;* as is
manifest in its cure of the *Yaws* and other Disorders. In
most of all the Oaks, grows a long Moss, whereof the Cattle
and Deer are very fond, which I have already mentioned.

The *White Scaly Bark Oak;* this is used as the former in
building Sloops, Brigantines, Ships, and other Vessells of
Burthen. And though it bears a larger Acorn, yet it never
grows to the bulk and height of the former. This kind of
Oak is found generally growing on dry stiff Lands and is so

H 2 called

called from the Scaly broken White Bark which covers the
Tree. This and the former produce good Mast for Swine to
feed on.

The *Red Oak* sometimes grows very large and lofty in
good Land, but it is not used as the former in building of
Vessels, being a very Porous Timber, and not durable, yet it
is sometimes used for Pipe Staves, and makes good Fences
and Clap-Boards, which are the only use made of it in this
Country; it is so called from the redness of its Wood. It
produces good Mast for Swine.

The *Spanish Oak* has a whitish smooth Bark, grows pretty
large in wet low Ground, and is very free from Limbs or
Boughs; it is durable Wood, and very easy to split, therefore
some use to build Vessels with it, it affords good Plank,
Clap-Boards, Rails, for Fences, and also excellent good Mast
for Swine; the Bark of this Tree is used for the Cure of the
*Yaws.*

The *Bastard-Spanish-Oak* is betwixt the *Red* and *Spanish-
Oak,* it is not as durable as the former, but makes good Rails
for Fencing, and Clap-Boards, and is very good Wood for the
Fire, this being all the Use that is made of it at present; it
likewise bears a very good Mast for *Swine* to feed on.

The *Black-Oak* grows large, and is durable Wood under
Water; it is seldom made use of in building Ships, but is
sometimes used in House-Work; it bears as good Mast as any
of the former for *Swine.*

The *White-Iron,* or *Ring-Oak,* is so called from the dura-
bility and lasting quality of the Wood; this Wood is found
to be one of the best *Oaks* we have in this Country, or in
*America,* for *Pipe-staves* and Building of all kind of Ships;
it is as large as the former, grows on dry Lands, and seldom
fails of producing a good Crop of *Acorns.*

The

The *Turkey-Oak,* so called, from the small Acorns it bears, which are sweet, and eat like the *Acorns* of the *Chestnut-Oak,* on which the Wild *Turkies* feed, and are very fat in the Season; this Wood is only used for Firing and Fences, not being so durable as the former are.

The *Live-Oak,* so called, from its being Green all the Year, it grows on dry sandy Ground, and is the most durable *Oak* in all *America,* but it is short, and will not afford Plank of any considerable Length, therefore unfit to build Ships with. There are some few Trees that will afford a Stock of twelve Feet, but it being so very firm and weighty, they never make use of it upon these Occasions, moreover the Wood being so very hard, the Sawyers seldom attempt the cutting of it: It is observable, that a Nail being once driven into it, it is next to an impossibility to draw it out again; the Limbs thereof are so cured, that they serve for excellent Timbers, and Knees and makes the best Trunnels of any Oak in the World for Ships and Vessels of any sort; the Acorns thereof are as sweet as any *Chesnuts,* and the *Indians* draw an Oil from them as sweet and palatable as that from the *Olive,* though of an Amber Colour; with these Acorns some have counterfeited and made *Chocolate* not to be distinguished by a good Palate; this Wood makes excellent Window Frames, Mallats, and Pins for Blocks. They are of an indifferent quick growth; there are two sorts of this Oak, and Swine that feed on its Acorns, are excellent fine *Pork.*

The *Fresh Water Oak,* grows in Ponds of fresh Water, in Swamps by the River sides, and in low Grounds over-flown with Water, they continue Green all the Year; there is little or no use made of it, except for Fire or Fences.

The

The *Cypress* is not an Ever-green in *Carolina,* and is therefore called the *Bald Cypress,* because the Leaves during the
Winter Season turn Red, and do not recover their verdure
till the Spring.   These Trees are the tallest and thickest of
any we have in this Part of the World; some of them being
above thirty Six Feet in circumference; the Nuts which these
Trees bear yield a most odoriferous *Balsam,* that most effectually cures all new and *green Wounds, Gonorrhœa's,* and old
*Gleets,* and being drank with *Alicant,* stop all kinds of *Fluxes*
of Blood, and consolidate *Ulcers* in stubborn Bodies, and dry
up excessive Moistures, and cure *Ruptures, Polypus, Carbuncles,* and many other disorders.   The *Planters* and *Indians* most commonly make their *Periaugers* and Canoes of
this Wood, with which they pass over large Creeks and Bays,
to Transport their Lumber from one River to another; some
of these *Periaugers* are so large that they will carry thirty
or forty Barrels of *Pitch* or *Tar* in them, though of one entire Piece of Timber; some trade in them to *Virginia* and
other Places along the Coast, with Pork and other Productions of the Country:   Of these Trees are likewise made
curious Boats for Pleasure and other Necessary Crafts; this
Wood is very lasting and free from the Rot by the Worms
in the Water, which often ruin many Vessels and Boats
made of Oak and other Wood, which I shall describe in its
proper Place, when I treat of those insects:   It is reported
that no Moth or other Vermine will abide in a Chest made of
this Wood.

The *Pine-Tree,* whereof there are four sorts, if not more.
The *Pitch-Pine* is a very large fair Tree, free from Boughs
or Branches, 'till you come near the top, and continues green
all the year like the *Fir-Tree,* it's Timber is much redder
than the former, and it's Leaves narrower, shorter and more

sharp

sharp pointed like the *Pine;* their Fruit is *Scaly,* the Bark of the Tree is blacker, tougher, and more flexible than that of the *Fir-Tree.* The Wood of this Tree being so full of *Bitumen,* or *Turpentine,* and is so durable, that it seems to suffer no decay, though exposed to all Weathers, or lying upon the Ground or in the Water for many Ages; and is used in many domesticks Affairs. This Tree affords four excellent Commodities, *viz. Turpentine, Tar, Pitch,* and *Rosin,* how they are made, I shall treat of in another Place.

The *White* and *Yellow-Pine,* grow to be very large Trees much after the same form with the former, but it's Leaves are larger, and the Wood is not so full of *Turpentine,* therefore more easy to be sawed, it affords excellent good Plank for Building, and several other uses, they make *Masts, Yards,* and several other Necessaries of this *Pine,* being the most useful Tree in the Woods.

The *Almond-Pine,* this last bears *Kernels* in the *Apple,* tasting much like *Almonds;* for which Reason it is so call'd, it much resembles the former in bigness and groweth, is used for *Masts, Boards, Piles, Fences,* and several other things.

The *Dwarf-Pine,* seldom exceeds above Seventeen Feet high, and is therefore of little or no use, except for shew, being an Ever-green, as all the rest are. There are many Virtues ascribed to the Produce of these Trees (which they rightly deserve) not only in external, but internal Disorders, which are well known amongst us.

The *Cedar,* whereof there are two sorts, the *Red* and the *White.* The *Red Cedar* is encompassed with a vast number of Branches, which grow gradually lesser and shorter, as they approach the top of the Tree, so that it grows exactly in the Form of a Pyramid. The Leaves are small and round like those of the Pine Tree, but shorter and not so sharp pointed;

it

it beareth Berries all times of the Year, which are sweet and pleasant to eat; it is a most beautiful Ever-green, and is here in great Plenty. Those near the Salts grow generally on Sand Banks, and that in the Freshes is found in the Swamps and low wet Grounds. It is a soft Wood like Firr, and of a reddish Colour, but hardens in process of time; of this Wood, Tables, Wainscot, and other Necessaries are made, 'tis esteemed for its sweet scent, and it is as durable and lasting a wood as any we have in *Carolina;* it is much used in Posts for Houses and Sills, as also to build Sloops, Boats, *&c.* by reason the Worms will not touch it, though it remain in the Water, or upon Land, for several Years. Of this Cedar, Ship loads may be exported, and it was formerly so very plentiful and common in this Province, that they have fenced large Plantations with it; the Coffins for the Dead are frequently made of it, by reason of its lasting Quality, the Wood of this Tree is profitable against the *French Pox,* and an infusion in Vinegar helps Scabs and other cutaneous Disorders.

The *White Cedar,* so called, because it nearly approaches the other Cedar in Smell, Bark, and Leaves, only this grows taller, is exceeding streight, very light, and free to split: It is tough and durable, and maketh good Yards, Top-masts, Boms, and Boltsprits, the best Shingles for Houses, Pails, and other Vessels, necessary for several uses, are made of it's Wood; with the Bark and the *Red Cedar,* the *Indians* most commonly use to make their Cabbins of, which proves firm, and resists all Weather.

The *Tulip* Trees, which are called by the *Planters* Poplars, as being nearest in grain to that Wood. These Trees grow exceeding large and tall, some being found Twenty one Foot and more in circumference as I have frequently seen in many

places

places in this Province. And I have been informed, that some are found ten Feet Diameter; several of these Trees bear a white Tulip, and others a party-colour'd one: The Wood makes handsome Wainscot Tables, Shingles for Houses, and Planks for several uses; it is very durable and lasting under Ground, and in the Water. The Planters frequently make an Oyntment of the Buds, which is excellent good to cure all manner of Inflamations, Scalds and Burns; The Cattle are fond of its Buds, which gives a very odd taste to the Milk.

The *Aspen* Trees are the same here as in *Europe,* but are scarcely to be found in this Province; the Bark is used inwardly in the *Sciatica,* and other *Rheumatick* Disorders, and in the *Strangury,* but the Leaves being taken inwardly, are said to cause Barreness.

The *Ash* Tree, whereof we have two sorts; the first is only like the *European* in the Grain of the Wood, for it differs from ours in the Leaves and the Bark, and Keys, it bears none; the Wood is very tough, but there is little use made of it at present. The second sort is what they call in these Parts by the Name of the *Water-Ash,* and differs from the former by only being brittel and the Bark is food for the *Beavers,* both these sorts of *Ash* grow in wet low Swampy Grounds, and on the Banks of the Rivers.

The *Sycamore* Tree grows in low and Swampy Land, and by River sides; the Bark is quite different from ours, but very beautiful, being mottled and clouded with several Colours, as White, Blue, &c. The Leaves of this Tree are exactly of the form and shape with those in *Europe;* Keys it bears none, but a Bur like the sweet *Gum,* or the *Chesnut,* but its Grain is fine and beautifully mottled with variety of

Colours, and is made use of for several domestick Necessaries, such as Wainscot, Tables, Chairs, Trenchers, Dishes, Stocks for Guns, and the like.   The Buds of this Tree boiled and applyed, help the hardness of the Spleen, and other hard swellings; the Fruit loosens the Belly and the Tears that issue out of the Tree in Spring, the biting of Serpents.

The *Beech* Tree is frequently to be met with very large, whereof there are two sorts; the first is much the same as in *Europe*, and is in plenty all over this Province, but is little regarded or made use of, only for *Fire-wood,* not being durable Timber, yet affords plenty of Sweet Mast for *Swine,* which makes the *Pork* very oily, except it be hardened with *Indian Corn* before it is killed or made use of.

There is another sort of *Beech* found here in several places called *Buck-Beech,* and differs little from the former, only in the Bark and Leaf there is some small difference, and the Tree is generally not so large.   The Leaves applied, help Swellings, Blisters, and Excoriations of the Skin; the Juice that comes out of the Tree bored, is excellent against Scruffs, Tetters, Ring-worms, Scabs, and sore Mouths; the Kernel of the Nut helps the Gravel and Stone in the Kidneys, so doth the Ashes.

The *Elm* Tree, whereof are two sorts, the first grows on high Lands, and is like the *European Elm.*   The *Indians* take the Bark of the Root of this Tree, and beat it to a *Pulp* whilst fresh, and then dry it in the *Chimney,* with which they heal a Cut or green Wound, very speedily.   The other kind of *Elm* grows in wet or low Grounds, and differs but little from the former, only the Bark is so very tough, that the *Europeans* and *Indians* make Ropes of it for several uses, which they strip of in *April* or *May,* when the Sap begins to run, this they can do with the greatest ease imaginable at

that

that time, there being such plenty of other valuable Timber, there is little or no other use made of it at present. The Decoction of the Bark and Leaves of the *Elm* is of a cleansing, drying, and binding Quality, and therefore good in Wounds and broken Bones; the Liquor that issueth out of the Tree takes away Scruff, Pimples, Spots and Freckles from the Face; one Ounce of the inner-Bark in Wine, Purges Flegm.

The *Mulberry* Tree, whereof there are three sorts here, beside the different bigness of some Trees Fruit. The first is the common red *Mulberry,* whose Fruit is long and taper at the Ends, and is the earliest in this Province (except the *Strawberries*) they are sweet and luscious, the Planters make use of their Fruit (which is above an Inch long) instead of *Raisons* and *Currans,* for several Dishes; they yield a transparent Crimson Liquor, which I do not doubt would make good Wine, if the Planters Inclination tended that way: The *Parakeetoes* and other Fowl feed upon the Fruit in the Season, and likewise the *Hogs,* as they drop from the Trees. These Trees grow to be very large, and make the most delightful and pleasant Shades to sit under in the Summer, of any in these Parts of *America,* by their large Boughs spreading at great distances, and growing as round as any I have ever seen; you shall see in most of their Plantations, and especially near their Dwelling Houses, these pleasant Arbours.

The other two sorts bear a smooth Leaf fit for the *Silkwork;* the first of these bear a white *Mulberry,* which is common: The second bears a Fruit like a small *Blackberry* which is very sweet; the Wood of these Trees are very durable and tough, and when the *Indians* can't get the *Locust* Tree, they use this, to make their Bows with. These Trees grow extraordinary round, and pleasant to the Eye, as any

I 2                                                                in in these Parts, the Fruit, Leaves, and Barke are used in *Gargarisms* for sore *Throats* and the *Tooth-ach.*

The *Hickery* Trees are of the *Wallnut* kind, and bears a Nut as they do, whereof there are three sorts, *viz.* the Common white, the red, and the flying Bark'd.

The common or white *Hickery* grows tollerably large, but is not a durable Wood, for if it be cut down and exposed to the Weather, it will be quite rotten and spoiled in three Years (as will likewise the Beech of this Country) but it is very tough, easy to split, and maketh the best Hoops I have seen. It bears a Nut much like the *Wall-nut* of this Country, with a Husk about it, but of an Oval Form; the Kernels are sweet, good to eat, and make Oil; the Hogs feed plentifully on them in the Season, by which means they become Fat, and make excellent Pork.

The *Indians* gather great Quantities of these Nuts, and the Black Wall-nuts (being ripe in *Autumn*) which they preserve and lay up in Stores for the Winter Season, whereof they make several Dishes and Banquets; this is generally done after the following Manner, they take these Nuts and break them very small between two Stones, until the Shells and Kernels are indifferent small, and this Powder they present to Strangers upon little Wooden Dishes, the Kernel dissolves in the Mouth, the Shell is spit out, and tastes as well as Almonds. They likewise thicken their Venison Broath with this Powder, whilst the Shell precipitates and remains at the bottom, making it very rich and agreeable in Taste; these Nuts have much the same Virtues with the Wall-nuts.

The *Red Hickery,* is so called, from the Heart thereof being red, firm, and durable, whereof are made walking-sticks, Mortars, Pestils, and several other fine Turners Ware.

Both

Both these sorts are plenty in this Province, and are the best Fire-wood they have.

The third sort is called the *Flying Bark'd Hickery,* from its britle and scaly Bark: It bears a Nut with a bitter Kernel, and a soft Shell; of this Wood they make Coggs for Mills, and several other Necessaries: The Leaves of all these sorts of *Hickery* have a fragrant smell, and are much like our Wall-nut in *Europe.*

The *Black Wall-nut* Trees are plenty and large in this Province, and the Wood firm and durable, whereof beautiful Wainscot Tables, Chests of Drawers, and several other Necessaries are made. Some of this Wood is very Knotty, but fine Grain'd, and partly of the Colour of the *Yew* Tree; it is so durable, that some have bottom'd Ships with it, it is likewise reported that it is never eaten by Worms bred in the salt Water. The Kernels of these Nuts are good to eat, but after some time they grow rank and oily. It grows exactly in the shape of the *European Wall-nut,* but the shell is much thicker and harder, as most of the native Nuts of *America* are. This Fruit is very agreeable and pleasant to eat; when it begins to grow ripe and hath its yellow Husk or Coat on, it looks exactly like a Lemon. The old Hogs feed plentifully on these Nuts, which make them fat, and good Pork, but the young Swine are not able to crack them, so that great quantities lye under the Trees. It is called the *Black Wall-nut* from its Black Barck, to distinguish it I suppose from the other *Hickery,* whereof it is a Species.

The *Ches-nut* Tree in this Province grows mostly toward the Heads of the Rivers, and hilly parts of the Country; it is large and durable Wood, and is useful in building of Houses and many other Conveniences. The Nut of the *Ches-nut* Tree is smaller than the *European,* but much sweeter and

better

better relish'd; they have the Virtues of Almonds and Hazlenuts, but more nourishing, the Leaves or Bark of the Tree boiled in Wine are good against the Bloody Flux, and all other kind of Fluxes.

The *Sweet-Gum* Tree, so called, from the sweet and fragrant Gum it yields in the Spring, by making an Incision in the Bark and Wood. It cures the Herps, Tettars, Inflamations, Morphew, and many other cutaneous Disorders: It is likewise a soveraign Balsam for several internal Disorders, as I have often experienced; it bears a Leaf partly like the Aspen Tree, a round Bur, with a kind of Prickle like the *Horse Chesnut,* wherein is contained the Seed; scarce any Wood has a finer or better Grain, being very durable, and is frequently made use of for Tables, Drawers, &c.

The *Black Gum* Tree, whereof there are two sorts; the first bears a black Berry well tasted, which the *Indians* commonly mix with their Pulse, and the kind of Soups they make, to which it gives a pretty flavour, and Scarlet Colour: The Bears crop these Trees for their Fruit, of which they are very fond, yet if they are kill'd at that Season, they eat unsavoury, which no doubt is occasioned by their eating those Berries, for at other times, when they feed on Beech and other Mast, their Flesh is well tasted and good Food.

The second sort bears a Berry in shape like the former, but bitter and ill tasted. This Tree the *Indians* report is never hurt or wounded by Lightning, as other Trees generally are. It has no certain Grain, and it is almost impossible to split it for Use; from whence I am persuaded the *Indians* took this Notion, that it is never hurt as above, from its being so very difficult to split.

The *White Gum* Tree bears a sort of long bunched Flowers, and is a beautiful knotted and curled Wood, and maketh

curious

curious Furniture of several kinds, if wrought by skillful Artists.

The *Locust* Tree bears a Leaf like the *Liquorish* Plant, and has large and long Prickles (like the *Hawthorn* Tree, but as long as the Quills of a *Porcupine*) in the Boughs and Body of the Tree: It is the most durable Wood we have, and is made choice of for all sorts of work that is exposed to the Weather; it grows pretty tall and large, there are two sorts of it, the White and the Yellow, it bears Cods like *Kidney-Beans,* but much larger, wherein are contained some few Seeds, and a certain Juice or Substance as thick and sweet as Honey, but of a dark brownish Colour. Of this Tree the *Indians* make their choisest Bows, being tough and flexible; the Fruit of this Tree is much of the same Virtues and Uses with *Honey.*

The *Honey* Tree is so like the *Locust,* that there is scarce any Difference between them, only the *Honey* Tree is more prickley than the former; and are a *Species* of the *Locust* though call'd by different Names; it bears long Cods like the former wherein is contained the Seeds and the *Honey.* This Tree grows as large as the *Locust,* and will bear in five Years from the time of Planting; they were first brought here by the *Indian* Traders, and propogated by their Seed, but from what part of *America* is not known: These Trees, if planted, would make the best of Hedges, being very prickley, and of quick growth; I have seen Orchards of these Trees in *Virginia,* where excellent *Metheglin* is made of their Fruit, they sometimes boil it to the consistance of *Honey,* and use it after the same manner.

The *Service* Tree groweth to be very large, and beareth long Leaves like those of the *Ash* Tree; the Flowers grow in great Clusters, and are of a whitish Colour, after which come

forth

forth small *Berries,* somewhat long, which are unpleasant to the Taste, 'till they have lain by for some time, then they become soft and mellow; they are in taste and operation like the *Medlar,* but seldom made use of but by the *Indians,* the *Planters* not regarding them: The Leaves are astringent, and stop Fluxes, and the Fruit is cooling, drying, and binding, (especially when they are hard, and not altogether ripe) they stop Fluxes in the Belly, and all other kind of Fluxes; they Strengthen the Stomach, stop vomiting, and outwardly heal Wounds, being dry'd and made into Powder.

The *Birch* Tree is plentiful in this Province, but generally towards the Freshes on the Banks and Heads of the Rivers, but never near the Salt Water; it differs something in the Bark from the *European Birch,* and the Leaves are sharper and smaller; it buds in *April,* and the *Parakeetoes* come from all Parts to feed on them at that Season. Where this Wood grows there are no Plantations; the Leaves are cleansing, disolve and purge watry Humours, help Dropsies and Stone in the Bladder, the Ashes of the Bark is effectual to heal sore Mouths, and take away Scabs. The *Mushrooms* are binding and cure the *Piles,* the Tears are pleasant to drink and quench Thirst.

The *Alder* Tree grows in wet low Grounds near the Freshes and heads of the Rivers, but is not common amongst the Planters, or near the Salt-Water; this Tree is so well known amongst us, that it would be needless to describe it. The Bark and Twigs are much used by the Planters in dying Wool and Cloath black; the Wood is soft, but durable and lasting in the Ground or Water, makes good Piles, and other Necessaries, the Leaves and Bark are cooling and binding, and used in hot Swellings or Ulcers in the Body.

The

The *Laurel* Tree is plenty all over this Province, and grows in low and swampy Ground, in height and bigness equalizing the lofty Oaks; the Planters dye a yellow Colour with the Leaves and Berries of this Tree, the Wood is not durable in the Weather, yet serves for several Uses when kept dry, its Virtues are doubtful, yet it is said to provoke Vomit, and bring down the *Menses*.

The *Ascopo* is a Tree, so called by the *Indians,* very like the *Laurel* in its Leaves, the Bark is of a hot spicy Nature, much like the *Cassa Lignea;* I never saw this Tree growing, but the *Indian* who procured me a Branch of it assured me, that they are plentifully to be met with at the Heads of the Rivers, and near the Mountains, and that they grow pretty large.

The *Bay* Tree delights to grow in the same Ground with the *Laurel,* it is a beautiful Ever-green, the Wood of this as well as the *Laurel,* are of little use only for Fire, and is plenty all over this Province; the Berries yield a Wax whereof they make Candles, which in burning afford a pleasing smell, besides it is useful in Chirurgery, the Leaves are of a bitter astringent Nature, but grateful to the Stomach, and resists Vomiting; when made into a Pulse, help all Inflamations, the stinging of Bees, and other venemous Beasts, the Bark of the Root in *Rhenish Wine* provokes Urine, opens Obstructions, cures Dropsies and Jaundice, but kills the *Fœtus;* the Berries expel Wind and ease all manner of Pains proceeding from Cold, therefore good in the Cholick, Palsies, Convulsions, Epilepsies, and many other Disorders; some have the Leaves tun'd up with Beer, which makes it pleasant and grateful to the Stomach.

The *Bay Tulip* Tree is another beautiful Ever-green, is very common, and grows in the same Ground with the former; its Virtues are uncertain, neither have I known any use made of it.

K

The

The *Horn-beam* Tree, grows in some places in this Province both plentiful and large, the Leaves are like those of the *Elm* or *Witch Hazel,* but tenderer; the Timber of the Tree becomes so strong, durable, and hard, in process of time, that it may rather be compared to a Horn than Wood, from whence it took the Name *Horn-beam,* or *Hard-beam;* it is excellent for making Arrows, Pullies, Shafts for Mills, and many other Necessaries; yet is little regarded, or made use of, by reason of the great plenty of other Wood in those parts; there may be an Oil drawn from it, which is of excellent use in the cure of the *French Pox.*

The *Maple* Tree, of which there are two sorts, the first has an exceeding white Grain, and generally grows in the plain and champion Country; the second has a much harder and more curled Grain, and grows in the Hilly and Mountainous parts; both these sorts are large, with a smooth Bark, great Boughs, and Leaves much like those of the Vine, hanging by long reddish Stalks, which make delightful and refreshing Shades to sit under from the Heat of the Sun: The Flowers which are of a whitish-green Colour, hang in Clusters, after which come forth long Fruit resembling the Wings of *Grass-hoppers,* with white and little Kernels in them: Of this Wood is made Wainscots, Tables, Trenchers, Dishes, Spinning-wheels, and the like; the Leaves and Roots are Astringent, stop all sorts of Fluxes, and the Root helps Pains of the sides and Liver.

The *Persimon* Tree agrees with all Lands and Soils, they are common on all Plantations, the Fruit when ripe is nearest to our *Medlar,* it is one of the greatest Astringents I have ever met with, for if eaten, or chew'd before it is ripe, it draws the Mouth up like a Purse. The Fruit when ripe, being apply'd to a Foul wound, presently cleanses it, but causes

exquisite

exquisite Pain: The Fruit soon rots after it is ripe, and contains four flat Stones, resembling those of the *Tamarinds.* The Planters make Beer of its Fruit, which they call *Persimon Beer.* There are two sorts of this Fruit, the one ripe in *Summer,* and the other not before the Frost visits those Parts; these Trees sometimes grow to two Feet diameter, some make use of the Bark, instead of the *Cortex peruviana,* or *Jesuits Bark,* for Agues, and it is reported that that Bark is from the *Persimon* Tree in *New-Spain.*

The *Holly* Tree, whereof there are two sorts, one with a large Leaf, and the other with a smaller, they generally are to be met with in low wet Grounds; both sorts are in plenty, and grow tollerably large, yet I have seldom seen any use made of their Wood, there being such plenty of much better. Their Berries are said to be good in the *Cholick,* for ten or twelve being taken inwardly, purge strongly by Stool. The *Birdlime* which is made of the Bark, being applied Plasterwise, consolidates Wounds, eases all manner of Pains, and strengthens the Nerves, but if taken inwardly, it is mortal, for it glues the Intrails together, so that the passages of the Excrements are intirely shut up.

The *Chinkapin* Tree is a kind of a *Chesnut,* and very plentiful, they bear great quantities of Nuts which are less than a *Hazle-nut,* and of a Piramedial Form, they are in Taste like a *Chesnut,* but sweeter: It's Nut has a Husk or Bur about it like the former, which opens when it is ripe, so that the Fruit falls to the Ground, which is good feeding for Hogs, making them fat and excellent Pork. The Grain of the Wood and the Leaves on the Trees are very like the *Chesnut,* but the Timber is not so large, yet it is used to Timber Boats, Shallops, &c. and makes anything that is to endure the Weather; this and the *Hickery* are very tough Rods to whip Horses with, yet this Wood is in Substance very brittle. This Tree the Vine delights to twist about, it is good Firewood, but very sparkling as well as the *Sassafras;* the Nut or Kernel of this Tree has much the same Virtues with those of the *Chesnut,* but more binding, and are of excellent use to stop Fluxes.

The *Sassafras* is very common, and grows large, its Wood being sometimes above two Feet over, 'tis durable and lasting for Bowls, Timber Posts for Houses, and other things that require standing in the Ground, notwithstanding it is very brittle and light, it hath a pleasant smell. The Leaves are of two sorts, some long and smooth, the others indented about the edges (especially those growing at the top of the Branches) sometimes like those of the *Fig-tree,* it bears a small white Flower, which is cleansing to the Blood, if eaten in the Spring with other Salating; it likewise bears a small Berry, which when ripe, is black and very oily, *Carminative,* and extremely prevalent in Coughs: The Bark and Root help most Diseases proceeding from Obstructions, and of singular use in Diets for the *French Pox,* it strengthens the whole Body, cures Barrenness, and is a Specifick to those afflicted with the Gripes, or defluctions of Rheum; the same in Powder, and strong lotions being made thereof, is much used by the Savage *Indians,* to mundify old Ulcers, and several other uses; it is a beautiful and odoriferous Ever-green, makes a delightful and fragrant Fire, but very sparkling.

The *Willow* Tree differs from the *European,* both in Bark and Leaves, but the Grain is not to be distinguished from the former, and is commonly to be met with growing on the River sides, and Banks of fresh Water, as the Birch does.

The

The *Black Wild Cherry* Tree, grows common in the Woods in several places, and especially on light Lands, to be very large, the Leaves and Grain are like those of the *European Black Cherry,* in *May* they are in their Bloom of Flowers, at which time they appear all over as white as a Sheet; it bears small black *Cherries,* in prodigious Quantities, which are ripe in *June,* the *Parakeeto's,* Wild Turkies, Swine, and several other Beast and Birds feed upon them at that time. These *Cherries* are very sweet and well tasted, and are better for making of *Cherry Brandy* than any I have ever met with in *Europe,* yielding a fine Colour, and most grateful Flavour to the Brandy, and have the same Virtues with the *European Cherries.*

The *Red Cherry* Tree, is very scarce, and rarely to be met with, it's Virtues and Uses are much the same of those with us.

The *Wild Plum* Tree, whereof there are two sorts, if not more, one is much sooner ripe than the other, and differ in the Bark, one being very Scaley like the *American Birch,* and the other smooth, these Trees are in great plenty in these Parts, and especially amongst the *Indians,* who are very fond of them. These Trees when they are in Blossom, smell as sweet as any *Jessamine,* and look as white as a Sheet, but are something Prickly, you may make them grow to what Shape you please; they are very Ornamental about a House, and make a pleasant sight in the Spring with their beautiful white Liverys: Their Fruit is red, and very cooling and palatable to the sick; they are of a very quick growth, and bear in five Years from the Stone. The *English* large *Black Plumb,* thrives well, as does the *Cherry,* being grafted thereon; this Fruit is in great Request amongst the *Indians,* which they sometimes dry and preserve for the Winter.

There

There is another sort of *Plum,* about the bigness of a *Damson,* the Tree is but small, and seldom exceeds ten Inches in thickness, the *Plum* has a very physical taste, what may be its Virtues is doubtful, but this I am sensible of, that when it is chew'd in the Mouth, it is apt to make that part sore; the Wood is something porous, but exceeds the *Box* for it's fine yellow Colour.

The *Damson* Tree, whereof there are two sorts, the black and the white, and are about the bigness of our *European Damsons,* they grow any where if planted from the Stone or Slip, they bear a whitish Blossom, and are a good Fruit, they are found growing in great plenty on the Sand-Banks, and all along the Coast, they never grow large, but are plentiful Bearers. The Fruit of this and the *Plum* Trees are very cooling and good in Fevers.

The *Fig* Tree, is to be met with growing wild in some parts of this Province, and especially near the Mountains, the Fruit of this is but small, notwithstanding the Tree grows to be very large. The Leaves and Fruit are good to dissolve and waste all hard Kernels and scrophulous Tumors.

The *Hawthorn,* or *white Thorn Tree,* of these there are two sorts, the first is exactly the same with ours in *Ireland,* and grows commonly near the Freshes and heads of Rivers, but never near the Salt Waters. The second sort grows plentifully in some parts of this Province, the Fruit, or Haws, are quite different from those with us being considerably larger and longer, and of a very agreeable taste. These Trees are near as large as the *European,* but have few or no Prickles: There is no use made of the Timber, neither do they plant this or the other in Hedges, because Timber is so plenty at present. The Leaves, Flowers, and Haws, are very binding, therefore good to stop all kinds of Fluxes; the Pow-

der

der of the Stone drank in *Rhenish Wine,* is of very great service in the Stone, Gravel, and Dropsie.

The *Black Thorn,* or *Sloe* Tree grows plentifully in several parts of this Province, (and is a Slender Tree about the bigness of our *Hazel*) but is quite different from our *Sloe* Tree in *Ireland,* the Fruit being generally twice as large and as long as ours; this is of a more astringent or binding Nature than the former. The Bark of this Tree being dryed and made into a fine Powder, and apply'd to inveterate old Sores (and especially in the Legs) very speedily cleanses and drys them up, and is one of the best Remedies on those occasions, I have ever met with.

The *Dog-wood* Tree, grows very plentifully in this Province, on light and rich Grounds, the Trunk or Body whereof, is covered with a rough Bark of a russet Colour with some Pith in the middle, like that of *Elder.* It flowers the first in the Woods, of any Tree in this Province, making the Forrest very beautiful at that Season; it bears a white Blossom in the Months of *February* and *March,* much like the wild *Rose.* The Leaves are full of Nerves or Sinews, in form like those of *Plantain,* of a loathsome smell and bitter taste. Some of these Trees are ten or twelve Inches diameter, and have a very fine and beautiful Grain, and serves for several uses within Doors, but is not durable, being exposed to the Weather. The Bark of the Root of this Tree, is frequently made use of by way of Infusion, and given to Children to kill the Worms; these being the only use made of it at present.

The *Sugar* Tree grows very beautiful and high, with a smooth Bark and large spreading Branches, which make an excellent Shade to sit under in the extremity of hot Weather. The Leaves are very large and broad like those of the *Vine,*

but

but I never observed any Flowers or Fruit growing on it, so can't satisfie the Reader as to that Point. It is of a very tedious growth, and is commonly to be met with at the heads of Rivers, and near the Mountains, but no where else. The *Indians* tap it at certain Seasons of the Year, and place *Gourds* to it to receive the Liquor, and when they have got a sufficient quantity of Juice, they boil it to the consistence of Sugar, which is as sweet, and serves for the same use, but what other Virtues, or Uses, it may be indued with, I am a stranger to.

The *Hazel-nut* Tree is so well known, that it would be needless to say much on that head, it grows plentifully in some parts of this Province, and especially near the Mountains and heads of Rivers, but its Nut is not as good as the *European,* having a much thicker and harder Shell, and so have most of the Fruits in *America* that I have seen. The *Hazel-nuts* before they are thoroughly ripe are an excellent Astringent, and stop Fluxes of all sorts, a Decoction of the inner Rind of the Tree, drank for some Days together, is good against the Strangury and kill Worms.

The *Papau* Tree is not large, being only about eight or ten Inches diameter, but has the broadest Leaves of any Trees I ever saw in the Woods of *Carolina;* it bears an Apple, about the bigness of a Hens Egg, which contains a large Stone in it, when it is ripe it is of a beautiful yellow colour, and as soft and sweet as any Fruit can be. The planters make Puddings, Tarts, and many other Dishes of the Fruit of this Tree.

The *Red-bud* Tree, so called from its red Buds; it bears a beautiful purple *Lark-heel* Flower, and makes the most agreeable and best Sallad of any Flowers I have ever met with; its Fruit is ripe in *April* and *May,* these Trees are

not

not large, seldom being above ten or twelve Inches through. The Flowers and Fruit are very cooling, and of an astringent Nature.

The *Sorrel,* or *Sower-wood* Tree, so called from it's Leaves, that taste exactly like *Sorrel.* I have never known any uses made of these Trees, which are but small, being not quite as large as the former.

The *Pellitory* is a small Tree that grows in this Province, especially near the Salts, Sand-banks, and Islands. The Planters use it frequently to cure the Tooth-ach, by putting a piece of the Bark in the Mouth, which is very hot, and causeth much Rheum and Spittle to flow from thence; and as I am credibly inform'd, is one of the Ingredients that the *Indians* use when they *Husquenaw* their young Men and Boys, whereof I shall treat in it's proper Place, when I come to describe the Customs of those People.

The *Myrtle* Tree, whereof are two sorts, different in Leaf and Berry. These Trees grow in great plenty in wet swampy Grounds, about ten or twelve Feet high, and bear small white Berries in great quantities, which the Planter's Wives and Children pull in the Months of *October* and *November,* at which time they are ripe, and boil them in Water in large Pans, and so skim off the Wax it produces, which is of a greenish colour (but in process of time becomes white) and yields a most fragrant and oderiferous smell. This they strain and make into Cakes or Candles, which are not only very lasting, but grateful and pleasant for Ladies to burn in their Chambers. Some mix half Tallow with them to make Candles, others without any mixture at all, and are more durable in burning than Tallow or Bees-wax; and the best in the World to burn in *Binnacles* in Ships that pass the Equinoctial Line, and all excessive hot Countries, because they will

6 L not

not melt with the extreamity of the heat, so readily as the former.  A Decoction of these Berries cure the falling out of the Womb, Tettars, and Scald Heads, by fomenting the Parts, and their Syrup is good in Coughs, and the like disorders in the Breast.

The *Sumach* Tree grows about nine or ten Feet high, and has tough and pliant Stalks, and Branches full of Twigs (like *Oziers*) of a brownish colour, whereon grow Leaves that are soft and hairy, having a red sinew or ridge growing through the midst of them, and indented all about the edges.   The Flowers which come forth in *July* are of a greenish yellow colour, and grow with the Leaves upon long and red Stalks in clusters, after which follow small reddish Seeds in bunches like Grapes, which are ripe in *Autumn*.  This Plant is in very great plenty all over this Province, but little or no use is made of it at present.   Yet it is of great value and use in *Europe* in dressing Skins, and especially the *Spanish* Leather. There are small Birds that feed on it and the *Myrtle Berries* in the Winter.   This is one of the Ingredients used in the cure of the *Yaws*.   The Leaves and Seeds stop all kind of Fluxes, and help the *Hœmorrhoides,* all Issues of Blood and weakness of the Stomach and Intestines; outwardly they resist putrefaction; drie up running *Sores,* heal old *Ulcers, Gangrens, &c.* the Gum put into the Teeth eases the Pains thereof.

The *Indico* Tree (which is a kind of Woad, such as Dyers use to dye Cloth) grows plentifully in this Province, but I have never known any uses made of it.

The *Indian-Nut* Tree grows to be very tall, large, and smooth, and free from Branches 'till you come near the top, whereon grow Leaves like those of the *Date,* but broad and sharp at the point as Thorns, whereof the *Indians* make Needles, Bodkins, and many other Instruments for their

uses,

uses, among these Leaves come forth clusters of Flowers like those of the *Ches-nut* Tree, from whence are produced large Fruit of an oval Form: In that end next the Tree, are two Holes, and sometimes three quite through the Fruit; the outside of this Fruit is covered with a substance not unlike Hemp, or Flax, before it be beaten soft: In the middle whereof is contain'd a great Nut, with a very hard shell, of a brown colour, wherein is contained a white Kernel, firm and solid, which tastes like an *Almond;* and within the Cavity or hollowing thereof is found a most beautiful Liquor like Milk, and of a pleasant Taste. This Tree continues green all the Year, the Timber, though large, is very spungy within and hard without. The *Indians* tie Ropes about these Trees for more ease in gathering the Fruit, and they sometimes cut off tender Twigs and Branches towards the Evening, at the ends whereof they tye Gourds to receive the Liquor that distills from the Branches thereof, which they drink as *Europeans* do Wine, and very much cools and refreshes their wearied Spirits. They sometimes make Canoes of this Tree, and of the Hemp that grows on the outside of the Fruit, Ropes for several uses; from the Kernel likewise is produced a most precious Oil, wherewith the *Indians* anoint their feeble Limbs after long Journies, which not only refreshes them, but likewise mitigates all manner of Pains and Aches. The Christians sometimes distil this Liquor, from whence is produced a strong and pleasant Spirit like our *Aquavitæ*, and is used as a great Cordial for many Diseases in these parts.

The *Palmeto* Tree, the Leaves whereof grow in great Clusters, only on the tops of the Trees are long stalks, exactly in the shape of a Fan. This Tree when it is at its utmost growth is about forty or fifty Feet in height, and about two Feet diameter; and it is observable that the growth of this

Vegetable is so very slow, that it is scarce perceivable in the age of Man, the Experiment having been often try'd in several places where it grows. The Wood of it is very porous and stringey, like some Canes, with the Leaves of this Tree the *Bermudians* make fine Hats for Women, Baskets, and many pretty Boxes for several uses, which are transported to the Northern parts of *America,* where this Tree does not grow, and to *Great-Britain* and *Ireland.* In *North Carolina,* this Tree is a Dwarfish kind, and the Planters make of the Fans of this Tree, Brooms to sweep their Houses with, which is all the use I have seen them make of it.

The *Hollow-Canes,* or *Reeds,* such as Angling Rods are made of, and Weavers use for their Reeds, grow in great plenty in many places in this Province, especially in wet low and Swampy Grounds, though there is none to be met with to the northward of *James's* River in *Virginia.* They continue green all the year, and are extraordinary good Pasturage for Cattle and Horses in the Winter, and in the Month of *March,* when the Planters are obliged by the Laws of the Country to burn off the old Grass in their Fields and Woods, as the Heath is burnt off the Mountains in *Ireland,* by the Farmers in those Places. They are so very large towards the Heads of the Rivers that one joint will hold a Pint of any Liquor. When they grow old they bear an Ear like Oats, wherein is contain'd their Seeds, exactly like the Grains of Rye (which being boiled is good Meat, and often made use of by the *Indians*) soon after which they decay both Root and Branch, but the Seeds never fail to grow again. These hollow Canes are Lodges for vast Numbers of Wild Beasts, which the *Indians* frequently set on fire to drive them out, by which means they kill vast Numbers of them, and you shall hear these Canes during the time that they are burning

at

at a great distance cracking and making a Noise like two Armies engaged, and firing at each other, which has deceived many, supposing it to be the *Indians* coming to War upon them.

The *Arrow-Wood,* so called from the *Indians* making use of it for Arrows for their Bows, and Rammers for their Guns. It grows very streight, of several sizes, and is tough and pliable, as the smallest Canes, of which it is a kind, and grows in great plenty on the Banks and River-sides. It is very strange to see how the *Indians* will harden the Points of their Arrows, and how artfully they can fix sharp Flint Stones to them, by which means they kill Deer, Turkies, and several other Beasts and Birds.

The *Prickley-Ash,* is so called from some resemblance it has to the Ash-Tree in its Leaves: It grows up like a Pole, whereof the *Europeans* and *Indians* make Poles to set their *Canoes* along the Shallow Waters, it is very light and full of *Pith* like the *Elder,* but is full of prickles and Thorns like the *Sweet Bryar,* but larger. It bears Berries of a purple colour in large Clusters like the *Alder* Tree. The Root of this Tree is *Cathartick* and *Emetick,* and is frequently made use of in *Cachexies,* with good success.

There is a kind of *Prim,* or *Privet,* that grows in this Province on dry barren and sandy Banks, by the Sound side, it differs little from ours, only this bears a smaller sort, and grows into a round Bush, and is beautiful to behold, when it's Flowers are full blown. The Leaves and Flowers are cooling and good in all Inflammations and soreness of the Eyes, Ulcers in the Mouth and Throat, looseness of the Gums, and to stop Fluxes.

The *Gallberry* Tree is a little Shrub, so called from its bearing a *Black-Gall* or Berry, with which the Women dye

their

their Cloth and Yarn.  It is a beautiful Ever-green, growing plentifully in Swamps, low Grounds, and Ponds of fresh Water; and sometimes on the Banks of the Rivers.

The *Savine,* is a low Shrub, and is plentifully to be met with in this Province, especially in dry Ground and Banks on the River sides.  It beareth Leaves and Berries much like those of the *Cedar,* it is a beautiful Ever-green, but is not as prickley, neither has it such a strong smell as the Barren *Savine* that grows in our Gardens.  The Virtues of this Plant are so well known, that it would be needless to repeat them.

The *Misseltoe,* or *Missteltoe,* that grows upon the Oak, was formerly held in great veneration amongst the *Pagans* in their Sacrifices; and it is much to be admired to see such a Dwarfish Shrub grow without any visible Root, on so tall, noble, and lofty Trees, as it does, and of a quite different Nature to them.  Various are the Opinions amongst Writers how this Plant is produced.  Some assign it's growth to a certain Moisture and Substance gathered together upon the Boughs and Joints of Trees through the Bark, whereof this vaporous moisture produceth and bringeth forth the *Missel-toe.*  Others assign it's produce from the Dung of *Wood-Quests, Black-Birds,* and several other Birds that feed upon it's Seeds, which they discharge upon several Branches and Barks of Trees, and that the Seed will not grow without suffering a change in these Birds Bodies.  But which of these Opinions may approach nearest Truth, I will not take upon me to decide.  But this I am certain of, that set the Seed after what manner you will, it will never grow.  It grows in this Province in as great plenty as in any part of the World, especially upon all the species of Oaks, and several other Trees.  It seldom exceeds above two Feet in height,

and

and there are two sorts of it. The first beareth Seed, and is full of green Branches all the Year. The second is barren and fruitless, and sheddeth its Leaves in the *Winter,* which it doth not recover 'till *Spring*: The Leaves of this Shrub is of a very bitterish Taste, and the Berries are so transparent, that one may see thro' them, and within is a small black Seed or Kernel. The Leaves and Berries are of a viscous and clammy nature, whereof the best *Bird-lime* is made, far exceeding that which is made of the *Holly Bark.* The Deer and Sheep are very fond of it's Leaves, croping them wherever they can reach, which makes them very fat. It's Uses in Physick are too well known, to be inserted here.

The *Indian-Tea* Tree, which in their Language is called *Yaupan,* and *Cassena,* grows in great plenty in this Province, especially on the Sand Banks and Islands, bordering on the Sea, none to be met with near the Freshes or heads of Rivers, that I ever could learn. This *Yaupan* is a Shrub, whereof there are three sorts. The first is a Bush of about twelve Feet high, and groweth in rich low Grounds. The second is about four or five Feet high, and grows on the Sand Banks. The third seldom grows to be a Foot high, and is found both on the rich low Ground and on the Sand Banks. It grows the most like *Box* of any Vegetable I know, being very like it in Leaf, only dented about the edges like *Tea,* but the Leaf somewhat flatter. It bears a small whitish Flower, which continues not long, after comes small Berries about the bigness of a grain of Pepper, which are at first of a reddish colour, but in the Month of *December,* when they are ripe, they become brown. All these sorts differ very little from each other in taste, when the infusion is made, neither is there any difference in the Leaves, that I could ever perceive, only those that grow in the low and rich

Ground,

Ground, are of a deeper Green, and larger than those growing on the Sand Banks, and this may be occasioned by the
richness that attends the low Grounds, thus situated.  The
Cattle, Sheep, and Deer are very fond of these Plants, and
crop them wherever they can reach or find them.  The Wood
is very brittle, and its Bark of a light *Ash*-colour.  The
Planters frequently make use of it with Physick, by reason
of it's safe and speedy passage through the Bowels and Ureters, which I have often experienced, and is of excellent use
in the Stone and Gravel, by it's diuretick Quality.  It is
likewise used as *Tea,* and in making *Punch.*  What request
it is of amongst the *Indians,* and how they cure it, I shall inform the Reader when I come to treat of these People.

The *Piemento,* or *All-spice* Tree, grows commonly in wet
and low Grounds, about eight or ten Feet high, though I have
known some transplanted to high Land, where it thrives very
well.  It bears a Berry different in shape from those in the
*East Indies,* being longer and taper, yet not inferior to any
of that sort.  The Leaves of this Tree are much like the
*Hurts,* and so is the Bark.

The *Hurts, Huckle-Berries, Bill-Berries,* or *Blues,* of this
Country, whereof there are four sorts that we are well acquainted with.  The first sort is the same *Blue* or *Bill-Berry*
which grows plentifully in the Mountains in *Ireland,* and
many other places.  The Juice of these Berries are of a very
binding and cooling Nature, therefore good in Fluxes and
Fevers, they cool and comfort the Stomach, and stop Vomiting.

The second sort grow on small Bushes in the *Savannas*
and Woods, their Leaves are of a dark Green colour, much
like the former, but larger, amongst which come little hollow
Flowers, which turn into Berries, and are longer than the
former.

The

The third sort grow on one single Stem, about three or four Feet high, in low rich Lands, and on the Banks of the Rivers; their Fruit are as large and good as the former, and are very plenty in many places of this Province.

The fourth sort grow on Trees about ten or twelve Feet high, and about the thickness of the small of a Man's Leg; are very pleasant, and bear wonderfully: These grow plentifully in wet low Grounds, in many places in this Province; the Planters gather great Quantities of them in the Season, dry them in the Sun, and make use of them for Puddings, Minc'd Pyes, and many other Uses as we do *Currans* and *Raisons:* All these sorts ripen gradually one after another. The *Indians* get many Bushells of them, which they likewise dry on their Matts in the Sun, and preserve and keep all the Winter, whereof they make Bread mix'd with *Indian-Corn-Meal,* like our *Plum-Cakes,* and several other Eatables, which are pleasant enough.

*Willow-Oak* is a kind of *Water-Oak,* so call'd from its Leaves, which very much resemble those of the *Willow.* It grows in low Grounds and ponds of Water, and is used for Fire, Fences, &c.

*April-Currans,* so call'd, from their being ripe in that Month, grow on the Banks of the Rivers, or where Clay has been thrown up; the Fruit when ripe, is red, and very soon gone. They are tollerable good Fruit whilst they last, and the Tree (for it is not a Bush they grow upon) is a pleasant Vegetable.

*Bermudas-Currans,* so call'd, from their growing plentifully in that Island, are very common in the Woods of *Caro-*

M                                                                *lina*

----

*This Tree by Omission, hath not been inserted in its proper Place, *viz.* amongst the *Oaks,* whereof it is a Species.

*lina* on a Bush, much like the *European Currans,* but not so agreeable to the Taste, being but an indifferent Fruit, though frequently eaten by the Planters.

*Winter-Curran,* so call'd, by reason it bears Fruit which are only ripe in *October;* it grows on a Bush about seven or eight Feet high, and the Fruit is like our *Bill-berry;* the Planters make the same uses of it as we do of *Raisons* and *Currans,* for Puddings, Minc'd-Pyes, &c. This Bush is very beautiful to behold, growing round, and is a plentiful Bearer. All these sorts of *Currans* are of a very cooling and binding Nature, therefore good in Fevers and Fluxes.

The *Brier-Rose,* or *Hip-Tree,* is to be met with in some places, especially on dry Lands, but is generally of a Dwarf-ish kind, but its Fruit is as good as ours. The Pulp is cooling and agreeable to the Stomach, good in Fevers or violent Heats, and is of excellent use in the Fluxes of this Country.

The *Rasberries* are of a purple Colour when ripe, very agreeable in Taste, but are not as rich Fruit as the *European.* They grow on a Stalk more like the *Bramble* than the *Rassberry-Bush,* and are in many parts of this Province, and its a difficult matter to root them out, when once planted; they have much the same Virtues with the *European Rassberry,* but are more binding.

The *European Rassberry* thrives and bears in *Carolina* to admiration, and is as grateful and pleasant Fruit in it's kind, as any in the World; and are to be met with growing in most of their Gardens. This Fruit has much the same Virtues with the *Black-Berry,* but is more Cordial and less Binding.

The *Black-Berry* grows after the same manner as those with us, but their Brambles or Stalks are not so thick or long, and their Fruit is not to be compared with ours, being ill

tasted

tasted and bitter, but has much the same Virtues, *viz.* cooling and astringent; the Juice, with Honey, Allum, and red Wine, fastens loose Teeth.

The *Dew-Berrys* grow on small Brambles or Stalks about two or three Feet long exactly like the *Black-berry*. This Fruit is sweet and good to eat, and like our *Black-berry* in shape, but is as red as a *Ras-berry* when ripe, and has much the same Virtues with the former.

I will in this place give an account of the *Straw-berry* though it be not a Shrub. The *Straw-berrys* in this Province are not only large, sweet, and good, but in as great plenty as in any part of the World, growing almost every where, and are the first Fruit the Hogs feed upon in the Spring. The Planters in their Canoes go to the Islands (which are to be met with in several parts of the Rivers) and pull what quantities they please, bringing generally home their Canoes full of this pleasant Fruit, from those parts where the Hogs can't come to feed. They quench thirst, help inflammations of the Stomach, comfort the Heart, and revive the Spirits, help diseases of the Spleen, and Reins, provoke Urine, are good against the Stone and Gravel, and are usefull in Fevers, by cooling and comforting the inward parts.

The *Honey-Suckles* or *Wood-bind* (whereof there are four Sorts I have already given an account of) are very plenty in this Province, and are much the same as those with us, but do not grow so large. The Leaves and Flowers are pectoral and Diuretick, and cure Asthmas and Coughs, outwardly they are Cosmetick, and take away Scabs and Pimples in the Face, the juice is vulnerary, eases wounds in the Head, strengthens the Nerves, and makes an excellent gargle for sore and dry mouths.

The *Yellow-Jessamine* is to be met with here in several parts of the Woods, and not only affords in the Summer-time,

when

when it is in it's splendor a most delightful prospect, but likewise a pleasant shade and a grateful and fragrant smell to those that pass through the Woods. The Flowers are an excellent perfume, an Oil made of them with Oil of Olive is of excellent use in Convulsions, Cramps, and Stitches in the side. The Flowers are of the nature of *Camomile,* and are good in all hard and cold swellings, in Clysters, help the Collick and pains of the Womb, and cure the Schirrus thereof, help delivery, Coughs, shortness of breath, Pleurisies, pain of the Stomach and Bowels.

I shall in the next Place give an account of the *Vines* that this Country produces; and first the *European Vines,* which thrive well, and their produce are extraordinary great, the Lands of *Carolina* being as proper for *Vines* as any in the World, yet there are but few *Vineyards* planted in this Colony at present, for I have seen but one small one at *Bath-*Town, and another at *Neus,* of the white Grape, the same with the *Madera,* I have drank of the Wine it produced, which was exceeding good. Though of late they have got Slips of several Sorts of curious *Vines,* which no doubt will soon come to perfection, there being nothing wanting but industry to make this as fine a Wine and Oil Country, as any in *Europe,* as may appear from the few Tryals that have been already made. Ripe Grapes eaten largely, often cause *Diarrhea's,* yet the Stones stop vomiting and Fluxes, being dried and given in Powder. When they are dried in the Sun, they are good against *Coughs, Asthmas, Colds, Obstructions, Ulcers* in the *Mouth, Lungs, Kidneys,* and many other parts; outwardly, they ripen *Tumors,* help *Gouts, Gangrenes* and *Mortifications.*

The *Vines* that are Spontaneous and produce Grapes in *Carolina,* are of six Kinds, and are as follows, The *Fox-*

*grape,*

*grape,* whereof there are four sorts, two of which are call'd the *Summer-Fox-grape,* because they are ripe in *July.*

The other two are call'd the *Winter Fox-grape,* because they are not ripe till *September* or *October.*

The *Summer Fox-grapes* do not grow in clusters or great bunches as the *European* do, there being only five or six upon one stalk, and are as big as a large *Damson.* The Black sort are very common and plentiful all over this Province, but the White are very scarce and seldom to be met with. These Vines always grow in Swamps and wet low Lands, running sometimes very high according to the growth of the Timber which they meet and twine about for their support. They have the largest Leaves of any *Vine* I ever saw, therefore wou'd make delightful and Shady Arbours to sit under in the extremity of the hot Weather. This Fruit always ripens in the Shade, and has a pretty Vinous taste, but is not so juicy as the *European* Grape, having a much thicker Skin, and is of a more glutinous Nature, yet pleasant to eat.

*Winter-Fox Grapes* are much of the same bigness with the former, and are very plenty in most parts, refusing neither Swampy, Dry, Hilly, or Sandy Grounds to grow in, and are greater producers than the former, and when thorow ripe, have a Vinous Flavour and eat well, but are as Glutinous, have as thick Skins, and the Leaves as large as the other sort.

The White are very clear and transparent, and have indifferent small Stones. They make very pleasant Shades in all parts of the Woods where they grow; and if they are transplanted, thrive wonderfully. I have seen Stems of these kind of Vines, that were thicker than a Man's Thigh.

The small *Black Grapes* grow plentifully in *Carolina,* and have large Clusters or Bunches growing together like the

*European.*

*European.* These Grapes, though very small, are well relish'd, and plentiful Bearers, they have a thick Skin and
large Stone, which makes them yield little Juice, which is
of a Crimson Colour, and hath a Vinous Flavour. The
*Black Grapes* and the following, are not ripe until *Autumn.*

There is another *Black Grape,* exactly resembling the other
small *Black Grape,* only the Juice is of a lighter Colour, but
as well relished as the former.

The small *White Grape* is to be met with in this Province,
but is very scarce, growing in few parts of the Woods, yet
its Bunches or Clusters are as well knit together, and as well
relish'd, as any of the former; all these Kinds of Grapes
might be indifferently used in Physick, as the *European's*
are.

The Planters pull and eat some of these Grapes when they
are ripe, and frequently juice them, whereof they make Vinegar, which is all the use I have seen made of them, as also
of all the other Spontaneous sorts growing in *Carolina.*
What remain in the Woods are devoured by several Beasts
(that climb high Trees) and the Birds.

I shall in the next place give an Account of several other
sorts of *Vines* (growing in this Province) that produce no
Grapes, some whereof are most beautiful Ever-Greens, others
affording most pleasant Shades and fragrant Flowers, and are
as follows.

*First,* the *Scarlet Trumpet Vine,* so called, from the glorious red Flowers like a Bell or Trumpet, which it bears, and
makes a fine Shade in the Woods where it grows, inferior to
none I ever saw. It loses its Leaves (which are large) in the
Winter, and remains naked until the Spring. It bears a
large Cod that holds its Seed, but I never saw any use made
of its Bark, Leaves, Flowers, or Seeds, in Physick or otherwise.

There

There is another sort of Vine which I know no Name for, but it is a beautiful Ever-Green, with Leaves like the *Jessamine,* but larger and of a harder Nature, this grows to be a large Vine, and twines itself round the Trees; it grows near, and makes a fine Shade. It bears a *Black Berry* which is not ripe till Winter. It is a very Ornamental Plant, and worth transplanting; for I never saw any thing make a more pleasant and delightful Shade to sit under in the extreamity of the Heat in the *Summer,* and likewise from the Rain and severity of Weather in the *Winter.* But what Virtues it may be endued with, is uncertain.

The *May-Cock,* is a Vine so called, from an Apple which it bears, and is ripe in that Month, it has a beautiful Flower, and the Fruit is of an agreeable sweetness, mixt with an acid Taste. It is a *Summer-Vine,* and is naked all the *Winter* 'till *Spring,* at which time it buds, and in the *Summer* Season is very Ornamental. The Fruit of this Vine is cooling and quenches Thirst.

The *Oak-Vine* is no Tree, but so called, from a Burr it bears like the Oak, and generally runs up those Trees, it's Stalk or Stem is so very porous, that you may suck Liquors through it at a length of two or three Feet; I know no other use it is for, never having seen it made use of amongst either *Christians* or *Indians,* in any manner of Disorder.

The *Poysonous Vine,* so called, by reason it colours the Hands of those that handle it, of a yellowish Colour, but what Uses or Virtues it hath, is uncertain, no Experiment as yet having been made of it. The Juice of it stains Linnen, never to be wash'd out by any Art. It dyes a blackish blue Colour, this is done by breaking a bit of the Vine, and pressing with it's End what Mark you think proper. It runs up any Tree it meets with, and clasps round it. The Leaves of

this

this Vine are shaped like *Hemlock,* and fall off in the *Winter.*

The *Small Bamboo* is another kind of Vine, grows in wet low Grounds, and is seldom thicker than a Man's Finger; the Stem is like the *Sweet-brier,* full of Prickles and Joints, but very rough. These Vines bear small *Black-berries,* their Root is like a round Ball, which the *Indians* boil (as we do any Garden Root) and eat, which they say is good and nourishing. When these Roots have been out of the Ground for some time, they become exceeding hard, and make Heads for Canes, on which several Figures may be cut. I know of no other uses made of them at present.

*Prickley Bind-weed,* or *Sarsaparilla,* is a kind of *Prickley Vine,* not unlike the former, it groweth plentifully in several Places, but especially on dry Lands, or the Banks of Rivers. It has many Branches set full of sharp prickles with certain clasping Tendrels (like several of the other Vines) with which it taketh hold upon Shrubs, or whatever is next to it. One single Leaf groweth at each Joint, like that of *Ivy,* frequently mark'd with little white Spots, and guarded or bordered about the Edges with crooked sharp Prickles. The Flowers are of a whitish colour, and fragrant smell. The Berries are like those of the wild Vine, green at first, and red when they are ripe, and of a biting Taste, wherein is contain'd a black Seed, like Hemp, the Roots are long, and grow deep in the Ground. It is good against *Catharrs,* all manner of *Defluctions, Gout,* and *Pox,* being of a *Sudorifick* Nature.

The *Indian Figg-Tree,* commonly call'd the *Prickley-Pear.* This strange and admirable Plant, call'd *Ficus Indica,* grows in great plenty, especially on the Sandbanks and dry Land, and seems to be nothing but a multiplicity of Leaves; that is, a Tree made of Leaves, without Body or Boughs, for the

Leaves

Leaves set in the Ground, do in a short Time take Root and produce other Leaves, that grow one above another, 'till such time as they are pretty tall like a Tree, their Leaves spreading out like Boughs, sometimes more or less according to the difference of the Soil it grows in, adding one Leaf above another, whereby it spreads over a great piece of Ground. These Leaves are long, broad, and thicker than a Man's Hand, of a deep green colour, set full of long sharp and slender Prickles. On the tops of these Leaves come forth long Flowers, not unlike those of the *Pomgranate*-Tree, and of a yellow colour, after which is produced the Fruit, like the common *Fig,* or small *Pear,* in shape. The outside of this is Fruit of a greenish Colour, but within it is full of red Pulp or Juice, staining the Hands of those that touch it with a sanguine or bloody colour. The tops of these *Figs* are invironed with certain scaly Leaves like a Crown, wherein are contain'd small Grains that are the Seeds, which being sown, bring forth Plants round bodied like the Trunk of other Trees, with Leaves placed thereon like the former, which being planted in the Ground, bring forth Trees of Leaves also. The Fruit of this Plant is luscious and sweet, and frequently eaten, but must be well cleansed from the Prickles, otherwise wherever they enter, it's a hard matter to get them out, and frequently leave Knobs in the Skin. Upon this Plant grow certain Excrescences, which in continuance of time become Insects, which are the *Cochenele,* so much valued, for dying the best and richest Scarlet Colours. I have already made mention of it's changing the colour of the Urine like Blood, whereby many at first sight doubted of their Recovery, imagining what they voided to be pure Blood, being altogether Strangers to its Effects upon the Urine;

7          N          whereas

whereas it only gives this high Tincture, without any Pain, as I have frequently experienced. We have no certain Account, from the Antients, of the temperature or virtues of this Plant; yet I am very certain, that it is indowed with many excellent Qualities, and that the Juice of it's Leaves are good against Ulcers of long continuance, Burnings, and Inflammations in several parts of the Body.

Thus having given you the most exact Account that I could learn of the Trees, Shrubs, and Vines, that this Country naturally produces (But undoubtedly there are many other Species that are not yet known, which time and enquiery must discover) I shall therefore proceed to give an Account of the *European* Fruit-trees that are to be met with here, most of which thrive well. And first of the *Apples,* and their different Species.

The *Golden-Russet* is an excellent Fruit, and thrives well; this Apple, and the following sorts, are soon ripe, and have great produce.

The *Red-strak'd* grow well, whereof they make *Cyder* in many places: But for the most part, these and the other Fruits are only Food for the Hogs, there being such plenty of most kinds, that they are little made use of or regarded.

The *Summer* and *Winter Pearmains* are apt to speck and taint on the Trees, especially the South-side of the Fruit, and the Trees are frequently damaged by small Worms, that breed in several parts of the Bark, which cut Circles about the Branches, and sometimes round the Body of the Trees, and destroy the Bark that it soon dies (especially above those Circles) for want of a sufficient quantity of Juice or Nourishment from the Roots, to produce Leaves and Fruit, this frequently happens in the heat of the Weather, when the Trees are loden with Fruit.

The

The *Winter-Queening* thrives well, and produces excellent and durable Fruit, of which the Planters make good Cyder, and is seldom prejudiced by the Worms.

The *Harvy-Apple,* likewise thrives well, whereof they make Cyder.

The *Leather-coats,* both Apple and Tree stand well, have as great produce, and thrive as well as any in this Province.

The *Jenneting* is an early Fruit, thrives well, but is soon gone, in this warm Climate.

The *Coddling* looks as fine and fair to the Eye as any Fruit in the World, yet the Tree suffers after the same manner as the *Pearmains* do, or rather worse, for they commonly dye before they come to their full Growth. The Planters make the first of their Coddling Cyder against the Reaping of the Wheat, which is in the beginning of *June,* as I have already made mention.

The *Long-stalk,* is the same here as in *Europe*, it thrives well, and makes good Cyder.

The *Lady-Finger,* or *Long-Apple,* is the same as in *Europe,* and full as good. There are several other sorts of Apples in this Country called by different Names, according to Peoples fancies, and most of them good for Cyder. All these Fruits are very cooling, therefore good in Inflammations and Fevers, they gently loosen the Belly, and are of excellent use in all Burnings, Scaldings, &c. and take away the Heat of St. *Anthony's* Fire.

I never met with the *Wilding* or *Crab Tree* growing in this Province, or any other part of *America* that I have been in.

There are several sorts of *Pears* in this Country, all which thrive well, and are as good as any in *Europe,* such as the *Katherine, Sugar, Warden, Burgomot, Jenneting, Quince* Pears, and many others, which are as well relished as any I

have

have met with, but all these Fruits are of short continuance, being soon ripe and almost as soon gone.

The *Quince*-Tree thrives well, and is in plenty, and it's Fruit is as well relished as in any part of the World. The Fruit eaten raw, is pleasant, of which the Planters make a Wine or Liquor which they call *Quince-drink,* and is the best Drink that Country affords at present, though they have plenty of Cyder, and some Perry made there. They likewise draw a Spirit from this Fruit, Apples, and Peaches, which is as pleasant and grateful as any Brandy I have ever tasted. This *Quince-drink,* most commonly purges those that make use of it, and cleanses the Body, which is a contrary Effect to what it hath in *Europe,* being of an astringent Nature there; which contrary Effect must certainly be owing to the difference of the Climates. The least slip of this Tree stuck in the Ground, comes to perfection, and will bear in three Years.

The *Peach,* whereof there are several sorts (these Trees do not differ in Shape, but in their Fruit only) *viz.* the *Queen's,* the *Nutmeg,* the *Newington,* and the grand *Carnation Peach;* the *Black,* the *White,* the *Roman,* and the *Indian Peach,* and many other sorts, called by different Names, according to Peoples fancies, are all standing Trees like the Apple or Pear, with us; for the Reader is to understand, that there is no such thing as Wall-Fruit in this Province, there being Heat enough, therefore do not require it. These Fruits thrive to admiration, coming to Perfection without any Pains or trouble, for the Ground in these parts is so natural for these sorts of Fruit, that a *Peach-stone* being Planted, or falling on the Ground, will grow and bring forth a *Peach-tree* that will bear in three Years, or sooner. And it is to be observed,

that

that in their *Peach Orchards,* and many other places where the Stones fall, they grow so thick, that they become a perfect Wilderness of Trees, that the Planters are obliged to pull them out of the Ground, as we do Weeds out of our Gardens. They generally bear in such plenty, that the weight of the Fruit frequently break off great Limbs of the Trees. The Planters sometimes take out the Stones and dry the Fruit in the Sun, which they preserve for the Winter; they are grateful to the Stomach, and cause a good Appetite: They also make a Liquor of them which is very cooling, and good in Fevers. The Flowers loosen the Belly, kill Worms in Children, and open Obstructions.

The *Indian-Peach* Tree, is a kind of Peach common amongst the *Indians,* which they claim as their own, and affirm that they had it growing amongst them before any *Europeans* came to *America.* This Tree grows as large as any Apple Tree, the Flowers are of a reddish Colour, the Fruit is generally larger than the common yellow *Peach,* and more downy, it is an extraordinary good Fruit, very soft and full of Juice, will freely part from the Stone, which is much thicker than any of the former. These Peaches are common amongst the *Indians,* and those that live remote from the Christians, haveing no other sort: They are a hardy Fruit, and seldom damaged by the North-East Winds, as the other are. Of this sort there is made *Vinegar,* therefore some call them *Vinegar Peaches;* though this may seem to be a Spontaneous Fruit of *America,* yet in those parts already inhabited by the *Europeans,* I never cou'd learn that any of these Peach-Trees were ever found growing wild in the Woods. The *Indians* have plenty of this sort of Peach, but scarce any other is to be found amongst them. They have much the same Virtues with the former.

The

The *Nectarines,* whereof we have two sorts, which are very fair and large, *viz.* the Red, which clings to the Stones, and the Yellow which parts from them. I see no foreign Fruit like these for thriving in all sorts of Lands, and bearing to admiration. The Planters raise them from the Stone, which never fails to produce the same sort the Stone came from; for I never observed much Pains taken in either Inoculating or Pruning their Fruit Trees, as is customary in *Europe,* notwithstanding they bear in as great plenty. This Fruit has much the same Virtues with the former.

The *Apricock*-Tree grows to be very large, exceeding most Apple Trees. They are great Bearers, if the Season proves favourable, but it often happens in an early Spring, and when the Trees are full blown, that the North-East Winds which happen in the latter end of *February* or beginning of *March,* blast and destroy most part of it's Fruit. The Flowers are of a whitish Colour, and the Fruit round like a *Peach,* Yellow within and without, wherein is contain'd brown smooth Stones, less than those of the *Peach,* having a sweet Kernel. These Trees are generally raised from the Stone, and never fail to produce as good Fruit as the Stone came from. The Fruit is cooling and pleasing to the Stomach, but apt to surfeit; an Oil made of the Kernel is much of the same Nature with the Oil of *Sweet Almonds.*

The *Medlar* Tree, I never observed growing in *North Carolina,* but do not doubt it would thrive as well as any other Tree from *Europe.*

The *European Wall-nuts* are very large Trees, and thrive as well here as in any part of the World. There are two of these Trees growing at *Bath-Town,* which were produced from the Nut, and are exceeding great bearers, and the most beautiful and fragrant, when in their prime, of any

Trees

Trees of that Sort, I ever saw. These Trees, arrive sooner to Perfection here than in any part of *France* or *Spain,* are excellent good Fruit (when ripe) and used in several Disorders of the Body, such as malignant Fevers, *&c.*

The *Cherry* Tree. The common red and black *Cherry* bear exceedingly well from the Stone, but would do much better had they been grafted in the *Indian Plum* Tree Stocks, because these admit of no Succors or Scions to grow round the Tree, which the *Cherry* Tree is subject to, and proves very prejudicial to the Trees and Fruit. *Cherry* Trees are not only liable to this, but several *Apple* Trees and other Fruit-Trees, which might be soon remedied by a skilful Gardener, or careful Planter, whose Genius tends that way. The *Cherries* are ripe here a Month sooner than those growing in *Virginia.* The Fruit of the *Black Cherry* is good in *Epilepsies, Convulsions, Apoplexies, Palsies,* and many other Disorders; the red is cooling, quenches Thirst, and good in Fevers, *&c.*

The large round *Black-Plums,* thrive well, and become large Trees, if planted in stiff Grounds; but they will not answer if planted in light sandy Ground, where they are subject to be torne up by the Storms and Squals of Wind, that are frequent in this Country. The same misfortune attends both Forest and Fruit Trees, growing in these kinds of Grounds. There are several other kinds of these Trees that bear Fruit of various Colour, Figure, Magnitude, and Taste, but have much the same Virtues with the *Cherries,* being of a cooling Nature.

The *Damson* Tree thrives well, and the Planter's Wives and Daughters make good Dishes of it's Fruit. The Leaves of these Trees are used with *Rhenish-Wine* for *Defluctions* and swellings in the Jaws and Throat.

The

The *Figg-Tree,* of which there are two sorts, *viz.* the greater
and the lesser. The large *Figg* Tree hath many Branches full
of Pith within, like *Elder,* and large Leaves of a dark green
Colour, divided into several Divisions. The Fruit comes out
of the Branches without any appearance of Flowers, that I
could perceive, which is in shape like *Pears.* This Tree, notwithstanding it grows to be very large, yet beareth the lesser
Fruit, which it produceth in abundance, especially if planted
in light Lands, for it thrives no where better than on the
Sand Banks, and near the Sea-shoar. This Fruit being
broken before it is ripe, yieldeth a white glutinous Liquor,
but when the Figs are ripe, the Juice of it is like *Honey,* and
as sweet.

The *lesser* or *smaller Fig* Tree, is like the former in it's
Leaves and Fruit, but seldom exceeds seven or eight Feet in
height, growing more like a Bush than a Tree. The Fruit
is ripe in *July,* very sweet and luscious, and considerably
larger than the former. If the Frost proves severe in *Winter,*
the Tops of this Shrub decay and dye. As soon as the *Spring*
approaches, it sprouts and bears vast quantities of Fruit. I
could never observe any Flowers it has, for it comes out of
the Branches, like the former. The Leaves of these Trees
are sharp, opening, and vulnerary; and being applied with
the Roots of *Marsh-mallows,* waste away the *King's Evil* and
all hard Tumors; the Fruit is likewise used with good success
in the same Disorders, the Juice or Milk is Cosmetick, and
with *Barley-meal* and *Lard,* help the *Gout* and *Piles,* &c.

The *Filberd*-Tree being planted here, in a few Years de-
generates into a small Dwarfish *Nut,* no bigger than the
Hazle, yet it's Fruit is as good as any in *Europe*, but few are
either so industrious or curious to plant these Trees, there
being such quantities of spontaneous Fruit.

The

The *Orange-Tree* groweth to be as large as a small *Pear* Tree, having many thorny Boughs or Branches; the Leaves are partly like those of the *Bay-tree,* these, and their Flowers (which are of a beautiful colour) yield a most fragrant smell. The Christian Inhabitants have planted many of these Trees of late, which thrive tollerably well, especially near the Sea-Coast and light Ground, where they chiefly delight to grow. The Flowers are of great Use in Perfumes; a Water made of them is *Pectoral,* and helps *Fevers,* the outward Rind is very hot, dry, and of thin parts; it expells Wind, and comforts a cold Stomach.

The *Bead*-Tree, so called from it's Fruit resembling Glass-Beads at a distance. It bears Flowers (much like those of the *Olive*) which smell sweet. It grows in a round Bunch about four or five Feet high, and is to be met with in many of their Gardens; their Fruit are as large as *Peas,* and hard when ripe, but easily drill'd, whereof are made *Bracelets,* and several other Toys. It is ornamental in Gardens, and the Flowers are good for *Obstructions* in the Head. The Decoction of the Bark with Fumitory and *Myrobalans,* help Agues. The Leaves and Wood are accounted deadly to Beasts, and the Fruit is very dangerous, if not poysonous.

The *Gooseberry*-Tree, or Bush, does not thrive here, though I have frequently met with it in their Gardens, but of a dwarfish Kind to what we have in *Ireland,* and other parts of Europe, but I am perswaded that if it had been planted in their *swamps* or moist low Grounds, it would thrive and bear well.

The *Red* and *White Currans* thrive much better here than the former, and bear tollerably well when planted near a shade, or in moist low Grounds. The Fruit is cooling and grateful to the Stomach.

O                    The

The *Barberry*-Tree or Bush, whereof we have two sorts which thrive well, *viz.* one with, and the other without Stones, wherein consists the difference; the colour and the taste of the Fruit being the same. The Flowers are of a yellow colour, and grow in clusters upon long Stems, after which are produced long slender red *Berries,* when they are ripe. The Leaves spring forth in *March,* and the Flowers in *August.* The Bark and Leaves open *Obstructions,* and are of singular Use in the *Jaundice.* The Fruit is very cooling in *Fevers,* grateful to the Stomach, and causeth a good Appetite.

The *Rose*-Tree, and it's Kinds. There are none to be met with growing Spontaneous in this Province. These Trees have been brought from *Europe,* and other Parts, and are to be met with in most Planters Gardens, especially the common *white* and *red Rose,* but few of the other sorts.

The *Rosemary* is not a Spontaneous Shrub in *Carolina,* as in *France, Spain,* and many other parts of *Europe,* in the same Latitude; but is to be met with in most of their Gardens, and thrives well.

There are many other Fruits in this Country, that I am a Stranger to, which are beneficial and advantagious to the Planters, not only for their own Use, but likewise in feeding their Swine, and makeing them exceeding fat, and as well tasted as any in the World.

OF

# OF THE BEASTS.

THE *Buffelo,* or *wild Beef,* is one of the largest wild Beasts that is yet known in these parts of *America;* it hath a Bunch upon it's Back, and thick short Horns, bending forward. *Pliny* reporteth in the eleventh Book of his *Natural History,* that the Horns of one *Buffelo's* Head were so large that they contain'd or held two Measures, call'd *Urnæ,* which is about eight Gallons. This Monster of the Woods seldom appears amongst the *European* Inhabitants, it's chiefest haunts being in the *Savannas* near the Mountains, or Heads of the great Rivers. Their Flesh is very course, and nothing to be compared with our Beef, but their Calves are said to be excellent good Meat, as in all probability they are: And it is conjectur'd that these *Buffelo's* being mix'd, and breeding with our tame Cattle, would much improve the Species for largeness and Milk; for these Monsters (as I have been inform'd)

O 2 weigh

weigh from 1600 to 2400 pounds Weight. They are a very fierce Creature, and much larger than an Ox. The *Indians* cut their Skins into Quarters, for the ease of Transportation or Carriage, and frequently make Beds of them to lie on; they likewise spin their Hair into Garters, Girdles, Sashes, and the like, being long and curled, and frequently of a black or red *Chesnut* colour. Of these Skins and the *Wild Bull's* the best *Buff* is made. Their Horns wou'd serve for several uses, such as drinking Cups, Powder-horns, Lanterns, and many other Necessaries, being transparent when wrought; Rings made of them are said to help the Cramp, and the Liver the Spleen; the other Parts have much the same Virtues with the Ox. There were two of the Calves of this Creature taken alive in the Year 1730, by some of the Planters living near *Neus* River, but whether they transported them to *Europe,* or what other uses they made of them, I know not, having occasion to leave that Country soon after.

The *Elk* is a monstrous, large, strong and swift Beast, in shape exactly like a *Deer,* but bigger than a Horse, and is reported to be fearful, and subject to the *Epilepsy* or *Falling sickness.* They have two large Horns, which exceed in weight all Creatures that are yet known in the New World. Their Neck is short and thick, but the Ears and Back very long: Their Colour is like a *Harts,* and sometimes all White. Their Flesh is not near so sweet as the *Fallow-Deer,* being much courser and stronger. These Creatures may be made Domestick, and it is said, that they are so swift, that they will run more Miles in one Day than a Horse can in two. Some take the *Elk* for the *Red Deer* of *America,* but I am credibly informed, that they are of two different kinds, and that they will never breed together. Their Horns generally

weigh

weigh twelve or fourteen Pounds. These Beasts are plentifully to be met with in the *Savannas* near the Mountains, and
Heads of Rivers: It is reported that some of them are seventeen Hands high. Several parts of this Animal are used with
good Success in Physick, and especially the Hoofs of the
Male's hinder Feet, which have a pleasant scent when they
are burnt.

The *Stags* are swift in Motion, and are said to be a long-
liv'd Creature, they are plentifully to be met with in or near
the Mountains, but are not so large as those in *Europe,* yet
much larger than any *Fallow-Deer.* They are fat all Seasons
of the Year, and it is said, that some *Deer* on the Mountains
afford the *Occidental Bezoar,* and not produced from the
*Goat,* as some have reported. The Flesh nourishes almost like
Beef, but breeds much more melancholy Juice. The *Tallow*
makes incomparable fine *Candles,* and their Horns and Skins
are a good Commodity. There are many valuable Virtues
ascribed to the several Parts of this *Deer,* and all the other
sorts, and not undeservedly, which are so well known, that it
would be needless to insert them here.

The *Fallow-Deer* are taller and longer Legg'd in *Carolina,*
than those that are to be met with in *Europe,* but neither run
so fast, nor are so well Haunched. Their Shingles are likewise much longer, and their Horns stand forward as the other
incline backwards. Towards the Salts, they are not commonly so fat and good as those on the Hills, and near the
Heads of the Rivers: They are in great plenty all over this
Province. Their Nostrils and Throats are frequently found
full of *Bots* or *Maggots* in the *Spring,* which make them very
poor at that time; but as the *Summer* approaches these *Bots*
become the most beautiful *Butter-flies* immaginable, being
large, having black, white, red, and yellow stripes in their
Wings.

The

The *Fawns* are beautifully mottled with rows or stripes of white and brown, which only continue 'till they are one Year old. Deer-skins are one of the best Commodities that *North Carolina* affords, which the Planters export in great Quantities for *England* and other parts.

The *Lyon* and *Jack-all,* are supposed to be in *Carolina,* from an Account the *Indians* give us, who report that near a Lake of Water, towards the Head of *Neus* River, there is a Creature that haunts those parts, and frightens them from Hunting. They say that it is partly in colour like a *Panther,* and that the only way they have to avoid it is by climbing up Trees, which it cannot do. They likewise say, that there is a swift Creature which remains with, and attends it, much like the *English* Man's Dog: This Account I had from several of the *Indians;* but whether or no there be any such Beasts in these parts, I cannot affirm the certainty thereof, for I never saw either them or their Skins.

The *Bears* are very common in this Province, though not quite so large as in more Northerly Climates, such as *Greenland* and *Russia.* Their Flesh is good and nourishing, not inferior to the best *Pork* in taste, and is betwixt *Beef* and *Pork:* The young Cubs are a most delicious Dish, as most of the Planters testifie, who prefer their Flesh before *Beef, Pork, Veal* or *Mutton,* and it looks as well as it eats, their Fat being as white as Snow, and the sweetest of any Creature in the World; for, if any Person drinks a Quart of it melted, it never rises in the Stomach, as other Oils and Fats are subject to do, and is preferr'd above all things for frying Fish, *&c.* Those that are Strangers to it may judge otherwise, as it happened to me not long after my arrival in *America,* who could not be prevail'd upon to eat *Bear's* Flesh; but travelling in the Country with some other Company, we were in-

vited

vited to Dine at a Planter's House, who entertaind us with a large Loyn of a roasted *Bear.* I imagin'd it to be a Loyn of *Pork,* and eat as heartily of it, which seem'd to me to be the most delicious Meat of that kind I ever tasted; that I could not forbear all that Day to extol the goodness of it, still supposing it to be *Pork,* tho' the Company knew the contrary, but did not undeceive me. The next Day we were invited to another Planter's House, who told us he had the finest piece of *Bear* that could be, just roasted and ready for the Table. The Company very readily accepted of his Invitation, but as for my part, I could not be prevail'd upon for some time to eat; the Company said, they were much surpriz'd because I prais'd it so much the Day before. For I never knew 'till then but that it had been *Pork.* I only mention this to shew what power Prejudice has over us.

But to return. The *Bacon* made thereof is extraordinary good, but must be well saved, otherwise it will rust. I have seen very good *Hams* (not inferior to the best *Westphalia*) made of these *Bear's*-flesh. These Beasts feed upon all manner of wild Fruits, and are great devourers of several sort of Fish, especially *Herrings,* which they catch at the Brooks side in the Months of *March* and *April.* The Flesh of those *Bears* that feed upon them is not good that Season, and eats filthily; neither are they good when they feed upon *Gum-Berries.* They are great devourers of *Swine,* that they take in the Woods, especially when they are hungry and can get no other Food, which is the only Flesh-meat they are fond of. They sometimes get into the *Indian Corn-fields,* or *Maze,* where they generally spoil ten times more than they eat. They are so fond of the *Potatoes,* of this Country, that they seldom fail to destroy and root out all clean whenever they chance to come where they are.

And

And notwithstanding they seem to be such a clumsy Creature, yet they will very nimbly climb Trees (when pursued by Hunters and Dogs) where they generally remain till shot; and it is strange to see with what agility they will go up and down the Trees, and in coming down they always run tail foremost. They are likewise very dexterous and expert in Fishing, catching vast Quantities of several sorts of Fish, as they run up the narrow Creeks and shallow Waters to Spawn. There you shall see these Beasts sit, and take up Fish as fast as it is possible for them to dip their Paws into the Water. There is one thing very strange and remarkable of this Creature, which is, that no Man, either *Christian* or *Indian,* ever killed a *She-Bear* with Young; for it is supposed, that after Conception (which is in the *Winter*) the *She-Bears* hide themselves in the most secret places 'till they bring forth their Young, which according to *Pliny* is in thirty Days. But *Elianus* affirmeth not 'till three Months, which is the most likely and credible, because all large Creatures bear their Burthens longer than such as are small; when they Couple together, the Female lieth on her Back, and the Male coupleth with her, which few other Beasts are known to do. They have commonly three or five Cubs at a time, which seem to be at first a lump of white Flesh, void of Form, without Hair or Eyes, only there is some appearance of Claws. This rude Lump they fashion by degrees, by their constant licking. It is likewise reported that after conception they will Sleep so soundly for fourteen Days that it is not possible by any means to awaken them, and that during their abode in those secret Places, they never appear abroad for Food, but only suck their Paws, which is all they subsist upon during that time.

It

It is most certain, that they hide themselves in the most Secret Places, otherwise the *Indians,* who constantly hunt in the Woods, and kill thousands of He ones, would at some time or other have found them. *Bear-hunting* is a very great Diversion amongst the *Christians* and *Indians,* the former have a Breed of Dogs fit for that kind of Sport, about the size of Farmers Curs; these by practice become acquainted with the Scent of the *Bears,* which as soon as they have found they run him by the Nose 'till they come up with him, and then bark and snap at him 'till he Trees. By the Noise of the Dogs the Huntsmen repair to the place, and find the *Bear* in a large Tree, where they generally shoot one after another, 'till they kill him: And though they are not naturally voracious, yet are they very fierce, and will fight most desperately when wounded, for which reason there are three or four of these Huntsmen together with Guns ready, for fear the first shot should miss, or not quite kill him.

If any of these Dogs should fasten on a *Bear,* the Huntsman looks upon him as not good, for the best Dog in *Europe* is nothing in their Paws, for when ever they get a Dog in their Clutches they either tear him in pieces, or blow the Skin from the Flesh like a Bladder, and sometimes kill him; but if he recovers, he never is good for any thing afterwards. As the Paws are accounted the best Morsel of this Creature, so is the Head esteemed the worst, and is therefore cast away, for the Brain is said to be Poisonous. They are not near so plenty now as they were some Years ago in this Province, where the Planters have kill'd four or five Hundred in one Season; the reason is because they are so very easily kill'd, for the least Dog will make them Tree, where they most commonly remain 'till shot, for the Dog continues barking about the Tree 'till the Planters come to their Assistance. The

Parts of this Beast are good in several Disorders. The Oil is used in many Cases, and especially by the *Indians* to paint their Bodies withal. The fine Furr at the bottom of their Bellies is used in making Hats, and the Skins for several Uses, such as Hammer-Cloths for Coaches, Furniture for Saddles, &c. and the black Cub's Skins for Muffs.

The *Tyger* is in shape somewhat like a *Lioness,* but has a short Neck.   His Skin is most beautifully mottled with several kinds of spots resembling the *Panther,* only the former are not so round, nor have such different Colours. They are large, strong and swift Beasts, but are never to be met with in the Settlements, being more to the Westward, *viz.* on this and the other side of the Mountains, but are very scarce and seldom to be found in this Province, by what I could learn from the *Indians;* and in our Journy up towards the Mountains we saw but one.   They have a great many young Ones at a time, and are very fierce and bold Creatures, and will spare neither Man nor Beast to satisfie their Hunger, as I have been inform'd by the *Indians* and some of the Planters who have seen and kill'd them.   *Pliny* reporteth that the young Ones are carried off in the following manner in *India, viz.*   The Hunters lie in wait to espy when the *Tygress* is abroad, that they may have an opportunity to carry off the whole Litter of Whelps at once, upon very swift Horses prepared for that End.   But when the *Tygress* returneth and findeth her young ones gone, she pursueth most swiftly those that carried them away, by the Scent.   But as soon as they perceive the *Tygress* approaching near them, they let fall one of the *Cubs,* which she taketh in her Mouth, and runneth back to her *Den* with it, and immediately pursueth again in quest of the rest of her Whelps, thus she runneth to and from her *Den,* until such time as the Hunters have an Opportunity to

embark

embark and get off with part of the young Ones. The Flesh of this Beast is eaten by the *Savage Indians,* who say it is as sweet and good as *Beef.* The *Tyger* is much larger than a *Gray-hound,* with shining Eyes, crooked Nails, sharp Teeth, and Feet having many Toes; they love their young extreamly, which may be tam'd by giving them *Opium,* as it is reported; the Fat is good against *Palsies,* &c.

The *Panther* is of the species or kind of *Cats,* is near as large as the *Tyger,* and much of the same shape, the Skin is of a reddish or whitish Colour, finely mottled with small round black Spots, and the Hair is short and *mossy.* It is said, all four-footed Beasts are wonderfully delighted and enticed by the smell of the *Panther,* but that their frightful Countenances soon scareth them away, wherefore they hide their Heads 'till they come within reach of their Prey, which they leap upon and quickly devour. They climb Trees with the greatest agility imaginable: They are very strong limb'd, and will catch and take a piece of Meat from any Creature they strike at. Their Tails are exceeding long, and their Eyes are large and of a grayish colour, yet look very fierce and sparkling. They are very destructive to the Planters, being a swift Beast of Prey, devouring *Swine, Deer,* or any other Creature they can Master. No Creatures are so nice and cleanly as these in their Food, and when they have got their Prey, they fill their Bellies with the slaughter, and carefully lay up the remainder, covering it very neatly with Leaves and Boughs of Trees, which if any other Creature happens to touch, they will never eat any more of it. They pur like a *Cat,* and such is the wildness of their Nature, that altho' taken young, they are never to be tamed. They will hollow in the Woods like a Man, by which means many have been deceived, supposing it to be some of their Acquaintance

that hollowed, yet I never hear'd of any Body being hurt by
them; and the smallest Dogs will make them take up into a
Tree, where they generally remain 'till they are shot by the
Huntsmen, and if it happens that they don't kill them out-
right, these and the *Bears* are a very dangerous Enemy when
they are wounded, to the Huntsmen; but more especially to
the Dogs that approach too near them. Their Flesh looks as
well as any Shambles-meat whatever, and abundance of People eat them as choice Food. The *Indians* make warm covering for themselves in *Winter* of the Skins, though it is not
esteemed amongst the choice Furs. Their Skins dressed,
make Upper-leather for Shoes, or Gloves for Men and Women.
The Fat is hot, dry, and cosmatick, and helps the *Vertigo,*
*Palsie, Scabs, Ring-worms,* and *Varices* (or swelling of the
*Veins.*) The Gall being drank, presently kills, for it burns
the Humours by its violent heat, causing *Convulsions,* vomiting of *Green Cholor,* and Death. It is reported that some
Poyson their Arrows therewith, that they may kill the sooner.

The *Mountain-cat,* so called from it's living in the Mountainous parts of *America,* seldom appeareth or approacheth
near the Settlements. This is likewise a Beast of Prey, as
the *Panther* is, and is nearest to him in bigness and Nature.
They seldom do any Mischief to the Planters, because they
are so remote from them, their continual haunts being in and
near the Mountains, otherwise they are most destructive and
fierce Creatures. They will nimbly climb Trees when pursued by Huntsmen and Dogs, where they remain till they
are shot, but if only slightly wounded, will fight most desperately, tearing the Dogs in pieces that they chance to meet
with, which seldom happens, by reason so many hunt in a
Body together, who are always well armed, and ready for

such

such Encounters, otherwise these Beasts would be dangerous Enemies to meet with thus wounded, in the solitary parts of the Woods. What uses are made of these Beasts are uncertain, because they seldom or never appear or are kill'd by the *Planters* near the Plantations, and what use the *Indians* make of them we know nothing of at present.

The *Wild-cat* is likewise another Beast of Prey, and is quite different from those in *Europe,* being more fierce, nimble, and large; they have a very large Head, yet their Tails do not exceed four Inches in length. They are of a fine Tabby colour, and as large as a *Fox.* They make an odd and frightful sort of Cry in the Woods at Night. They are dextrous in climbing of Trees, which they do with the greatest Agility imaginable, and Prey as the *Panthers* do, being great destroyers of young Swine. They take most of their Prey by surprize, for they get up into the Trees and kill Deer as they feed or pass by near them, by leaping directly upon them, and so fasten their Teeth into their Shoulders, and thus suck their Blood 'till they die, as a *Weesel* does a *Rabbet* with us, so that you shall see the Deer run through the Woods in this manner, 'till at length for want of Strength he falls to the Ground, and becomes a prey to his Enemy. Thus they take every thing by surprize, not being able to catch any thing by running. They destroy *Hares, Birds,* and every thing they meet that they are able to conquer. The Furr is made use of in Stomachers for weak and cold Stomachs, in lining of Muffs and Coats in cold Countries. Their chiefest haunts are in *Swamps, Perkorsans,* and amongst the *Hollow-Canes.* They are not near so numerous now as they were some years ago, the Planters continually meeting and killing them as they

hunt

hunt in the Woods. Their Fat is externally us'd for several Pains, and Aches, for which it is good.

The *Pol-cats* (by some called *Scunks*) of *America,* are different from those in *Europe,* being much thicker, larger, and of various Colours; not all alike, but each differing from another in their particular Colours. They smell like the *European Fox,* but if possible, ten times stronger, and more offensive: When a Dog encounters them, they piss on their Tails and sprinkle it on him, by which means he shall smell a Month or more, so that he is not to be suffered to come into the Houses; and if it should happen to touch ones Cloths, the smell by no means can ever be discharged, except they be buried in the Ground for some time, which Method ends generally in the loss of the whole Suit.

The *Indians* love to eat their flesh, which has no manner of ill smell when the Bladder is out. They feed in the Woods on Rats, Mice, Birds, and sometimes Fish. They are easily made tame (and frequently come about the Planters Houses at Night) yet few covet to entertain Guests so offensive in their smell. There is another sort of *Pol-cat* in most respects like those in *Europe,* and I have been informed, that there are white ones to be met with in and near the Mountains: I know no use made of their Furs, or any part of them in Physick.

The *Minx* is a small Animal, much like the *English Filli-mart* or *Pol-cat,* being long, slender, and every way like him. The haunts of these Beasts are chiefly in the Marshes by the Sea-side and Salt-water, where they live on Fish, Fowl, Mice, and Insects. They are very bold Thieves, and will steal Fish or Fowl from you in the Night, and will venture to take it even from under your Head when you are asleep. They are likewise found a great way up the Rivers, in whose Banks

they

they make Holes and live, which is known by the great quantities of fresh Water *Mussel-shells,* that lye at the mouth of their Holes. They are great Enemies to the *Tortoise* and *Terebens,* whose Eggs they find and scratch out of the Holes in the Sand, which they quickly devour, as the *Raccoons* and *Crows* do.

These Beasts may be made tame, and are the greatest destroyers of Rats and Mice in the World, and were it not for their paying unseasonable Visits now and then to the Poultry, they would be in great esteem amongst the Planters. Their Skins are good and valuable, provided they are kill'd in the Season; I never knew any use made of this Animal in Physick, except the Fat for Pains and Aches.

The *Wolf,* is the *Dog of the Woods,* for it is reported that the *Indians* had no other Curs before the arrival of the *Christians* amongst them. These *Wolves* may be made domestick, but they are not so large or fierce as those in *Europe,* they are no Man-slayers, neither are there any Creaturs in *Carolina* (except they be wounded) will attack Man, Horse, or Dogs. They go in great Companies together in the Evenings and at Night (especially in the Winter-time) and will hunt down a Deer in full Cry, as well as the best Pack of Hounds, one of them will hunt down a Deer, but they are frequently so very poor that they can hardly run or pursue their Prey. When they are very hungry, and can take no Game, it is reported, they go to the *Swamps* and fill their Bellies full of Mud, and if afterwards they chance to get any Flesh, or stinking Fish, they will readily discharge the Mud, and eat the other. They make a most hideous noise when they are in pursuit of their Prey, and will follow the *Indians* in great droves through the Woods, who only kill the Deer and other Beasts for their Skins and generally leave most part of the dead Carcass behind

hind them, on which the *Wolves* feed, this being what induces them to follow the *Indians* after that manner. Formerly there was a Reward (in this Province) for all those that kill'd them, which made the *Indians* so active, that they brought in such vast quantities of their Heads, that in a short time it became too burthensome to the Country, so that it is now laid quite aside, and the *Indians* will not kill them. The Planters formerly made Holes or Pits in the Earth to take them in, where they killed great Numbers, but their dogs being led to those Places by the Scent of the Baits that were laid for the *Wolves*, most of them were destroyed, so that this method is entirely neglected, and they are become as numerous as ever, being as great Breeders as our Dogs and Bitches. They are but small, many being no bigger than midling Dogs, they are very crafty, but fearful Creatures, for they seldom or never attack or kill either Foles or Calves, but are very destructive to Sheep, if they are not carefully put up in their Penfolds at Night, and especially if it prove stormy Weather, at which time they will come about the Planters Houses, and strive to devour their Sheep, but in good Weather they never dare appear so near their Dwellings, which if they had done, the Dogs would soon chase them away, so sensible and crafty are they to come when the Dogs are all under some Cover to protect them from the violence of the Weather, and they generally kill all before they begin to eat, as many have testified. It is the Opinion of the most judicious Hunters in these Parts, that if they did not die for Hunger, or some secret unknown way, which they have for destroying one another, they would be the most numerous Beasts in *America,* being such prodigious Breeders. Their Skins drest to Parchment make the best Drum Heads, and if Tan'd, good Shoes for *Summer*

Countries

Countries, and being laid on Beds, are said to banish Fleas, Bugs, and all other kind of Vermine from thence. The Skin worn about the Belly is good in the *Cholick,* and all cold Disorders. The Flesh being boiled helps the *Gout,* and many other Disorders. The Fat is much of the same nature and uses with that of a Dog, being externally used in all kinds of *Aches, Palsies, Luxations,* and *Fractures.* The Dung and Blood are excellent good to expedite the Birth, and after-Birth.

The *Beavers* are amphibious Animals, like the *Otter,* living both on Land and Water, yet they never go into the Sea, their Haunts being altogether in the Freshes. They are very numerous in *Carolina,* there being abundance of their Dams in most parts of the Country where I have travelled. They are like an *Otter,* but larger, and have broad flat Tails, in shape like a *Soal,* and covered with a Skin like the Scales of a Fish, upon which they carry the Mud and Earth, with which they make their Dams. Their Heads are short, and the Ears are very small and round, and the Teeth so long and Sharp, that they will cut down Trees growing by the River sides, as if it were done with an Ax or Chizel. Their Fore-feet are like a Dogs, and their hinder Webbed like a Water-Fowl, and they are one of the most industrious Beasts in the World. They are very subtil, and cut down Trees in the Night (for they are scarce to be seen in the Day) with which they make their Dams. The Food which they chiefly feed on are Fish, and the Barks of several sorts of Trees and Shrubs, such as *Sassafrass, Sweet-gum, Ash, Birch,* and many others. If they are taken young, they become tame and domestick, but are very mischievous in spoiling Orchards, by barking the Trees, and blocking up the Planter's Doors in the Night with the Sticks and Wood they bring thither. If they eat any thing that is

Salt, it presently kills them. Their Flesh is very sweet Food, and especially their Tails, which is held as a great Dainty. They have such a Jargon amongst them when they are at Work, that one would immagine them Discoursing, or in a grand Debate about their Building, wherein it is said, they have such an orderly Government, that each knows his proper Business and Station, and that the Overseers beat the Young ones that loiter in their Business, and will make them cry, and work stoutly. It is very surprizing to behold with what Pains and Labour they make their Dams, and how artificially they build their Houses, one Appartment above another, until they lie dry. They are sometimes shot, but are taken most commonly after the following manner. The Planters break down part of their Dams, and lay Traps in those places, which the *Beavers* attempting to repair and mend at Night, are caught in them. Their Furr, which is of a brownish colour, is softer and finer than any Plume or Down of Feathers, and a good staple Commodity in this Country. Their Skins being dress'd, make thick Leather, fit for Shoes, and wears well, it is likewise used in Mittens for Hedgers, and several other ways. From this Beast comes the *Castoreum,* which is it's *Stones,* the Virtues whereof are so well known that it would be needless to insert them.

The *Otters* are plentifully to be met with near the Heads of the Rivers, and live on the same prey in *Europe, viz.* on Fish, and sometimes Fowl, and are the same in most respects as those with us: Yet there have been seen some *Otters* to the Westward of this Province, which were of a whitish gray Colour, a little inclining to Yellow. Their Furr, if Black, is valuable to make Hats, Muffs, and several other Necessaries. Although the Flesh be cold and ill-scented, yet some eat it, the Blood mixed with Vinegar, helps swellings of the

*Sinews;*

*Sinews;* their Skins worn about the Body, help *Palsies,* and other cold Disorders; the *Testicles* are good in the *Epilepsy* and *Fits of the Mother,* and have much the same Virtues with the *Castoreum.*

The *Raccoon* (which I take to be a Species of the *Monkey*) is of a dark grey Colour, and in shape and bigness it partly resembles a *Fox,* but has large black Eyes, with great Whiskers like a *Cat*, the Nose like a *Pig,* and the Feet are form'd like a Hand, or those of a *Monkey.* If these Animals are taken Young, they are easily made tame and familiar like a Dog, yet they are very Apish, and the drunkenest Creatures in the World, if they can come at Liquors that are strong and sweet; and, if possible, are more mischievous and unlucky than a *Monkey;* they are very subtile and crafty in taking their Prey. Those that live near the Salt-Waters feed much upon *Oysters,* which they are fond of. These Beasts watch the *Oyster* when it opens, and nimbly put in their Paw, and pluck out the Fish, yet it sometimes happens that the *Oyster* shuts and holds fast their Paw 'till the Tide comes in, by which means they are frequently drown'd notwithstanding they swim very well. This animal is very fond of *Crabs,* which are plenty in this Province, and the way they take them is very remarkable and diverting, for when he intends to make a Prey of this Fish, he goes to the Marshes on the Water side, and standing on the Land he lets his Tail hang down in the Water, which the *Crab* takes for a Bait, and fastens his Claws therein, as soon as the *Raccoon* perceives it, he of a sudden springs forwards a considerable way on the Land, and brings the *Crab* with him; as soon as the *Crab* finds himself out of his Element, he immediately lets go his Hold, and then the *Raccoon* encounters him, by getting him crossways in his Mouth, and so devours him. There is a sort of

*Land-Crabs* in *Carolina,* which are commonly called *Fiddlers,* these live all along the Sea-shoar, and have Holes in the Sand, into which they run when pursued by any kind of thing. These *Crabs* the *Raccoon* takes by putting his fore Foot into their Hole and pulling them out, which is very diverting with a tame one. The chief of his other Food is wild and tame Fowl, all manner of Fruits, Green Corn, and the like. This Beast and the *Possum,* are much of a bigness. They are very dexterous in climbing of Trees, and often make unseasonable Visits among the Poultry. The *Indians* and *Negroes* frequently eat them, and esteem them very much. The Furr makes good Hats, and Linings for Coats in cold Countries, and the Skins dress'd make fine upper-Leather for Women's Shoes, and Gloves for Men. The parts of this Beast are much of the same Nature and Virtues with those of the *Otter,* and may be indifferently used after the same manner.

The *Foxes* are as large as those in *Europe,* but generally of a gray Colour, they have redish Hair about their Ears and are most commonly fat, yet I have never known any Person eat them, notwithstanding they have not that strong smell that the *Foxes* in *Ireland,* and other parts have; yet they are as mischievous in their Nature. When they are Hunted, they run up the first bending Tree they meet with for Security from the Dogs, where they generally remain 'till forced down or shot by the Huntsmen, but whether they Burrow in the Ground, I cannot inform the Reader, (for I never met any *Fox-Holes* in the Country) They are never to be made tame or familiar as the *Raccoons* and other Beasts in that Country are. The Furr of this Animal, if taken in the Season, is very good, and is used for Muffs, and many other Ornaments. Their Food is chiefly Birds, Fowls, Rabbets, and such like small Prey. The Fat or Oil helps *Nodes, con-*

*tracted*

*tracted Sinews,* Pains of the *Joints, Gout, Palsie,* and many other Disorders.

The *Possum* is to be met with no where but in *America,* that I could ever learn, and is the wonder of all Land Animals; it is near as large as a *Badger,* and partly of that colour, but lighter. The Males Pisel is retrogade, and in time of Coition differs from most other Animals, turning tail to tail as Dog and Bitch when tied together. The Female no doubt breeds her young ones at her Teats, for I have frequently seen them stick fast thereto, when they have been no bigger than the end of a Childs little Finger, and seemingly to move and be alive. The She one has a false Belly or Pouch, which covers her Teats, and wherein she carries her Young; in the middle of which is a Hole where the young ones creep in and out, for the Female will lye down upon a Bank, and the young come out to sun themselves, and return in at Pleasure, yet the Female will contract this Pouch so secure and close together, that she will swim over large Ponds and Creeks of Water with her Young, without any danger of their being drowned. They have about five or six young ones at a Time, which remain sporting in and out of this false Belly, till they are able to fend for themselves. They have long Tails without Hair, like a Rat, but as thick as a Man's Thumb; and appear as if they were Scaly, which they will readily twine about your Finger or Cane, in which Posture you may carry them where you please. They are a very stupid Creature, being altogether negligent of their own Safety, and never strive to flie from their Enemies, as it is natural for all other wild Beasts to do. In shape, they are most like Rats of any thing, and have very wide Mouths and sharp Teeth. They are hard to kill, for I have known their Sculls mashed and broken in pieces, so that they seemed to be

quite

quite dead, yet in a few Hours they will recover and creep about again; and it is a common saying in *Carolina,* that if a *Cat* has nine Lives, a *Possum* has nineteen. Their Feet are very white, soft, smooth, and without Hair, and have five Toes upon each Foot, but the hinder Feet more resemble a Man's Hand, with a Thumb and four Fingers, than the fore-Feet do. Their Flesh is generally fat, white, and well tasted, several Persons eat of them, especially the *Indians* and *Negroes,* who prefer them before *Pork,* but their ugly Tails are enough to put one out of Conceit with them. They climb Trees as the *Racoons* do, and feed on Flesh, Poultry, Roots, and most kinds of Fruits. Their Furr is not esteemed, and therefore made very little use of, only that the *Indians* spin it into Girdles and Garters. The Fat of this Beast is much of the same Nature of that of Hogs. The Testicles given with Honey stir up Lust and cause Conception.

That Animal which the People of *Carolina* call a Hare, is nothing but a *Hedge-Coney,* for I never met with or heard of any of the Species of the *European Hares* being in this Province. The *Hedge-Conies* never Burrow in the Ground, but continually frequent the Woods and Thickets, and if you start one of them and pursue it, it generally runs up as far as it can into a hollow Tree, in which case the Hunters make a Fire and smoke the Tree, which brings it down, and most commonly smothers it; though I have frequently seen them pursued and taken by Dogs, yet I never observed any taken after that manner, but their Bladders were ready to burst, which the People in that Country would perswade me was a Distemper amongst them, whereof they frequently die. They hide their Young in some secret place from the discovery of the Bucks, as the *European Rabbets* do, and are of the same

Size

Size and Colour. At certain Seasons of the Year, great *Bots* or *Maggots* breed betwixt the Skin and the Flesh, which turns into most beautiful *Butterflies,* like those in the *Deer.* They eat much after the same manner as those in *Europe* do, but I never observed any of them so fat. The Planters frequently fire the Marshes and Thickets, by which means they kill abundance of them. The Flesh of these nourishes more than that of the *Hare.*

Those of the *European* Species of *Coneys* or *Rabbets* are very scarce in this Province, and are to be met with but in few places, so that it is thought that they are not natives of this Country, but that they have been brought from *Europe,* to these parts. They Burrow in the Ground (but in two places that I know of) like those with us. These as well as the former breed Maggots in their Testicles and other parts of the Body, which become most beautiful *Butter-flies;* they eat after the same manner as those with us, and their Furr is for the same uses, and the parts of this Animal have the same virtues in Physick with the former.

The *Squirrels* whereof there are four sorts in this Province, *viz.* The *Fox-Squirrel,* the *Gray-Squirrel,* the *Flying-Squirrel,* and the *Ground-Squirrel.*

The *Fox-Squirrel,* so call'd, from its being the largest, and smelling like a *Fox.* It is most commonly larger than a *Rabbet* and of a gray colour, yet I have seen several Pyed ones, and some white, red and Black. Their chiefest haunts are in Piney Lands where the *Almond-pine* grows. They feed on pine Nuts and all other sorts of Nuts, and Fruits, of which they lay up a sufficient store in hollow Trees for the Winter, during which Season they never appear abroad. They may be made tame, and are very plenty, and good Meat in this Province, but very distructive and pernicious in Corn

Fields

Fields. The flesh is sweet and good like that of *Goats* or *Rabbets*.

The small *Gray-Squirrel* is much of the same nature and bigness with those in *England,* there being only some small difference in the colour. They feed like the former on Corn and Nuts, *&c.* and like the *Bear,* are never found with Young, neither are they to be met with in *Winter,* but lie in the hollow Trees during that Season: Their Flesh eats rather better than the former. The Fat of these *Squirrels* is *Emollient,* and good against Pains in the Ears, and the Teeth, are said to be used by *Magicians* in foretelling things to come.

The *Flying-Squirrel* is of a light dun Colour, or Gray, like the former, but much smaller than any of the other two. It has no Wings (like a *Bird* or *Bat*) only a fine thin Skin covered with Hair, as the rest of the Parts are. This is from the Fore-feet to the Hinder-feet, which they puff full of Wind at pleasure; and this buoys them up, that they will fly with incredible swiftness, and at greater Distances than any other kinds of *Squirrels* do, by their jumping or springing. They lay in a sufficient Store of Provisions for the *Winter,* which are generally Nuts, Corn, and several sorts of Fruits. They are a tender Creature, lie very warm in their Nests (which are made of fine Down) not appearing all the *Winter,* being unable to bear the Cold and severity of the Weather, and generally half a dozen or more lie together in one Nest, which is always in a hollow Tree, and have their Stores of Provisions near them, whereon they feed during the cold Weather. They are easily made tame, but Enemies to Cornfields (as all the other *Squirrels* are) and only eat the germinating Eye or Bud of the Grain, which is very sweet. The Flesh of this *Squirrel* is as good as any of the former.

The

The *Ground Squirrel,* so called, because they seldom delight in running up Trees, or leaping from Branch to Branch, as the other *Squirrels do.* They are the smallest of all *Squirrels,* being not much bigger than a large *Mouse,* and their Tails are not so long or bushy as the former, but more flattish. They are of a reddish colour, and finely striped down each side with black Rows like the young *Fawns,* which make them very beautiful; they may be kept tame in a little Box with Cotton in it, because these as well as the *Flying-Squirrels* never stir or appear abroad in the *Winter,* being a very tender *Animal,* and not able to bear the Cold. These have much the same Virtues and Uses with the other sorts of *Squirrels.*

The *Weesel* is likewise to be met with here, but not so common as in some parts of *Europe;* I see no manner of difference between them in shape, colour, or bigness. It is very strange what some Writers have said of the Generation and Conception of this Animal, who confidently assure us, that they Ingender at the Ear, and bring forth their Young at the Mouth. *Pliny* reporteth, that when they encounter and fight with *Rats,* they use *Rue* as a preservative against their Bite. The Parts of this Animal are good in Fevers, Gouts, and Pains of the Joints, Head-aches, Falling-sickness, Epilepsies, and many other Disorders.

There are four sorts of *Rats* in this Province, *viz.* the *Musk,* the *Marsh,* the *Water,* and the *House-Rat.*

The *Musk-Rat* is partly of the colour of a *Rabbet,* and is in all things shaped like our *Water-Rat,* only something larger, and has Hair or Down upon it's Tail, longer than the former. It frequents the Marshes near the Fresh-Water Streams (as the *Beavers* do) and no where else, and builds in the Marshes, having three lodging Rooms, one higher than the other, very neat and finely daubed within, where it lies dry and secure from the violence of the Weather. It has a Cod of Musk that is very valuable, so is it's fine Furr. It is the Opinion of many in these parts, that this Animal lives mostly on Fish.

The *Marsh-Rat,* so called from its frequenting the Marshes; it differs from the former, being less and of a darker colour, but is more Hairy and larger than the common *House-Rat.* It is a very destructive and mischievous Animal, especially to Corn, and all manner of Fruits; of what use it may be in Physick, is uncertain.

The *Water-Rat* is found here the same as in *England,* and other parts of *Europe,* the *Water-Snakes* frequently devour these Rats, for I have killed several of these Snakes and found these Rats in their Bellies; they feed upon little small Fish and Water-Insects that they meet with in Rivers and Ponds of fresh Waters.

The *House-Rats* are the same here as in *Europe,* and in great plenty all over this Province, and as mischievous in these parts, as in any part of the World, destroying Corn, Fruit, and many other things. The Tail of this Animal is Poysonous, and frequently kills Cats that eat it: The Urin falling upon the bare Skin, causeth the Flesh to rot even to the Bones, if there be not good care taken to prevent it, by a speedy Cure, yet the Fat is of excellent use against the Palsie.

The *Moles* in this Province are of the same sort as those to be met with in *England* and other Places, but are not plenty here, being destroyed by Snakes, and several other kinds of Vermine, which this Country produces in great abundance. Many are the Virtues ascribed to this little Animal, such as curing the King's-Evil, Gout, Leprosie, and Fistulas, the Ashes being outwardly applied, and inwardly drank in Wine for several days. The fresh Blood put on

bald

bald places causeth the Hair to grow, and the Liver being applied, is said to waste away Wens, and the Powder of the Heart to cure Ruptures. They are most effectual in *May.*

The *Mice,* whereof there are four sorts, *viz.* The *House-mice,* the *Shrew-mice,* the *Dor-mice,* and the *Bat,* or *Rear-mouse.*

The *House-mice* are the same here as those with us, and these and all other kinds of Mice are scarce here (except the *Rear-mouse*) which may reasonably be supposed from the great quantity of Vermine that continually destroy them, such as *Hawks, Owls, Rattle-Snakes, Black-Snakes,* and the like. It is a short-liv'd letcherous Creature, and breeds often in the Year. The Flesh being applied, helps the biting of Serpents; the Fat is good against the *Scirrhus* and Baldness. The whole Mouse being calcined, helps *Tetters, Ringworms, Piles, Epilepsies,* and many other Disorders; the Gall with Vinegar, dropt into the Ears, bring out living Creatures got in; the Urine corrodeth after the same manner as the *Rat.*

The *Shrew-mouse,* or *Poysonous-mouse,* so called, from poysoning Cats after they have eat of them; it is very like the former, but is a Field-mouse, for it never resorts or comes near the dwelling Houses. It is said, if it go over the Back of any Beast he shall become lame in the Chine, and if it bite, he swelleth to the Heart and dieth. This Animal being burnt to Ashes, and applied with Goose-grease, helps all Swellings in the Fundament, Felons and Tumors behind the Ears. Their biting is cured by the application of their own Flesh bruised, as also, oxymel Cupping Glasses, Scarification, Wormwood, Vinegar, Garlick, Cummin Seed, Vervain, *&c.*

The *Dor-mouse* is of the same kind here as in *Europe;* these Animals are but scarce in this Province, and it is said,

R 2                                                        they

they will sleep a Month or two in *Winter,* and can hardly be
revived 'till just the time of their going abroad.   The Body
being roasted with Oil and Salt, and eaten, helps wonderfully Ulcers in the Lungs; the Fat dropt into the Ear, helps
Deafness.   The Body burnt to Ashes, mixt with Honey, and
eaten every Morning, clears the Eye-sight; and with Oil,
helps burnings.

The *Bat,* or *Rear-mouse,* whereof there are two sorts, *viz.*
one a large sort with long Ears, and particularly long strag-
ling Hairs.   The other is of the same kind here as with us in
*Europe,* only something larger, and is plentiful all over this
Province, yet it never appears all the Winter.   The *Bat* alone,
of all Creatures that fly, brings forth its young alive, and
suckleth them with *Paps,* and giveth *Milk;* it likewise will
convey or carry them from one place to another as it flies.
I have put this Animal amongst the Beasts, tho' it partakes
of both Natures, of the *Bird* and *Mouse* kinds.   The Flesh
is abominable Food, yet some eat it, and it is frequently
Roasted, and given to Children that eat Dirt (which is very
common amongst the *Christians* and *Negroes* in this Province) and is held as an infallible Medicine for that purpose.
The Blood causes the Hair to fall off, the *Gall* helps the biting
of the *Shrew-mouse,* and dimness of Sight.

Having thus given an Account of the *Terrestrial,* or *Land-
Animals,* which are to be met with in *Carolina,* and are
already known to us; I shall in the next place proceed to
describe the *Reptiles* and *Insects.*   Not that I pretend to give
an ample Account of all the different Species, (which would
require a larger Volume than is here designed) they being
very numerous; my Purpose is to discribe such only as I can
perfectly remember, and whose Qualities are best known;
there being too great a diversity of various kinds, many
whereof are not yet thoroughly discovered, and others have

slipt

slipt my Memory; besides what the Mountainous parts of this Land may hereafter lay open to our View; for whoever consider what a small part of this large Province is inhabited at present, can't imagine but there will still be greater Discoveries made, by Time and Industry, when the back parts of this Country, and near the Mountains are once settled; for the farther we Travel *Westward,* we meet greater Differences in the Soil, Air, Weather, growth of Vegetables, and several Animals, which we at present are intire Strangers to; only what little Account we have from the *Indians,* so that no doubt every Age will make new Discoveries.

The *Alligators* are Amphibious Creatures, living both upon Land and Water, and by the best Description I can learn concerning the *Crocodile,* I see little or no difference between them, only in the Name; this being the receiv'd Opinion of the Naturalists, that it is no other than a *Crocodile* not arriv'd to it's full growth. They are a large Creature with four Feet, which are like a *Bears,* except that they are covered with *Scales,* instead of Hair, the Claws are sharp and the Tail long, with *Fins* upon it. They have a large broad Head and wide Mouth, the Snout is like a *Swines,* and the Teeth, which are exceeding sharp, meet within each other like the Edges of two *Saws.* The Tails of these Animals are near as long as the whole Body, and the same is very rough and armed with a hard Skin. Their haunts are chiefly between the Freshes and Salt Waters. They make their Dwellings in the Banks on the River-sides, a great way under Ground, the entrance whereof is generally two or three Foot under Water, which rises gradually as they burrow under Ground, 'till it rises considerably above the surface of the Water, where they lie dry all the Winter, at which Season they never appear abroad, but as it is supposed, sleep all that time without any

manner

manner of Provision, which some report to be the space of
threescore Days. In *Spring* they come forth from their
Holes or Caves, and continually swim up and down the Rivers and Creeks in the Day time, but at Night they are to be
met with in the Woods and Marshy low Grounds. They
always breed near the fresh Water streams, or clear Fountains, yet seek their Prey in brackish and Salt-waters, not
near the open Shoar, but in the Rivers and Creeks. They
are never known to devour Men in *Carolina,* but on the contrary, always strive to avoid them, as much as possibly they
can. Yet they frequently kill Swine and Dogs, the former
as they come to feed in the Marshes and at the sides of the
Rivers and Creeks, and the latter as they are swiming over
them.

The *Alligator* lays Eggs as Ducks do, only they are longer
shap'd, and have a larger and thicker Shell than they have;
but how long they are in Hatching their Eggs I never could
be satisfied, or rightly informed, for the *Indians* with whom
I conversed, say, it is most part of the *Summer,* and only by
the heat of the Sun; but some of the Christians assured me,
this was performed in sixty Days, or thereabouts: Their
young ones are shaped exactly like a *Lizard, Asker,* or *Effit,*
and they have short flat and large Tongues. I saw one of
the young ones taken and brought to a Planters House who
had a Pond of Water before his Door (out of which he dug
Clay for Building) wherein he put the young *Alligator,* it
remained there for half a Year, feeding on Guts of Fowl and
other Flesh-meat and *Frogs* that happend to come into the
Pond. It grew so very domestick, that it would frequently
come into the Dwelling House, and return again to the Pond:
But at length it stole away to the Creek before the Planters
Dwelling House, as was supposed, for it never could be seen
or heard of afterwards. But to return to their Breeding

their

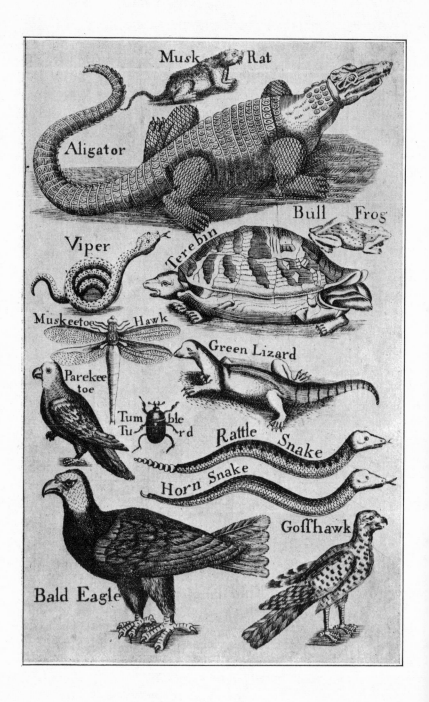

their young ones. The old ones throw up Banks of Mold in the wet Swamps, in form of a Sugar-Loaf, near the sides of the fresh Water-Rivers and Creeks, whereon they lay twenty or thirty Eggs, if not more, in the Season, where they remain 'till such time as they are Hatched, and then they tumble into the Waters, and fend for themselves in the like manner as the young *Frogs* do: I am perswaded they are one of the largest Creatures in the World to be produced out of so small a Beginning as an Egg not so large as a *Goose's,* for they sometimes exceed eighteen Foot in length, they have Sixty Teeth, Sixty turning Joints, and are said to live no longer than Sixty Years. They are very crafty and subtile in taking their Prey in Waters, whereon they float as if dead, or like a log of Wood, 'till they come within reach of their Prey, which they will most nimbly seize by leaping upon them, and then dive under Water with it, which they quickly devour. They are likewise very destructive and mischievous to Wairs made for catching Fish, into which they come to prey on the Fish caught in them, from whence they cannot readily discharge themselves, so break the Wairs in pieces, being a Creature very large, and of great Strength. It is almost impossible to kill them with a Gun, except you chance to hit them in or about the Eyes, or under the Belly, that part being softer than any part of the Body; the rest of the Skin being so hard, that it will resist a Bullet like Armour. They are very easily avoided upon Land, being a very slow Creature, by reason of the shortness of their Legs, and they cannot readily turn themselves, for their Bodies are so stiff and hard, that they are obliged to go streight forward, so that they may be avoided by the least turning out of their way, but they are very nimble and active in leaping either upon Land or Water. Some of these Creatures afford a great deal of *Musk,* and when their

Tails

Tails are cut off, they look very fair and white, seemingly like the best of Vail, and some People eat thereof, and say it is most delicious Meat, when they are not Musky. Their Teeth are as white as Ivory, whereof I have seen Chargers for Guns of several sizes, Snuff-Boxes, and many other Toys made. The upper Jaw of this Monster is movable, and not the under, and it is doubtful whether they have any Passage for their Excrements, except the Mouth. After the Tail is cut off from the Body of this Creature, it will freely move for four or five Days, as if it had been alive, and still joined with the other parts. I saw two of them killed during my stay in that Country, in the Bellies whereof (after they were opened) were found several sorts of Snakes, knots of Lightwood, and particularly one of them with a large solid Stone, that weighed about four Pound weight.

These Monsters roar and make a most hideous Noise against bad Weather, and before they come out of their Dens in the *Spring.* I was very much frighted by one of them in a Creek near *Bath-Town,* where these Animals are very plenty, which happened after this Manner: As I was walking near the Creek side one Evening, not long after my arrival in those parts, on a sudden this Monster began to roar after such a dreadful manner, that the very Earth seemed to tremble where I stood. I am not able to express the consternation I was in; for I am satisfied it gave me the greatest dread and surprize I was ever in, never having heard so terrifying a Noise before; it continued thus roaring for eight or ten times, like a *Bittern,* but if possible, a hundred times louder, which at first I imagined to be some diabolical Spirit breaking through the Bowels of the Earth, for in the fright I was in, I could think or imagine nothing else. I made all

the

the haste I could to a Planters House, where I had lain the Night before, who soon undeceived me, and told me what it was, and that in a few Days I should see the Creature that made that hellish Noise in the Creek before his Door, which happened in a Day or two after. Their Flesh if not Musky, is accounted good Meat, and helps those that are afflicted with the Gout and Rhumatick Pains. The Blood clears the Eyes, and the Fat is prevalent against all manner of Pains, Aches, Ulcers, and Cancers, by Unction. The Gall is of excellent use in taking away the *Cataract* and *Web,* growing in the Eyes; the Teeth of the right Jaw bound about the Arm, are said to provoke *Venery.* The Skin calcined, and mixed with *Lees* of *Oil,* is said to stupefie the Parts so much, that they cannot feel, though cut. I have ranked the *Alligator* and the *Tortoise* among the *Insects,* because they lay Eggs.

The *Tortoise,* vulgarly called the *Turtle,* whereof there are three sorts. The first is the *Green Tortoise,* which is not common, but is sometime found on these Coasts; it lives both on Land and Water, and has a large strong Shell on it's Back, which defends it from it's Enemies. The Lean of this Tortoise looks and tastes like *Veal,* without any fishy savour, and the Fat is as green as Grass, yet very sweet; some are so large, that they weigh four hundred Weight.

The second is the *Hawks-Bill,* which is common here, the Flesh of these two sorts are incomparably good Food, being inferior to none, and is useful in several Disorders, such as the *Gout, Hecticks, Epilepsy, sore Eyes,* and is said to be an Antidote against Poyson.

The third is called the *Logger-Head,* which scarce any one covets to eat, except it be the *Negroes* and *Indians,* yet the Eggs of this and all the other sorts (which are covered with a Skin and not a Shell) are extraordinary good Food and nourish very much, yet none of these sorts of Creatures Eggs will admit in boiling the White to be harder than a Jelly, notwithstanding the Yolk with boiling becomes as hard as any other Egg. They make Holes in the dry Sandy-Land, and on the River sides, where they lay above an hundred Eggs in the Season as large as Pullet's, afterwards they cover them carefully with Mould, which they beat hard and smooth with their Breasts, where they remain till they are Hatched, and they lay Eggs two or three times a Year, which causeth a prodigious Increase. The common way of taking these Turtles is, to turn them on their Backs, in which Posture they cannot dive under the Water, so that those that Fish for them tye a Rope about them, and hawl them into their Boats, or tow them to Land, and it is reported, that they will shed Tears when they are taken; and though they have large Lungs within their Scales, yet according to *Pliny,* they are without Blood. They are commonly found floating upon the Water, and sometimes fast asleep, at which time they will snort very loud. They have neither Tongue nor Teeth, but a very sharp Bill, which serves them instead of Teeth; they feed on *Cockles, Muscles,* and other Sea-shel Fish, for their Bills are so hard and strong that they will readily break those Fishes and eat them.

The *Terebins,* whereof there are divers sorts, which I shall comprehend under the distinction of Land and Water *Terebins.*

The Land *Terebins* are of several Sizes, but generally round mouthed, and not *Hawks-bill,* as some of the other sorts are, they are exactly in shape like the *Turtles,* and move very slowly, and if any thing touches them, they readily draw their Head and Feet within their Shells; (being

speckled

speckled with reddish spots, which are hard and strong) that scarce any thing can hurt them. The *Indians* eat them, and most of them are good Food, except the very large ones, and those that are Musky. These, as well as the *Tortoises,* make Holes in the Sand-Banks above High-water-mark, where they lay vast quantities of Eggs in the Season, which are hatched by the heat of the Sun, and the young Ones, as soon as they are out of the Shell, crawl back to the Water, where they seek their Living. They are mortal Enemys to the *Rattle-Snakes,* killing them wherever they meet, which they do by catching the *Snake* a little below the Neck, and so draw his Head into their Shell, which makes the *Snake* beat his Tail, and twist about with all the strength and violence imaginable to get away, but the *Terebin* soon dispatches him, by pressing him to Death between his Shells, and there leaves him. In *Europe* they are called the *Land-tortois,* and are plenty up and down the Woods of *Carolina;* they feed on *Snails, Tad-pools,* or young *Frogs, Grass, Mushrooms,* and Dew and slime of the Earth and Ponds. Their Eggs are very nourishing, and exceeding good Food. They never appear in Winter, but lie all that Season in Holes in the Earth, without any manner of apparent Provision.

The *Water-Terebins* have a Shell on their Backs and another underneath, like the former; they are but small, containing about as much Meat as a Pullet, and are extraordinary good Food in *May* and *June,* at which time they make Holes in the Earth, where they lay vast quantities of Eggs, which are hatched by the heat of the Sun and Sands, as the former are. They come out about the bigness of a small *Chesnut,* and seek their own living: It is incredible what quantities of Eggs, these as well as the others will lay in the Season, but they have so many Enemies that find them out (especially *Hogs, Racoons,* and *Crows, &c.*) that the hundredth part never come to perfection. For during the time they are laying, you will see the *Hogs* and *Racoons* hunting all along the Water sides till they find their Eggs, which they root out of the Earth, and so devour them; this is the reason they are not so plenty in this Province as formerly they were, though they are still numerous enough. I have frequently eat of them, which are as delicious a Morsel as ever I tasted, if well dress'd. Their Virtues and Uses are much the same with the *Tortoise.*

The *Frogs,* whereof there are several sorts, but none so remarkable as the *Bull-Frogs,* so called, from their bellowing like a Bull, which makes Strangers wonder (when by the side of a Marsh) what's the matter, for they hear the *Frogs* bellow, and can see no Cattle: They are the largest that are known in *America,* being generally as big as a *Rabbet,* I have known no Use made of them in Physick.

The *Green Frog,* so called from it's Colour, it is one of the smallest sort I ever met with; these climb up Trees, and sing or make a noise much like the *Grass-hopper,* but much louder. The *French* eat the hinder Quarters of them.

The common *Land-Frog* is like a *Toad,* only it leaps and is not poysonous. These *Frogs* are great devourers of *Ants,* and the *Snakes* devour them. These Animals baked and beat to Powder, are taken with *Orrice-*Root, to cure the Tympany, and many other Disorders.

There are several other coloured small *Frogs* in these parts; and what is worthy of Observation is, that they in general have such variety of Notes from the Spring to the Fall, that it is very strange to hear them, representing as it were all the Crys, Calls, and Notes of Beasts and Birds in these Parts.

The

The *Scorpion-Lizard,* but why so called I know not, for it is not like a *Scorpion* in any respect: It is of the *Lizard* kind, but much bigger than any I ever saw in *Europe.* Its Back if of a dark Copper-colour, and the Belly of an Orange. It is very nimble in running up Trees, or upon Land, and is accounted very Poysonous. This Animal hath the most Sets of Teeth in the Mouth and Throat of any I have seen, but what they prey or feed upon, I am an intire stranger to, and likewise their Use in Physick.

The *Green-Lizards,* in this Province are as large as those to be met with in *Europe,* and are very harmless and beautiful, they frequently resort to the Walls of the dwelling Houses (especially in the *Summer* season, for in *Winter* they are not to be seen) and stand gazing on the Inhabitants, without any dread or fear, being very tame: They are of a most beautiful Green colour and have a little Bladder under their Throat, which they fill with Wind, and evacuate at pleasure.

There are several other sorts of *Lizards* of various and changable Colours, but none so beautiful as the Green ones. These *Lizards* are mortal Enemies to the *Spiders* and *Toads,* yet their Flesh eaten is hurtful, causing Inflammations, Tumours, and Blindness; the Head being outwardly applied with Salt, draws out Darts, Thorns, and things sticking in the Flesh, it likewise wasteth Wens, and other hard Swellings. The Gall causeth the Hair to fall off, and their Eggs kill speedily, except a sudden Remedy be exhibited made of *Falcon's* Dung and Wine. If they bite, they leave their Teeth behind them, which causeth continual Pain, until they are taken out. The *Gray-Lizards* are very common, and the *Snakes* feed upon them; for I have taken several of them out of the Bellies of the Snakes.

In

In the Month of *June,* 1730, as I was travelling in the
Woods together with other Company, we found an Insect
sunning itself at the Root of a large Pine Tree, about the
thickness of a Man's Finger, and three Inches long, it was
beautifully striped with Circles of Black and White.  The
Mouth was partly like the Mouth of a Frog, but not so large,
it had four short Feet, but no Tail; it was very soft, but the
Skin exceeding tough, and it moved very slowly.  Not one
of the Company could give me an Account what it was, neither could I ever learn from any I conversed with, or shewed
it to, having preserved it a considerable time in Spirits; but
I take it to be a Species of the *Lizards,* and have therefore
ranked it amongst them, not knowing by what other Name
to distinguish it.

Having thus given an Account of the *Frogs* and *Lizards,*
I shall in the next place proceed to give an Account of the
SNAKES that this Country produces, beginning with the
most poysonous, and concluding with those that have none.
And first,

The *Rattle-Snake,* so called from the Rattles at the End
of their Tails, which is a connexion of Joints (and seem as
if decayed) with a thin covering of an excrementitious Matter, between the substance of a Nail and a Horn; Nature
undoubtedly designing these on purpose to give Warning
of such an approaching Danger, as the venemous Bite of these
Snakes are.  Some of them grow very large, as six or seven
foot in length, and about the thickness of the small of a Man's
Legg.  They give Notice to such as approach their Danger,
by rattling their Tails, which may be heard at a great Distance; they are sharp sighted, and quickly discover any thing

approaching

approaching them a great way off. Their Skins are all over full of thin tender Scales, with a Ridge through the middle of them, of an Orange-tawny, and blackish colour, beautifully mottled on their Backs, and their Bellys an Ash colour, inclining to Lead. The Male is easily distinguished from the Female, by a Spot on his Head of a black Velvet colour, and his Head is smaller shaped and longer. Their Bite is very venemous if not speedily remedied, and especially if it happens in a Vein, Nerve, Tendon, or Sinew, where it is difficult to be cured. The Wound grows black, or of a livid colour, causing a swelling in the Parts; dimness of the Eyes, paleness of the Face, Swooning, and Death, if a Cure be not applied in time. They are a majestick sort of Creature, and will seldom or never bite (except they are provoked) which they cannot do until they gather themselves into a Quoil or Circle, and then will spring at a good distance to bite whatever provokes or injures them, otherwise they are most peaceable Creatures, and never attack or molest any one. The *Indians* pretend to charm them, so that they can take them up in their Hands, without any danger of being bit; but how far they may be expert in this kind of Practice, is still a Secret among them, but this I am certain of, that they are famous in curing the Bite of these and most other sorts of venemous Creatures in these parts. They have of late communicated the Method how to cure the Bite of the *Rattle-Snake* to the *Christians,* which almost every Planter is very well acquainted with. This Cure is perfected by chewing in the Mouth the Root of an Herb that beareth Tuffts or Buttons at the top like *Scabions,* but not of that Colour; this Root is as hot in the Mouth as *Ginger,* and about the same thickness, it is called the *Rattle-Snake-Root*, from its curing

the

the venomous Bite of that Snake; there are three sorts of it
to be found almost every where, this (as I said before) they
chew in their Mouths, swallow some part of the Juice, and
apply the rest to the Wound, which perfectly cures those
that are bit in a few moments.    It is surprizing to observe
how these Snakes will allure and charm *Squirrels, Hedge-
Conneys, Partridges,* and many other small Beasts and Birds
to them, which they quickly devour.    The Sympathy is so
strong between these, that you shall see the *Squirrel* or *Par-
tridge* (after they have espied this Snake) leap or fly from
Bough to Bough, until at last they run or leap directly into
it's Mouth, not having power to avoid their Enemy, who never
stirs out of the Posture or Quoil until he obtains his Prey.
It is reported, they have a Rattle for every Year they are
old, which does not begin to grow until they are three Years
old, which I am apt to believe, for the young ones have
none, and I have seen and killed several of these Snakes, with
thirteen, and fifteen, and one with thirty Rattles.    They
have several small Teeth, of which I cannot see they make
any Use, for they swallow every thing whole, but the Teeth
which poyson, are only four, two on each side of their upper
Jaws; these are bent like a Sickle and hang loose, as if by
a Joint.    Towards the setting on of these, there is in each
Tooth a little Hole wherein you may just get in the point of
a small Needle; here it is that the Poyson comes out (which
is as green as Grass) and follows the Wound made by the
point of the Teeth.    Their Bite is not always of the same
force, but more or less venemous according to the Season of
the Year, for the hotter the Weather, the more poysonous they
are, especially in *June, July,* and *August.*    In *Winter* they
never appear, but lie hid in some secret Places in the Earth,
as all the other Snakes do, not being able to endure the cold

                                           Weather;

Weather; for you shall see several sorts of them lying dead, at the approach of the Winter, not being able to reach or crawl into their Holes. Neither can we suppose that they can renew their Poison as soon, or as often as they please, for we have known Instances to the contrary of two that were bit in the Leg by one *Rattle-Snake,* as they were travelling in the Woods. The first was very painful some Days, not having an opportunity to get the Rattle-Snake Root, in some Hours after he was bit. The other received no more harm by that Bite than if he had been bit by a *Mouse,* or any other Creature not venemous; so that we may reasonably conjecture from this Observation, that their Poyson is not always of the same efficacy. I enquired of the first Person, what he felt when the Snake first bit him; he said, it seemed as if a flash of Fire had run through his Body. The *Indians* frequently pull out their Teeth, so that they never afterwards can do any Mischief by biting; this may be easily done, by tying a bit of red Wollen Cloth to the upper end of a long hollow Cane, and so provoking the *Rattle-Snake* to bite, and suddenly pulling it away from him, by which means the Teeth stick fast in the Cloath, which are plainly to be seen by those present. They have two Nostrils on each side of their Nose, which is not common in many of the other sorts of Snakes. They are so venemous that they frequently bite and poyson themselves: For, oftentimes when we have found out where they are (which is easily known by their continual Rattling with their Tails, which they shake and shiver with wonderful nimbleness when they are any way disturbed) we cut down long Poles or Reeds and make the tops thereof sharp, wherewith we tickle their sides, and provoke them, that at length they become so enraged, they bite themselves, and dye in a short time.

I hope it will not be unpleasing to the Reader to insert the following Account in relation to a *Rattle-Snake* and a Dog, as it happened during my residence there, *viz.* A Planter having taken a *Rattle-snake* in a Noose, put it into a Barrel, and brought it to *Edentown,* and told the Inhabitants, that if they would make him drink, he would shew them some Diversion; that he had a living *Rattle-snake,* and a Dog that would fight it, who had killed several in his time; the proposal was readily consented to by all that were present. The Planter immediately turned out the Snake (which was very large) whilst another held the Dog, as we generally do our Bull-Dogs. A large Ring was instantly made and every one cry'd out for *fair Play, viz.* That the Snake should have time to gather itself into a Quoil, or posture of Defence, which it very quickly did, and immediately began to Rattle it's Tail: Every thing being ready, the Dog was let loose, and attacked the Snake; his usual way of killing them, was, to shake them at full length out of their Quoil, in which Posture they can neither leap nor bite; but this Snake being so large, the Dog had not strength enough to do it. In the first encounter he only bit it, which the Snake as readily returned, biting the Dog by the Ear, which made him cry and quit his hold, and seemed to be stun'd, or like one in a Megrim. But the Company encouraged the Dog, and set him on again: In the second encounter it bit the Dog by the Lip, and immediately after bit itself, the Dog in a little time began to cry and reel about as if drunk or in a Megrim, grew regardless of his Master's calling him, and in half an Hour dyed, and the Snake in about a Quarter. I had not related this, had I not been an Eye-witness to the whole proceeding. The Poyson both of Viper and Mad-dog (I conceive) kill, by thick-

ning

ning of the Blood after the manner that Runnet congeals
Milk when they make Cheese.

These Snakes cast their Skins every Year, and commonly
remain near the Place where the old Skin lies, these cast
Skins are frequently pulverised, and given with good success
in Fevers, so is the Gall mixed with Clay, made up in Pills,
and given in pestilential Fevers and the Small Pox, for which
it is accounted a noble Remedy, and a great Arcanum, which
only some few pretend to know, and to have had the first
Knowledge and Experience of for many Years; so are the
Rattles good to expediate the Birth, and no doubt but it has
all those excellent Virtues that the *Viper* is indued with.

The *Ground Rattle-snake,* but why so improperly called,
I know no Reason for, because it has no Rattles, and only
resembles the *Rattle-snake* a little in colour, but is darker,
and not so large, seldom exceeding a Foot or sixteen Inches
in length, and is reckoned one of the most poysonous and
worst of Snakes, and is said to be the latest Snake we have
that returns to it's Hole in the fall of the Leaf. It's Uses
and Virtues are unknown to any in these Parts, except the
*Indians.*

The *Horn-snakes,* so called, from a Horn growing in their
Tail like a Cock's Spur, with which they strike and kill
whatever they wound with it, except a speedy Remedy be
applied. They are like the *Rattle-snake* in colour, but a
little lighter. They hiss exactly like a Goose when any thing
approaches them. This Horn in their Tail is all the Weapon
they have with which they strike and destroy their Enemy,
for they never bite as the *Rattle-snake* and other Snakes do.
They give warning to such as approach their Danger by Hissing. They are a very venemous Snake, hardly admitting
of a cure from the *Indians;* yet the most effectual Method

to perfect this Cure is by the *Rattle-snake* Root, cupping Glasses and Scarification, or cutting off the Flesh to the Bone, and lastly by Amputation of the Parts. These Snakes are near as long as the *Rattle-snake,* but are not plenty in this Province, and I have been credibly informed by several of the Planters, that they have seen them strike their Horns into Trees, and particularly into the *Pine* and *Locust,* which in a few Hours decayed and died, though before that it was in it's full Bloom. But be that as it will, I am certain of this, that it is a dangerous Snake, and it's Wounds very difficult and tedious to be cured.

The *Water-snakes,* whereof there are four sorts. The first is of the Horn-snake Colour, but not so large, and is as poysonous as any of the other sorts. The second is a long Snake, and differs from the other in colour, being more dark. These Snakes will frequently swim over large Rivers, and often hang upon the Boughs of Birch, and several other Trees by the Water side, and sometimes drop into the Cannoes as they are passing by, they are also very poysonous. The third is of an *English Adder* colour, but always frequents the Salts, and lies generally under the drift Sea-weed, where they are in abundance, and are accounted very mischievous when they bite. The fourth is of a sooty black Colour, and frequents Ponds and Ditches, and is as Poysonous as any of the former. When these Snakes bite (if a Remedy be not speedily applied) there ensueth great Pain, Inflammation, blackness in the Wound, the Vertigo, and Death within three Days; for the Poyson is so malignant, that it forthwith disperses through the whole Body, which when it comes to the Heart, the Creature immediately falls down dead. These and all the other Snakes lay Eggs, except the *Viper.* The Cure for the

bite

bite of these, is much the same with that of the Horn-snake, and their Virtues and Uses the same with the *Viper.*

The *Swamp-snakes,* whereof there are three sorts, and are very like the Water-snakes, and may properly be ranked amongst them. The first is of a dirt Brown colour on his Back, and the Belly is of a Carnation or Pink colour, and is large, but not venemous. The second is large, and the back is of the colour of the former, but the Belly is of a tawny and light Copper colour, beautifully mottled; these always abide in Swamps and Marshes, and are poysonous. The third is mottled, with a dark brown Colour on the Back, and the Belly of a livid and Orange colour. They are very poysonous, and remain likewise in Swamps and Ponds, and have prodigious wide Mouths, they are commonly as thick as the Calf of a Man's Leg, though they are not very long, they feed on Water-rats, Mice, and several sorts of Insects. The cure of these is much the same with the former, and may indifferently be used after the same manner.

The *Red-back Snakes* (so called from their Red-backs) are long slender Snakes, they are rare to be met with, and are very poysonous; it is reported that the *Indians* themselves cannot cure the venemous bite of them: I never knew any one bit by them, and I saw but one during my abode in those Parts.

The *Vipers* whereof there are two sorts. The first is of a grayish colour like the *Italian Viper,* the other black and short. Both these sorts are venemous, and spread their Heads flat when they are provoked. They lie hid in the Ground all the Winter Season, and are generally about a Foot and a half, or two Feet in Length. Their Heads are very broad compared with the Body, and the Neck much narrower than the Head. Their Tails are small sharp, and

curled

curled at the end. The Teeth upon the upper Chop are very long and crooked like a *Sickle,* and upon either side it hath four; those upon the lower Chop, are so small that they can scarce be observed by the naked Eye, neither can the length of the Teeth be seen except you take away the little Bladder in which they lie concealed, in this Bladder it carries Poyson, which it infuseth into the Wounds it makes with its Teeth. The Scales of a *Viper* are more sharp than a *Snake's;* it lies for the most part Quoiled up like a *Rattle-Snake.* In the *Viper* there is nothing venemous but the Head and Gall, which are cast away as useless. It is a sharp sighted, crafty, and venemous Creature, biting those that suddenly pass by it. The Viper is said to conceive Eggs within her, which she does not lay after the manner of other Serpents; but in her Body they are hatched into living *Vipers.* For as *Pliny* reporteth, that of all Creatures that want Hair, the *Viper* and the *Dolphin* only bring forth their Young with Life. It is likewise reported, that after they have ingendered, the Female destroys the Male, and feeds on him; and that the Young Ones eat their way out of their Female's Belly, when she is ready to bring them forth, and feed on her 'till they are able to fend for themselves. But how true this may be, I will not take upon me to determine; but this I am certain of, that I have killed several of them and after having opened them, have found fifteen or more young ones alive in the Female's Belly. The bitting of the *Viper* is mortal, and kills within three Days at farthest, if not speedily cured; the Poyson is universal, as if the Body were set on Fire with violent Convulsions, Weakness, cold Sweats, Vomiting, and then Death. At first the Poyson may be sucked out by applying the *Anus* of a Hen to the part after Scarification, or else a Plaster of *Garlick, Onions,* and *Venice-Treacle, ice-Treacle,* drinking *French Wine, Garlick Broth,* with *Mithridate, Bazoar-mineral, Myrrh,* and the *Rattle-snake* Root. The Virtues of the *Vipers* are so well known, that it would be needless to trouble the Reader with them, only that they are more valuable than any of the other Snakes.

The *Red-belly-snakes,* these frequent the Land, and are so called, from their Red-bellies, which inclines to an Orange colour: They are not very venemous, for I have known several Persons bit by them, some whereof were not much hurt, and others have suffered much by them. But I am perswaded that there are two different sorts of these Snakes, but so like each other, that there has been no difference made between them at present; otherwise their bites would not produce such contrary effects, as they are known to do.

The *Chicken-snake,* or *Egg-snake,* so called, from it's frequenting about Hen-yards, and devouring Eggs and Chickens. They are commonly of a dusky soot colour, though I have seen some of them dark, yellow, and mottled. They are about four Foot long, and the thickness of a Man's Wrist, they frequently climb up large Pine Trees, will rowl themselves round, and stick to the side of it, where there seems to be no manner of hold, above twenty or thirty Feet high; there sun themselves, and sleep in the heat of the Day. I cannot find that they are venemous, but are mischievous about Houses, and will imitate exactly the call and cry of Chickens, and allure and decoy them, which they will quickly seize and swallow.

The *Brimstone-snake,* so called, from it's being almost of that colour. They might as well have called it, the Glass, or brittle-Snake, for it is as brittle as Glass, or a Tobacco-Pipe, for give it the least touch with a small Twig it immediately

breaks,

breaks, or rather disjoynts into several pieces; and several in these parts confidently affirm, that if they remain in the same place untouch'd, they will joyn together again. What harm there may be in this brittle-ware, I cannot tell, for I never knew any Person hurt by them.

The *King-snake* is the longest of all other Snakes in these parts, but are not common; the *Indians* make Girdles and Sashes of their Skins, and it is reported by them, that they are not very venemous, and that no other Snake will meddle with them, which I suppose is the Reason that they are so fond of wearing their Skins about their Bodies as they do.

The *Corn-snake,* so called, from it's being met with in Corn-fields, and scarce any where else. They are not venemous, neither do they gather themselves into a Quoil like the Viper or Rattle-snake. They are near a Yard long, and of a Brown colour, mixt with Tawny.

The *Green-snakes* are very small, and are so called, from their beautiful green Colour (if any Beauty may be allowed to Snakes) the Planters make themselves very familiar with them, and will frequently put them in their Bosoms, without any dread or fear, because there is no manner of harm in them.

The *Black-truncheon-snake* might have very well been numbered amongst the Water-snakes: they are so called, from their shape, being the thickest and shortest kind of Snakes I ever saw; they lie on the Banks, and at the Roots of Trees by the Water sides, and when any thing disturbs them, they dart themselves into the Salt-water like an Arrow out of a Bow. What good or harm there is in them I know not, some of these Water-snakes will swallow a black-land Snake, half as long again as themselves, as I observed in one of them that I shot.

The

The long *Black-snake* is very common, and generally six Feet in length, it frequents the Land altogether, and is the nimblest Creature living, it has no manner of Venom in it's bite, but the part sometimes swells and turns to a running Sore. These Snakes are the best Mousers that can be, for wherever they frequent, they destroy *Lizards, Frogs, Rats,* and *Mice,* leaving not one of those Vermine alive. They are very mischievous about Dairies and amongst Eggs, skimming the Cream of the former, and swallowing the latter. They will sometimes swallow all the Eggs from under the Hen that sits, and Quoil themselves under her in the Nest, where they are often found by the House-wife: They kill the *Rattle-snake* where-ever they find him, by twisting their Head about his Neck, and so whip him to death with their Tails; and notwithstanding the Agility of this Snake, yet it is so brittle, that when it is pursued, and gets it's Head into the hole of a Tree or Wall, if any one gets hold of it at the other end, it will twist it self in pieces. One of these Snakes, whose Neck seems to be no thicker than a Woman's little Finger, will swallow a *Squirrel* or *Rat,* which I have taken out of their Bellies; so much does that part stretch in all those Creatures. It likewise feeds on small Insects and Flies, taking them betwixt the forks of its Tongue.

The *Eel-snake,* though improperly so called, because it is nothing but a kind of *Leech* that sucks and cannot bite, as other Snakes do, but is very large, being commonly eighteen or ninteen Inches long, and has all the Properties that other *Leeches* have, and lives in Ponds as they do. There is likewise a *Leech* in this Province, of the same bigness of those with us in *Europe.*

Having given as large an Account as is yet known of the *Snakes* in these Parts; I will in the next Place proceed to

U                              treat

treat of some of the smaller Reptiles or Insects that are most remarkable, and to be met with in this Country; but to give a large Description of all the different Species that this Country produces, would require too large a Volum, which is not my intention at present. Besides the *Indians* give us many strange and uncouth Names for various kinds of Beasts, Birds, Fishes, Snakes, and Insects, that we are intire Strangers to; for the greatest part of this spacious and large Country lies waste at present, and undoubtedly there will be many curious and considerable Discoveries made, when once this Country is well settled and inhabited by the Christians, for the Indians whilst they remain in their Idolatrous Practices, never will be brought over to cultivate this rich and noble Country, or even to make Discoveries of what they know of it already. But to proceed to the *Reptiles* and *Insects.*

The *Bees* are in great Plenty, not only in Hives, in the Planter's Gardens, but are likewise to be met with in several parts of the Woods in hollow Trees, wherein are frequently found vast quantities of Honey, and Wax. The Uses and Profits of these noble Insects, are so well known amongst us in *Europe,* that it would be needless to trouble the Reader about them. Their *Bee-hives* are generally made of some piece of hollow Tree, and especially the sweet Gum Tree, which they cut at proper lengths for that purpose, with a Board at the top for a Covering; these are all the sorts of *Bee-hives* made use of in this Country, some whereof are larger than our Barrel. The *Humble-bees* are of the same sort in this Province as those with us in *Ireland,* and other parts of *Europe.*

The

The *Silk-worms:* In several of our Journies in this Province, we found great numbers of them, with quantities of Silk as large as our ordinary *Wall-nut.* And no doubt these profitable *Insects* might be brought to great Perfection in *Carolina,* as in any part of *Europe,* if the same Care were taken there as is in *France, Spain* and many other Places, since this Country doth naturally produce them. In process of time, they leave off Spinning, and receive Wings like *Butterflies,* and after three or four Days Copulation, the Male presently dies, and the Female having lay'd many Eggs, dies also. The whole Worms dried, powder'd and laid to the Crown of the Head are good in *Megrims, Virtigoes* and *Convulsions,* and the Ashes of the Silk cleanseth Wounds, *&c.*

The *Butter-flies* are produced from small Eggs as the *Silk-worms* are, and are very plenty all over this Province, and of several sorts: some large, and others small, and most beautifully Mottled with variety of fine Colours. They generate in *May, June* and *July,* and lay vast quantities of Eggs in the Season, from whence they are produced. There are some of them larger in this Province than any I have met with in *Europe,* for you shall frequently see them chace the *Humming-birds* away from the Flowers on which they feed. It is a long lived Insect, after the Head is off; for I pulled off the Head from one of them in the middle of *Summer,* that lived about thirty five Days, and could flie all that time. This any one that pleases may try and prove the Truth of it. The Powder of these Insects taken inwardly, provokes Urine, and have much the same Virtues with the *Silk-worm.*

The *Grass-hoppers* are very plenty, whereof there are two Sorts; the first are of a much larger size than any I have met

with

with in *Europe*.   The second are much of the same bigness
as those with us.   Both these sorts seem to be more lazy and
dull Insects than those in *Europe,* for they are seldom heard
singing, but commonly are groveling in the Dust.   They are
likewise bad sighted, for they will scarce stir 'till you almost
tread upon them.   Of all Creatures that are known to live,
the *Grass-hoppers* alone have no Mouth, only a sharp Pipe
in their Breasts, wherewith they suck in the Dew, on which
they live.   Their Breasts are full of small sharp Pipes, with
which they make that ringing Noise we hear, and their Bellies, for the most part, are found empty.   They engender
with their Bellies upward, and have a roughness on their
Backs, which is sharp, and it is with this that they make Holes
in the Earth, where they lay their Eggs, and breed.   When
these Eggs are hatched (which is by the heat of the Sun) there
appear first little Worms or Maggots, which in process of
time become *Grass-hoppers*.   The Males are only said to sing,
and the Females to be always silent.   They are never to be
met in these parts in the *Winter* Season. The Powder of them
dried and given with Pepper, helps the Cholick, difficulty of
Urine, and the Ashes with *Rhenish* Wine the Gravel.

*Sows,* or *Hog-lice,* breed in most places, especially under
Stones and rotten Wood, whereof there are two sorts in this
Province, but not so plenty as with us, by reason that the
*Wood-peckers,* and several other Birds and Creatures continually devour them.   When they are touched, they gather
themselves up as round as a Pea.   The whole Insect is thin,
and of volatile Parts, digesting, cleansing, opening, and a
great disolver of all tartarous Matter, therefore good in all
Obstructions, Jaundice, Cholick, King'ʮ Evil, old sordid and
rebellious Ulcers, Convulsions, Stone and Gravel, Rickets in

Children,

Children, dimness of Sight, *French* Pox, and many other stubborn and lingring Disorders.

The *Fire-fly.* (I would not have the Readers be mistaken, and take these Insects for the *Pyrales* or *Fire-flies* that are represented by *Pliny* in his *Natural History*, as bred and living in the Fire). These live in the open Air, and are so called, from their appearing at Night like so many shining Sparks of Fire. They are as long as the Drones amongst the *Bees,* but much thicker, and are of a brownish colour. Their Light is under their Wings, which appears frightful to Strangers at first sight, although they have no manner of harm in them. I have frequently taken them and broke off their Wings, that they could not fly away, and placed them on a Book in a dark Room, and whatever way they went, I could plainly see and distinguish each Letter. They appear in *May,* and remain most part of the *Summer,* and are at sometimes in such plenty, that the Woods seem to be altogether Sparks of Fire; they are never to be seen in the Day, but fly all the Night. What Virtues they may be indued with, are uncertain; for I never knew any use made of them in this Country.

The *Crickets* are winged Insects like the *Locusts,* or *Grasshoppers,* and are plentifully to be met with in this Province. They seldom frequent the dwelling Houses as those with us in *Ireland* do, but are often heard and seen in the Woods and Corn-fields (especially in the *Summer*) where they Sing almost continually, in *Winter* they approach near the Houses and other warm places, they are very mischievous, for they frequently cut large holes in Linnen and Woollen, and are likewise great devourers of Corn and all kinds of grain. The Powder of them is said to provoke *Urine,* and strengthen the

Sight,

Sight, their Juice has the same effect, and their Ashes excellent against *Fluxes* and the *Gravel.*

The *Lady Bird* is a beautiful small Insect (with red Wings and black spots thereon) which the Children in *Ireland* frequently play with; it is to be met with in *Carolina* in the *Summer* time, and is a wonderful Cordial, curing all Fevers how poysonous or malignant soever, by its sudorifick quality. The Powder of its Body is of a deep Purple colour, and emits its Tincture into Water and Spirits of Wine, being not inferior to Saffron.

The *Cantharides* or *Spanish-flies,* are here likewise to be met with in the *Summer* time. These Insects are produced from small Worms like the *Catter-pillar* in *Fig*-Trees, *Pear*-Trees, Wild-*Pines* or *Pitch*-Trees and the Eglantine-*Brier:* Their uses and virtues are so well known, that it wou'd be needless to trouble the reader about them.

The *Pismire* or *Ant,* is a small, but industrious and wise insect, gathering its food in the *Summer* in the full Moons and resting in the new ones: They are like a common wealth, and gather Corn for their Winter provisions, which they dry and bite at both ends that it may not grow: They wear away Stones by their assiduity and make beaten Road ways; they help one another in drawing their Burthens; dam out Water and bury their Dead. The greater lead the way, and lesser drag the Corn; and when dirty, they cleanse themselves before they enter into their habitations. They teach their young to Labour, but expel the Idle, and when they carry their grain, it is said to be a sign of fowl Weather. They cast up the Earth over the Mouths of their Caves (that the Water may not enter in) wherein they have three Cells; in the one they live, in another they breed and bury their Dead, and in third they keep their Corn. They generate in *Winter,* and bring

forth

forth Eggs, which in Spring are *Ants;* when old they grow winged, then suddenly after die. The *Ants* are of a hot and dry Nature, excite lust, and wonderfully refresh the Spirits, their Eggs help deafness, and many other excellent virtues are atributed to them.

The *Spider* is a poysonous Insect, which hurts by stinging. There are divers sorts of these Insects in America, but the most remarkable is the *Mountain-Spider,* so called, for its being found commonly in the Woods near the Mountains, and scarce any where else. It is the most poysonous and largest of all *Spiders* that are yet known in *America.* Several sorts of these *Spiders* make their Webs or nets so strong that they often take small Birds in them. Those that have the Misfortune to be stung by these insects, are afflicted with different disorders, according to the Nature of the Spiders, which have communicated the poyson. For you shall some-time find them afflicted with violent pains at the heart, short-ness of Breath, heats and colds all over the Body, tumors, Inflammations, tremblings, cold sweats, vomiting, singing, laughing, talking, sleeping, starting, and sometimes fear, frenzy, and madness, with many other griveous symptoms, which often end in Death, without a speedy remedy be ap-plied. The cure is done by bathing with decoction of stink-ing Trefoil and Oil; fomenting the part with Spunges dipt in Vinegar, by application of the mullet, lees of Wine and Juice of Ivy; giving inwardly an electuary made of *Tamarisk, Mith-ridate,* and sometimes *Musick.* The Indians cure it by suck-ing the part with their Mouths, and continually spitting out the venom. These Insects being made into a Plaster and ap-plied to the wrists and Temples, cure Agues.

The *Ear-wig* is to be met with in this Province in the *Sum-mer* time, and is the same as in *Europe;* these Insects being

boiled

boiled in Oil and applied to the Arteries of the Temples and Wrists, are said to cure Convulsions, by causing a Fever. Their Powder mixt with Hare's piss, and so put into the Ears Evening and Morning, cure Deafness.

The common *Small-black-flies* are plenty in these parts, and are more troublesome here than in *France* or *Spain,* especially about the Legs, and no where else, for they will pierce through a pair of Stockings, and bite like the *Clegs* or *Gad-flies* in *Ireland.*

The large *Black-mackrel-flies* are also plenty, especially in the *Summer* time, and are the same as those with us in *Europe.* The powder of these Insects and their Juice cures Baldness.

The *Ox,* or *Gad-flies,* are so called, from their tormenting the Cattle in the *Summer* time; they are of various colours, but mostly yellow and green, and are plenty in this Province in the Months of *July* and *August,* at which time they are troublesome to Horses, especially about the Ears and head, and no where else; for which reason you shall see those that ride in the Woods, fix green boughs on the Horses heads, to defend them from these mischievous Insects.

The *Moth* is there likewise, and differs in nothing from those in *Europe,* being as mischievous and destructive to Woollen Cloths and Books as those with us. An Oil made of them is said to cure Deafness, Warts and the Leprosy, and being mixed with Tar, to be good in all sorts of rebellious Ulcers, Botches, Scabs, Whittles, &c.

The *Weevil,* is a little small Worm, not much bigger than a *Mite,* and is very distructive to Trees, but more especially to Corn, for I have seen Barrels full of *Indian* Wheat or *Maiz* intirely ruined by these Insects, when there has not proper care been taken, to prevent their doing mischief. They never

meddle

meddle with any grain (exposed in the weather) but when it is put up in close places, such as barrels and the like, yet this may be easily remedied by shaking a little Salt at the bottom and top of those vessels the Corn is in.

The *Chinch Wall-louse,* or *Buggs;* these are flat, red, and in shape and bigness like the *Sheep-louse,* they have an offensive smell when they are killed, they haunt Beds, suck Men's Blood very greedily, especially about the Neck and Face, which in many appeareth for a Day or two, as if stung with Nettles, and are as numerous in this Province as in *France* or *Spain.* *Pliny* saith, they are good against all Poysons and biting of *Serpents.* *Marcellus* saith, that the Powder of them cures all Fevers, their Scent, the Fits of the Mother, and that they are successful to force away the Birth, and After-birth.

The *Cock-roch,* is a kind of *Beetle,* something larger than a *Cricket,* and of a dark brown Colour; they frequent the Houses, and are very mischievous among Books and Linnen, by eating innumerable Holes in them, if there be not care taken to sweep and keep those places clean where those things are laid up. When they are killed, they stink like *Buggs;* their Uses in Physick are uncertain.

The *Tumble-turds,* are a Species of the *Beetles,* and so called, from their constant rowling the Horse-dung (whereon they feed) from one place to another, 'till it is no bigger than a small Bullet. They are one of the strongest Insects, of the same Size I have ever seen; they frequently fly into Houses, and I have seen one of them move a Brass Candlestick from one place to another upon a Table, which seem'd very strange to me at first; for not long after my arrival, being one Night at a Planter's House, who had secretly conveyed two of these

Insects under two different Candle-sticks; amongst other Discourses, he told me, he would made the Candle-sticks move about the Table by a certain Spell, as he pretended: He had all this time kept the Candle-sticks in his Hands on the Table. I was very desirous to see this performance; he immediately takes his Hands from the Candle-sticks, and struck three times under the Table, and seemed to mutter some few Words (as Juglers are known to do) which he had no sooner ended, but the Candlesticks began to move backwards and forwards, to my great surprize, for I could imagine nothing else but that it had been some secret Charm he had got from the *Indians,* who are great Conjurers. After the Company had sufficiently diverted themselves at my surprize, and how desirous I was to have this Charm communicated to me, one of the Company takes up the Candlesticks and discovers these Insects, which are of the same Shape, but something larger than the common *Beetles,* that are to be met with in *Ireland,* which feed on the Cow-dung, and make Holes in the Ground. There are several other different Species of *Beetles* here, but none so remarkable as these, or so beautiful, with a variety of Colours, such as Red, Green, Black, Yellow, &c. (except the *Horned-Beetle, Bull-Fly,* or *Flying-stag.*) These *Beetles* seem to be infected with little small Insects of a light brownish Colour, which are commonly called the Lice of the *Beetles.* Their Powder is used against the falling out of the Fundament, to expel Urine, and cure the bite of a Mad-dog. The Juice cures Wounds, and in Plasters Buboes and pestilential Carbuncles.

The *Muskeetoes* (in the *Indian* Language called *Toquani*) whereof there are two sorts. The first is small, but pernicious and troublesome, of a dark colour, and are so mischievous, and plentiful in some places on this Continent (and espe-

cially

cially on the Marshes and low Grounds) that scarce any one can live there, except the *Indians,* whom they do not bite or molest; this I am perswaded is owing in a great measure to their so frequently anointing themselves with *Bear's-grease,* and many other Ointments, which they make and daub their Bodies with.

The second sort are exactly the same in shape and size with the former, but are of a whitish Colour; these are not troublesome to the Inhabitants, neither do they bite like the former, they are generally brought here by Southerly Winds in *July* and *August,* in such vast quantities, that it is strange to behold them, they either die suddenly, or are carried away with the Winds, shifting from the South. What Virtues they may be indued with is uncertain.

The *Muskeetoe-Hawks,* are Insects, so called, from their continually hunting after *Muskeetoes,* and killing and eating them; they are a large Flie, with a long Body, great Head, and Wings, resembling the *Dragon-flie,* whereof they are a Species. They are very plenty all over this Province, especially in the latter end of *Summer.* They seldom appear in the Day-time, but hunt the *Muskeetoes* all night long. I know no other use they are good for than in destroying those Insects, so pernicious and mischievous to Mankind; so that the Planters seldom kill them.

The *Horned Beetle, Bull-flie,* or *Stag,* are to be met with in several parts of *Carolina.* These Insects have no Stings, but a large pair of Horns on their Head, exactly resembling the Horns of a *Deer,* for which reason they are called the *Flying-stag,* these Horns they can at pleasure bring together and bite withal. These *Beetles* are hung as an *Amulet* about Children's Necks for several Disorders.

X ₂                                    The

The *Sand-flie,* so called, from their breeding, and always being found in the Sand-banks, and near the Rivers, they are very small, not much larger than a *Gnat,* and are almost as pernicious and troublesom as the *Muskeetoes,* especially about the Face and no where else.

The *Wasps* are very plenty in this Province, they build their Nests in Trees, the substance whereof seems like Cobwebs, or a kind of brown Paper, and it is said they ingender in *Autumn,* but never in the *Spring,* and are bred out of the softer parts of Horse-flesh, they live upon Flesh, and several sorts of Insects, which they hunt after and kill for their Provisions. The *Wasps,* like many other Insects, are not to be seen all the *Winter,* but lie in Holes or hollow Trees all that Season, and they live not above two Years. They seldom are mischievous, or do any harm, except you provoke them, or approach too near their Nests, which the Planters frequently set fire to, by shooting at them with Gun-powder. (This is commonly done late in the Evening, or early in the Morning) and then they run away as fast as possibly they can, to avoid being stung, for when they are provoked, they will pursue in great Numbers those that have molested them. Their Sting is worse than that of the *Bees,* and is cured by application of *Cow-dung* mixed with *Barly-meal,* or *Leaven* mixed with *Oil* and *Vinegar.* The Powder of them is good to open Obstructions of the Reins and Bladder, some use them in all Cases where *Sows* or *Hog-lice* are used, and with the same success.

The *Hornets* are in great plenty in this Province; they build their Nests in Caves and Holes in the Earth, much like the former, and are said to be produced out of the harder parts of Horse-flesh, as the other is out of the softer. Their Decoction, or distilled Water, if touched on the Skin, makes the place swell as if there was a *Dropsie,* or the Parts had

been

been poysoned, yet without pain. The Cure for this, and their Sting is *Venice-treacle* taken inwardly, and applying outwardly *Cow-dung, fasting Spittle, Barley-meal, Oil* and *Vinegar,* &c.

The *Labourers,* are a Specie of *Hornets,* and are so called, from the pains and labour which they take in building their Nests with a kind of yellow Clay, they make Rooms or Cells wherein they breed their young, which is wrought so close, and after such a manner, that it is hard to break it when dry, to get the young ones out. They are near as large as a *Hornet,* and of the same shape and colour, they have long Legs, and always breed their young ones in the *Summer* time. They are more mild than the *Hornets,* and seldom or never sting; I have often observed these Flies to scrape the Sand by the River sides and moist places, where they make deep Holes and are buried under Ground before they can come at the yellow Clay. Some of them have Stings, yet they do little harm, only they are very troublesome in the Houses by fixing Clay to the Ceiling, if there is not proper Care taken to prevent them. Their uses in Physick are unknown.

The *Fleas* are very plenty in some parts of this Province, especially in those places where the *Indians* dress their Deer Skins, they have no Physical Virtues yet known, but are certainly most troublesome Guests. They are generated by Dust, as also of putrefied Sweat, and are destroyed by Decoctions made of *Coloquintida.*

The *Louse* is not plenty in this Province. They are eaten by Rusticks for the *Jaundice,* and *Consumption,* and to provoke *Urine.*

The *Tick* is a filthy Creature, or kind of *Louse* that troubles *Oxen, Horses, Deer, Goats, Sheep, Dogs,* and sometimes Men.

These

These Vermine are plenty in this Country, whereof there are
two Sorts, *viz.* the *Dog,* or *large Tick,* and the *small* or *Sea
Tick.*

The large or *Dog tick,* is the same as with us in *Ireland,*
only it has a brown Spot on the Back, which disappears as it
grows large.   It's Food is the Blood of several Animals,
which it most greedily sucks, yet it hath no passage to void
the excrements by, and generally sucks till it falls of, being
so full, and in process of time bursts and dies.   The juice of
the *Dog-tick* is a Depilatory, kills Ring-Worms, the Erysipe-
las, and Itch.   These vermine are destroy'd by the Powder or
decoction of *Coloquintida.*

The Sea *Ticks* are so call'd from their being so plentiful in
the marshes on the water sides, they are so small that they are
scarce as large as a small pins head, and are very troublesome
to those that travel in the Woods and near the sides of the
Rivers, for they stick so fast in the Skin, that it is impossible to pluck them out, and are apt to occasion Inflammations,
Fevers, or inveterate Sores, by scratching the part:   And notwithstanding they are so troublesome, yet they are easily destroyed by washing the parts in the Rivers, or by a decoction
of the leaves of *Tobacco* or *Coloquintida.*   Those that travel
the Woods in their Boots are never pester'd with these vermine, or if they anoint their limbs with Bears-grease, as the
*Indians* do, who are never troubled with them.   They seldom
appear till the Month of *May,* and continue till *August;*
and are supposed to be the spawn of the former, which I
am apt to believe, for I have frequently found the large *Ticks*
(after they have bursted) with vast quantities of young ones
in them.

The *Locust,* is an Insect or fly with a head like a Horse,
six Legs and as many Wings, and are of divers colours.   They
lay Eggs in *Autumn,* which lie all *Winter* in the Ground,

but

but in the latter end of *Spring* they are hatched, and in *Summer* become *Locusts.* These Insects burn Corn, Grass, and most kinds of plants by touching, and devour the residue; and it is reported that in *India,* there be of them three Foot in length, which the People of that Country do eat and use their Legs and thighs for Saws when they are thoroughly dry: St. *John* the *Baptist* fed upon them in the Wilderness. They are often carried over great Seas, and continue their flight for several Days together, in such vast Numbers that they are said to darken the very Sun as they flie, and to be certain prognostications of a Plague or famine, in whatever Country they settle, and burn and destroy every thing before them, and 'tis likewise said, that they will kill *Serpents;* yet these pernicious and distructive Insects are not very common in *Carolina.* Their Eggs given in *Rhenish* Wine, help the Dropsie, and the fume of the fly helps stoppage of Urine in Women.

The *Caterpillar, Palmer* or *Canker-worm,* is the same in *Carolina* as is to be met with in *Ireland,* and many other parts of *Europe.* These Insects are very destructive to Herbs and Corn, if there be not care taken to prevent them, which is done by the fume of Brimstone. They change like *Silk-worms,* and in process of time become *Butter-flies.* Their Ashes put into the Nostrils, stop Bleeding. A powder made of them is said to be good in the Epilepsy, and their Web is said to stop the Flux of Women's courses.

The *Gally-worm* is a short kind of *Scolopender,* exceeding in Number of Feet all other Insects. Some of them are smooth, others hairy all over, they are about the thickness of a Man's little Finger, and near two Inches long. They are not plenty in this Province, having several enemies that destroy them. Their Ashes wonderfully provoke Urine,

the

the Blood with the Juice of *Hog-lice,* take away white Spots in the Eye.

The *Tobacco-worm;* I am not certain whether it is call'd by any other Name, but I have call'd it so from its feeding on the Tobacco-Leaves, it is exactly shaped like the *Gally-worm,* but is something larger, and not hairy, and has two sharp horns on its Head, the Body is white and Black, with as many Feet as the former. This Insect I take to be another Species of the *Scolopenders* and is destructive and pernicious in the *Tobacco* Plantations, if there be not care taken to Search for and kill them, which is a business that the Negroes are very much employed in during the Tobacco Season. I don't find that they are any way Poysonous, for I have known some of the Planters make their Negroes eat them by way of punishment, when they have been negligent in their Tobacco Fields, and have not carefully gathered them from amongst the Tobacco Leaves: what physical virtues they may be indued with is uncertain.

The *Glow-worm* has Wings, and it shines in the dark like Fire; their light is under their Wings, and they are generated of Dew, they are most commonly to be met with in Swamps, and wet low Grounds, where they are plenty they shine at a great distance like a Fire, which has deceiv'd many in the dark Nights. They are *Anodyne,* and are given with good Success in the Gravel, being made into Troches, with *Gum Tragacanth,* and Oil of *Almonds.*

The *Land-wood-worms* are of a shining Copper colour, and never exceed four or five Inches in length, and scarce as thick as a Man's little Finger. They are so called from being found in old rotten Trees, and accounted venemous in case they bite; yet I have never known any one hurt by them.

There

There are many other different sorts of Worms found, not only in rotten Trees, but likewise in several Trees in their Bloom, and especially the Apple Trees, which I have already made mention of.

The *Teredines* or *Water-wood-worms,* so call'd from their breeding in Ships and other Timber lying in the Salt-Waters. They have small soft white Bodies and large, hard Black-heads; I have frequently seen some of them no thicker than a Horse-hair, and others the size of a Childs finger. These ver-mine are only mischievous in the extreme heat of the *Sum-mer,* and the fresh Water is an utter Enemy to them, wherein they perish and die. They are very destructive to Ships and Timber, especially if they lie in the Mud or Sands, but whilst they float they never come to any damage by them. I have seen several planks taken out of Ships and Boats, that have been eaten by these Worms like a Honey-comb in six Weeks time, by the negligence of the Masters to whom they belonged, that suffered them to lie in the Mud and Sands all that time, and notwithstanding they cut such large Holes within side of the Plank, yet the Holes on the out side are scarce to be seen, and no larger than for the point of a small Needle to enter. The Ashes mix'd with an equal weight of Anniseeds, and a little Oil, are good against all sorts of Ulcers and Cankers.

The *Earth-worms,* whereof there are several sorts, and are the same here as with us in *Ireland.* This Insect is a great Diuretick, Sudorifick, and Anodyne; it discusses, mollifies, increases Milk, opens obstructions, and cures Wounds, princi-pally of the Sinews and Ligaments, and many other disor-ders, being both externally and internally made use of.

The *Snails* are here likewise, but not so plenty as with us in *Europe;* having many Enemies that continually destroy

Y                                        them,

them, such as Birds, Snakes, Frogs, &c. The flesh cools, thickens, consolidates, is pectoral, and Strengthens the Nerves, cures Coughs, Asthma's, spitting of Blood, and Consumptions. Outwardly they Ripen Tumors, Imposthumes, and Carbuncles, especially if mix'd with Ox-gall, they heal wounds of the Nerves and Ulcers of the Legs, cure Ruptures and stop Bleeding at the Nose, and many other Disorders too tedious to Name.

Having thus given an Account of some of the most remarkable *INSECTS* that are to be met with here, I shall in the next place proceed to give a Description of the BIRDS, and FOWLS that this Country produces, many whereof are not known, or to be met with in *EUROPE*.

OF

# OF THE BIRDS.

**T**HE *EAGLES* being accounted the King of the Birds, I shall therefore begin with them. Of these there are three Sorts, *viz.* the *Bald,* the *Black,* and the *Gray Eagle.* The *Bald Eagle* is the largest, and is so called, because his Head to the middle of the Neck is covered with a white sort of downy Feathers, whereby it looks very bald, and the Tail is as white as Snow, the rest of the Body being of a dark brown colour. These Birds are very great breeders most part of the Year, and always build their Nests in old decay'd *Cyprus,* or *Pine-trees* near the River's side, where they generally lay two Eggs, and sometimes three, but they seldom have four; as soon as they are hatched, and the young *Eagles* have down on them, with white woolly Feathers, the *Hen Eagles* lay again, which Eggs are hatched by the warmth of the young ones in the Nest, so that the flight of one makes room for the others that are just hatched; thus they continue breeding most part of the Year. They not only prey upon Birds, Beasts, and Fishes, but upon any thing they are able to destroy. They are very destructive to Poultry, Lambs, young Fawns, and Pigs, which they frequently carry Squalling into the Air, and so bring them with ease to their young ones. They can fly from Morning till Night, and that very high, notwithstanding they are heavy of flight, and cannot get their food by swiftness, to help which, there is a *Fishing-Hawk,* that catches Fish, which it suffers the *Eagle* to take from it, notwithstanding it is a large and swift Fowl, and can make far better way than the *Eagle* can, and it is very pleasant to behold the flight of these two Birds, which sometimes continues for above half an Hour, at length it lets fall the Fish which the *Eagle* frequently catches before it touches the Earth or Water. These *Bald Eagles* will likewise attend the Hunts-men, in the *Winter time* for several Hours together (but at a great distance) till they shoot some game, which they frequently flie away with, dead or wounded. Their Nests are made of Twigs, Sticks, and several kinds of Rubbish, and generally so large that it is enough to fill a handsome Cart's Body, and commonly so full of nasty Bones and Carcasses that it smells most offensively. It is the opinion of most People in those parts that these *Eagles* are not Bald till they are two or three Years old. They are the strongest Birds of prey that are yet known in these parts of *America.*

The *Black-Eagles* are much the same sort as are to be met with in *Ireland,* but not altogether so large as the former, yet in all other respects as mischievous, and build Nests after the same manner in old Trees naked of Boughs, and nigh the River side, from whence as I suppose, they may have a prospect of the *Fishing-Hawks,* for when they see the *Fishing-*

*Hawk*

*Hawk* strike a Fish, immediately they take Wing and pursue Her. The *Fishing-Hawk* as soon as she perceives herself pursued, will Scream and make a most terrible Noise, till at length she lets fall the Fish, to make her own escape.

The *Gray Eagle,* is much of the colour of our *Kite* or *Glead,* it is not quite as large as the former, but Builds and preys after the same manner, and is frequently to be met with all over this Province. All these sorts of *Eagles* are very sharp sighted, view their prey at great distances, and have the best smell of all living Creatures. They are very bold Thieves, and live to be very old, and die not for Age nor any Sickness, but of meer hunger, by reason that the upper Beak of their Bill is so far over grown, and turneth inward so much, that they are not able to open it, to feed themselves. They seldom seek their prey in the Forenoon, for they are found sitting Idle and perched upon Trees all the Morning. It is reported that the Quills or Feathers of *Eagles* laid amongst those of other Fowls, will rot and consume them, which I have not faith to believe. The Flesh, tho' scarce fit to be eaten, is medicinal against the Gout; the Bones of the Skull, in powder, are good against the Megrim; the Brain drank in Wine, helps the Jaundice, and the Gall is of excellent use in most disorders of the Eyes, and applied helps the bitings of Serpents and Scorpions, &c. The Dung opens obstructions, and applied outwardly, ripens Tumors and pestilential Buboes.

The *Fishing-Hawks,* are so called, from their continual catching of Fishes on which they live. They may likewise be called the *Eagles Jack-all;* for commonly after they have taken their prey (as I have already observ'd,) they will flie at a great height in the Air, and cry and make a noise till such time as the *Eagle* comes, and then they will let the Fish

fall

fall from them, which the *Eagle* immediately carries off. They are a large and strong Bird, being above two thirds as big as the *Eagle,* they build their Nests after the same manner as the *Eagles* do, and that generally by the sides of Rivers and Creeks, and the *Eagles* and these Birds are seldom or never known to sit upon any living Tree. They are of a Gray Pyed colour, and the most dexterous Fowl in Nature at catching of Fish, for they never eat any Flesh-meat. They are a quick and sharp sighted Fowl, will fly at a good height, hover above in the Air, and watch their prey, which as soon as they have discovered, they will dart themselves like an Arrow out of a Bow into the Waters, and breaking the force thereof with their Breasts, quickly catch up the Fish and flie away. But it sometimes happens that they strike their *Tallons* so fast in a large Fish which they are not able to carry, that the fish suddenly takes them under the Water (before they can discharge themselves) and so drowns them. This I have been Eye-witness to, and in an Hour after it happened, got both the Fish (which was a large *Drum*) and the *Fishing-Hawk.* Their virtues and uses are much the same with the *Eagles.*

The *Turkey-Buzzard,* is a kind of small Vulture, which lives on all manner of dead Carcasses. Their Head and red Gills resemble very much those of a *Turkey,* from whence it has it's Name. They are near as big as an *Eagle,* and their Feathers are of a sooty brown Colour. They are in great plenty here, and in the Northern Provinces, and have the most offensive and nasty Smell of any Fowl I have ever met with. They are a clear and sharp sighted Bird, and their Flight is like that of our *Kites;* they soar at a great height in the Air, for Hours together over the Carrion, 'till such time as they find an Opportunity to prey on it. They smell at vast

Distances.

Distances, and will very readily find out where the Carrion or Prey is, if it be even under the Leaves, or Boughs of Trees, or slightly buried in the Earth by wild Beasts or Dogs. They are said to be utter Enemies to all manner of Snakes, killing all they meet with, for which reason the Planters seldom or never destroy them or their Eggs. They do no manner of Harm, feeding for the most part on dead Carcasses, which I suppose is the cause that they are the stinkingest of any Birds in these Parts. The Fat of this Fowl made into an Oil, is recommended against old Aches, and Sciatica Pains.

The *Kites* are much the same here as those with us in *Ireland,* but not commonly so large. These Birds most commonly frequent the Northern parts of the Country, there being but few to be met with in this Province; and in *South Carolina* they are seldom to be seen. It is said that they are mortal Enemies to the *Snakes,* for which reason the Planters seldom kill them, or destroy their Eggs. Their Flesh, though it be of gross Nourishment, yet it is eaten by the poorer sort of People in several parts of *Europe.* They are a very bold Bird, and a great destroyer of young Poultry, and it is remarkable when they see a young Duck, Chicken, &c. far from shelter, and lying exposed, how they will fly round it for several times, marking it, then of a sudden they dart down as swift as Lightning, and catch it up before it is aware. A Powder made of them eases the Gout, and helps the Epilepsy; the Grease is Effectual to the same Intention, and the Gall is an excellent Remedy in most Disorders of the Eyes.

The *Snake-Hawk,* or *Herringtailed-Hawk,* so called, from it's beautiful forked Tail (like a *Swallow*) and it's killing and feeding on *Snakes,* which it will do with the largest in these parts, with a great deal of dexterity and ease. It is

about

about the bigness of a *Falcon,* but a much longer Bird. They are a beautiful Fowl, of a delicate *Aurora* Colour, the Pinions of their Wings, and ends of their Tails, are of a jet Black. They never appear abroad in this Province but in *Summer,* and what becomes of them in *Winter* is unknown. They are in the greatest Request amongst the Planters (who will not suffer them to be killed) by Reason of their destroying those pernicious Insects, so hurtful to Mankind. They are a tame and familiar Fowl, will fly near one, and take their Prey, which is both diverting and pleasing to the *Europeans* especially; as for the *Indians* they do not regard them. It is strange to see how they are brought to those places where the Snakes are, about which they will flie for Hours together, 'till they have an Opportunity of killing some of them; and it is always a certain sign of Snakes being near those places where ever you meet them thus flyng. I have observed, when they take a Snake, that they always seize it in their Tallons near the Head, and flie or drag it some distance before they prey upon it, which they do by tearing it in pieces. It's Virtues and Uses are unknown to any in those Parts.

The *Goss-Hawks* are very plenty here, but do not appear to be as large as those from the *Northern* parts of *Europe,* yet seem to be a very bold, swift and active Bird in pursuing and taking their Prey, which is Geese, Ducks, Cranes, Hares, Rabbets, and the like. The Flesh is fat and sweet, may be used as Food and Hath much the same Virtues with that of the Kite. The Dung is exceeding hot, and being drank fasting in Wine, is said to cause Conception.

The *Falcons* are much the same as in *Europe,* but seem to be not altogether so large, yet they are a brave, brisk, and

quick-sighted

quick-sighted Birds; I have frequently seen them kill *Part-ridges, Parakeetoes,* and the like. These *Hawk*s are most commonly to be seen in Evenings, flying to the *Westward,* having, as it is supposed, their abode and Nests in or near the Mountains, where we may reasonably expect to find them, and several other Species that we are intire Strangers to at present.

The *Merlin,* is a small Bird in *Europe,* but much smaller in *America;* yet it, as well as the other Species of Hawks, is a bold, ravenous, and quick-sighted Bird, and nimbly kills several sorts of small Fowl, and sometimes Partridges. It is a most beautiful Bird, and would be a great Rarity, if it could be caught alive, or their Young ones found, but they never breed near the Settlements, but as is supposed in the Mountains.

The *Sparrow-Hawk* is not as big as a *Fieldfear,* it sometimes flies at, and kills small Birds; but it's chiefest Food is Reptiles, such as Grass-hoppers, Butter-flies, Beetles, and such like small Insects. This Hawk is exactly the same Colour of the Sparrow-Hawk in *Ireland,* only it has a Black-hood by it's Eyes.

The *Hobbies,* are a Species of the Hawks, something less than the *European* Sparrow-Hawks, and much of the same size and colour with them; yet there are but few of these kinds of Hawks to be met with in these Parts of *America.*

The *Ringtailed-Hawk,* so called, from it's round Tail, is another small Species of Hawks, with very short Wings. They are frequently to be met with in several parts of the Woods: they prey chiefly on Mice, Rats, and such like Vermine, that are to be met with in the Marshes near Rivers and Creek's side.

The *Owls,* whereof there are three sorts, *viz.* the *White,* the *Brown,* the *Barn,* and the small *Screech-Owl.*

The first is the great large *Owl,* which is as big as a middling Goose, and has a prodigious large Head: It is a delicate Feathered Bird, all the Feathers upon the Back and Breast being Snow-white, and tiped with a punctal of Jet-black. They are a bold and ravenous Bird, especially in the Night, at which time they make such a fearful howling, like a Man, that they have often deceived Strangers, and made them loose their way in the Woods, as I have been credibly informed by many in those Parts.

The second is of a *Brown,* or dark *Ash* Colour, and is as large as the former. These two build their Nests in hollow Trees, where they lie concealed all the Day, but at Night flie up and down the Woods, where they seek their Prey; yet they sometimes approach near the Planter's Dwelling Houses, and kill Hens, and other Poultry.

The third is the common *Barn-Owl,* about the bigness of a *Pigeon.* This Bird has a beautiful Circle or Wreath of white, soft, downy Feathers, encompassed with yellow ones, passing round the Eyes, and under the Chin, so that the Eyes appear sunk in the Head. The Breast, Belly, and inside of the Wings are white, marked with a few dark Spots; being the most elegantly coloured of all Night-birds.

The fourth is the small *Screech-Owl,* and is the same as those in *Europe.* These *Owls* and the former, are frequently attacked by other Birds, when they find them abroad in the Day-time; and when they find themselves overpowered, it is pleasant to see how they will place themselves on their Backs, where scarce any thing is to be seen but their Beaks and Tallons, in which posture they will fight, and defend themselves. The Flesh of these Birds is eaten by the *Indians* and *Negroes.* It is accounted good in Palsies and Melancholly.

The

The Grease and Gall is good against Spots in the Eyes, and to strengthen the Eye-sight. The whole Bird, not plucked, calcined, and taken into the Throat, opens the Imposthums of the Quinsie to a wonder, and the Brain, eaten, helps the Head-ach.

The *Parakeetoes,* are for the most part of a fine Green colour, only their Head, and part of their Wings, are of a beautiful Orange colour. They have thick Beaks or Bills, exactly like those of the Hawks. They are a Species of the *Parrots,* and generally about the bigness of a small Pigeon. In *April* they feed on the *Birch-buds,* and seldom come down amongst the Planters until the *Mull-berries* are ripe, which they eat, and are extreamly fond of. They are likewise very mischievous to Orchards, and peck the Apples to eat the Kernels, so that the Fruit quickly rots and perishes. They build their Nests in hollow Trees, in low swampy Grounds. They lie hidden in the *Winter,* when the Weather is extream hard and frosty, and never appear all that time. There are none of these Birds or *Alligators* to be met with to the North-ward of this Province, by the best Information I could learn, during my Residence in those parts. They are often taken alive with Traps, Bird-lime, &c. and will become tame and familiar in two or three Days time; yet they are not so docile or apt to learn to speak as *Parrots* generally are. They are most commonly very fat in the *Mullberry* and Fruit time, and are excellent good Food, preferable to any *Pigeon.*

The *Cuckow* of *Carolina* is a Bird of the same bigness and Feather with these in *Europe,* and sucks the small Birds Eggs as they do, yet it is never known to cry or sing *Cuckow* in the *Summer* time like the former, neither are these Birds to be seen in the *Winter,* at which time they hide themselves in

Z 2        hollow

hollow Trees, and their Feathers come off, and they are Scabby, they usually lay but one Egg, and that in the Nest of the Hedge Sparrow; like those in *Europe*. Their Flesh is sweet and good Food, and eaten by many in these Parts. Their Ashes are good against the Stone and Epilepsy. The Dung given in Canary is good against the biting of a Mad Dog.

The *Rail, Jackdaw,* and *Magpy,* are not to be met with in *Carolina* or any of the other Neighboring Provinces as far as I cou'd be informed.

The *Ravens* are very scarce to be met with in these Parts, yet they are the same sort as those with us in *Ireland,* and other parts of *Europe,* they are said to live to a great Age, and lay about five or six Eggs (before they begin to Sit) which are of a Pale Greenish Blew colour, and full of Black Spots. The Flesh is unwholsom, because they feed upon dead Bodies, yet the Ashes given for two or three Days together, cures the Epilepsy and Gout. The Brain performs the same thing, the Grease, Blood and Eggs, make the Hair Black. The Eggs help the Spleen, but cause Abortion.

The *Rooks* are less in *Carolina* than in *Europe*. They are good Food when Young (because they never feed on Carrion) but their Skins are tough, Black and bitter. They are very great Enemies to Corn Fields, if there be not care taken to prevent them. They build their Nests after the same manner as the *Rooks* with us do, but differ much in their Cry or Notes, which are more like the barking of a Dog, than that of Rooks. And it is said that when Rooks build, one of the Pair always sit to watch the Nest until it be finished; otherwise if both go abroad, and leave the unfinished Nest, the other Rooks rob it, and carry the Sticks away to their own; hence perhaps the Word *Rooking* is used for *Cheating*.

                                                            The

The *Black small-Crows,* whereof there are two sorts. The first is bigger than our Black-bird, and exactly of that Colour, but different in it's Notes. These Crows are the most hurtful and pernicious Vermine (especially to Corn) in all *America.* They flie sometimes in such vast Flocks, that they destroy every thing before them. Their Flesh is white and excellent Food.

The second are bigger than the former, and that part of the Head next the Bill and the Pinions of their Wings, are of an Orange and most beautiful Crimson Colour; and the rest of the Body Black. These are as good Meat as the former, though very few trouble themselves to kill or dress them, where large Fowl are so plenty. Both these kinds continue here all the Year, are generally fat, and excellent good Meat, and I have frequently eat of them. They build their Nest in hollow Trees as the *Parakeetoes* do; I look on them to be a sort of *Sterling,* for they cry something like them, but do not sing, and are about the same bigness.

The *Turkeys* are here wild, in great plenty, and exceeding large; I have shot some of them which weighed forty pounds, and I have been credibly informed, that some of them weighed sixty. You shall see five hundred or more of them in a Flock together; sometimes the wild Breed with the tame, which they account makes them very hardy. I am satisfied it does, for the *Indians* frequently find their Nests, and bring their Eggs to the *Christians,* which are hatched under Hens, Ducks, tame Turkies, &c. As soon as they are out of the Shell, they will fend for themselves, and are more easily brought up than a Chicken with us. Notwithstanding they are thus hatched, and familiarly bred up, yet they still retain a wild Nature, and commonly, when they are a Year and a half old, and grown large, run wild into the Woods, and can

never

never be brought into the House to Roost, but perch on some high Tree near it, and are always observed to seperate themselves from the tame sort, although (at the same time) they Tred and breed together.   There is no manner of difference that I can see between the wild Turkeys and the tame, either in their Shape, Gobling, Call, or Notes, only the Feathers of the wild are always of a blackish shining dark Gray, that in the Sun, shine like a Duck's Neck, very specious, and they have thicker and larger Legs.   They are a sharp sighted Fowl, and excelent good Food.   They feed on *Acorns, Huckleberries,* and several other Berries and Fruits that the Country produces, which makes them exceeding fat.   I have been credibly informed, that if one take these wild Turkey Eggs, just when on the point of being hatched, and dip them (for some small time) in a Bowl of Milk, or warm Water, that it will take off their wild Nature, and make them as tame and domestick as the others.   But how true this may be, I know not, never having made an Experiment that way; neither can I see any Reason to believe it; yet I thought fit to insert it, that others may try.   The *Indians* have frequently these wild Breed hatched at home, to be a Decoy to bring those that are wild near their Houses, by which means they shoot many. They are seldom to be met with but in the Morning and Evening, for at Sun-rise they go off to feed, and at Sun-set they return and perch on high Trees, and so continue all Night.   At any other time of the Day you shall scarce find one, except it be when they are Breeding, or in Snowy Weather, and then they are to be seen in great Flocks together.   They are a wary Fowl, and seldom shot but whilst they are perching on the Trees.   They may be heard call or gobble, at a great distance (Morning and Evening, but at no

other

other time) which brings the Huntsmen to those places where they are. They are a heavy Fowl, and cannot flie far, but will run exceeding fast, for if you should chance to break one of their Wings in Shooting, without a Dog, you seldom catch them. Their Uses in Physick are the same with the tame Turkey.

The *Pheasants* are something less, and differ some small matter in their Feathers from those in *Ireland,* but are no ways inferior in delicacy, but rather better and finer Meat. They are very plenty, but their chiefest Haunts are backwards in the Woods, and near the Mountains; for they are seldome to be found near the Inhabitants. The *Pheasant* is accounted better Meat than almost all other Fowl, because it is of a most delicate Taste, and yields such excellent Nourishment. They feed on Acorns, Berries, Grain, and several sorts of Seeds of Plants. Their Flesh is good in hectick Fevers, the Gall sharpens the Sight, and the Blood resists Poyson.

The *Wood-cocks* are not near as large in these parts of *America,* as those in *Europe;* they differ nothing in shape and Feather, only their Breasts are of a Carnation colour, and they make a Noise (when on the Wing) like the Bells about a Hawk's Legs. They breed and continue here all the Year, and though they are not as plenty here as they are in the Northern parts of Europe, yet they are as fine and delicate Meat as any of that kind in the World. They are to be met with in most parts of this Country, but especially in the low Grounds, Springs, Swamps, and Percoarsons. Their Flesh is best in *Winter* being then fattest. It and all it's Parts have the Virtues of *Partridges.*

The *Snipes* are plenty in several parts of this Province, and are the only wild Bird that are not different from the same species in *Europe.* They frequent the same Places as

those

those with us do, *viz.* Springs, Wet Ground, *&c.* Their Flesh is tender, sweet, and of excellent Nourishment.

The *Tut-cocks,* are a Species of *Snipes* in these parts, and are almost like the former in Size and Feather; they are plenty in several Places of this Province, and nothing inferior to the former in the delicacy of their Meat; but these, as well as most other small Birds, are little regarded or made use of at present, where large Fowl are so numerous.

The *Curliew,* whereof there are three sorts, and vast Numbers of each : They have all long Bills, and differ neither in Colour or shape, only in size, from those in *Europe.* The largest being as big as a good Hen, and the smallest as large as a small *Wood-cock,* and those sorts are excellent Meat, and nourish very much.

The *Sea-Pie,* or *Gray Curliew.* This Bird is about the bigness of a large *Wood-cock,* and has a long Bill as the other *Curliews* have, which is of a yellowish colour, and so are it's Legs. It frequents the Sand-banks on the Sea-side. When killed, is inferior to no Fowl I have seen or eat of; It's Flesh being tender, well relished, and nourishing.

The *Will-Whillet,* is a Bird so called, from it's Cry, for it exactly repeats, or calls *Will-willet,* as it flies. The Bill is like a *Curliews* or *Wood-cocks,* and has much such a Body as the other, but not so tall; it is good Meat, being nourishing and well tasted. They are plenty along the Shore, and the sides of Rivers, and are much of the same Nature and Virtues with the *Curliews.*

The *Lapwing* or *Green-Plover:* These Fowl are very plenty in several parts of this Province, especially in the Savannas, and near the Mountains. Their Cry is pretty much like those with us, they differ little or nothing in the Feathers, but are not near so large, yet not inferior to any

of

of that Species, in the delicacy and goodness of their Meat. Their Ashes drank in Wine, is good against the Cholick, and a Cataplasm thereof, helps the biting of Mad Dogs.

The *Grey,* or *Whistling-Plover.* These Fowl are very scarce, and seldom to be met with near the Settlements, but there are great Numbers of them in the Vallies and Savannas near the Mountains, and Heads of Rivers, where they are to be met with in great Flocks. They differ little from ours, either in Feather or Size, as far as I could discern, and eat as well as any of the same sort in *Europe;* the Flesh is pleasant, and much better Nourishment than the *Green-Plover.*

The *Partridges* are not as large as those in *Ireland,* being not much bigger than our *Quail.* They frequently perch upon Trees, and have a kind of Whistle or Call quite different from those with us; but the same Feathers, only the Cock has a half Circle over each Eye, instead of the Horseshoe. They are a beautiful Bird, but great destroyers of Pease, Wheat, and *Indian* Corn, in the Plantations, where the Boys set Traps and catch vast numbers of them; I have frequently bought a Dozen of them for less than a twelve penny Bill. They are generally exceeding fat, and are a far more delicious Morsel than ours. *Sed de gustibus non est disputandum.* They might be easily transported from one Place to another, because they take to feeding immediately after they are caught. The *Rattle-Snake* frequently destroys them, however they are in great Plenty in this Province, and resort in Covies as ours do. It is a very libidinous Bird, for they will seem to couple with their own Image in a Glass: they lay ten or fifteen Eggs, and sit twice in a Year, and are said to live about fifteen or sixteen Years. The Blood helps the Eyes, wounded or Blood-shot, and the Gall is one of the most eminent things in the World for defects in the Eyes.

The *Turtle-Doves* are very plenty in these parts of *America,* and breed and remain here all the Year; they are something less than a common *Pigeon,* the head and back are of a duskish blue, or ash Colour; they have a more melancholly Tone or Note, than any of the other Species of *Doves,* that are to be heard up and down in the Woods, as you travel through them. They live eight Years, are destructive to Corn-fields and Pease, for which reason the Planters make Traps, and catch great Numbers of them. I have frequently eat of them, and they are a most delicious Morsel. Their Flesh has the same Virtues with the *Pigeon,* but is peculiarly good against the Bloody Flux.

The *Wild Pigeons* are like the *Wood-quest,* or *Stock-dove,* only they have longer Tails. They seldom or never appear amongst the Planters, or near their Settlements, but in the *Winter* (as *Wood-cocks* do with us) they come down in large Flocks, that it is surprising to behold them. After Sunrise I have seen them fly, one Flock after another, for above a quarter of an Hour together. They come at this Season of the Year in quest of a small sort of *Acorn,* that is called the *Turky-Acorn,* which groweth on the *Turky-Oak,* whereof I have already made mention. It is common in these Parts, and thereon these *Wild-Pigeons* feed in that Season, and are very fat. It is observable, that wherever they settle, or roost at Night, they frequently break large limbs of Trees, in several places in the Woods. When they come in these numerous Flocks, they generally clear all before them, scarce leaving one *Acorn* on the Ground. It is said they breed in the Mountains (and I am persuaded, considerably to the *Northward* of us, because they never appear here but in the

extremity

extremity of the *Winter,* when it is hard Frosty or Snowy Weather) but whether they make their Nests in the Rocks, or in Trees, is not known, by any that ever I conversed with. I should rather think they made them in Trees, because of their frequent sitting and roosting on them at Night. Their Dung will lie above half a Foot thick about those Trees, which kills Shrubs, Grass, and everything that grows near where it falls. Notwithstanding these Flocks are so numerous, yet they are not to be mentioned in comparison with the great and infinite number of those Fowls that are to be met with to the Westward of those Places, where the *Christians* at present live (especially on this and the other side of the Mountains) many of which Species we are little acquainted with, because they seldom appear or come where we are already settled. The Flesh is very nutritive and excellent Food. The Blood helps disorders in the Eyes, the Coats of the Stomach in Powder, cures bloody Fluxes. The Dung is the hottest of all Fowls, and is wonderful attractive, yet accompanied with an *Anodyne* force, and helps the Headach, Megrim, pain in the Side and Stomach, Pleurisy, Cholick, Apoplexy, Lethargy, and many other Disorders.

The *Moor-hen.* I never saw any in this Country, yet I am credibly informed, that they are to be met with in the Mountains, and high Country, for they never appear in any part of the Settlements.

The *Wood-pecker,* whereof we have five sorts, if not more. The first is as big as a large *Pigeon,* of a dark brown Colour, with a white Cross on the Back, and a white Circle round the Eyes, and on it's Head stands a Tuft of beautiful Scarlet Feathers. Their Cry is to be heard at a great Distance, and they fly from one rotten Tree to another to get *Grubs* and *Worms,* which is what they live on.

Aa 2                                        The

The second sort are of an Olive colour, striped with Yellow. They are about the bigness of those in *England*. They feed after the same manner with the former, on *Grubs* and *Worms*.

The third sort is about the same bigness with the second, and is pied or mottled, with black and white, and it's Head is of a beautiful Vermilion colour, but hath no Topping on it; they are destructive to Corn and Fruit, especially Apples. They likewise open the Covering of the young Corn, so that the Rain gets in and rots it.

The fourth sort are finely speckled or mottled, with beautiful white and black Feathers, the finest I ever saw. The Cock has a beautiful red Head, but not near as big as the former. Their Food is *Grubs* and other creeping Insects, and Corn. They are not wild, for they will let one come near them, but then they hop and shift themselves on the other side of the Tree from your sight, and this they will do for a considerable time; yet it is very difficult to shoot one of them by their shifting so often from you, notwithstanding they will scarce leave the Tree. These are about the bigness of our *Lark*.

The fifth sort is about the bigness of a *Jay*. The top of the Head is of a Crimson or Vermilion Colour, spoted with Black, round each Eye is a circle of Black, and on each side is a Vermilion spot. The Throat, Breast, Belly, and Wings, are of a Pale Green, the Rump of pale Yellow, or Straw Colour. Its Tongue is of a great length, with which it strikes *Ants,* and other *Insects*. The Bills of all these sorts are so sharp, hard, and strong, that you shall hear the stroke of them sound like a Chizzel against a Tree. They are well acquainted in what Trees Worms are bred in by the Sound. They Climb Trees upright, after the manner that *Cats* do, and bend their head and look backwards on those that ap-

proach

proach near them. They make Holes in Trees where they build their Nests, and it is reported that if these Holes were stopt up ever so secure with a Wedge or Pin of Wood, that they will soon take it out again, so dextrous are they to work in Wood with their Bills. The Flesh of these Birds is not good for Meat, being harsh and hard of Digestion, outwardly it helps Inflammations, and the Gall with Honey and Juice of Rue is used in disorders of the Eyes. There is a Tradition amongst them, that the Tongue of one of these *Wood-Peckers* dryed, will make the Teeth drop out if pricked therewith, and cure the Tooth-ach (though I believe little of it, but look on it as ridiculous) yet I thought fit to hint it, that others may try the Experiment; for sometimes such odd Stories refer to some particular Virtues, though all that is said of them be not true.

The *Cat-Birds* so called, from their crying or making a Noise exactly like the Young *Cats,* for I never could discover or hear any other Note amongst them. They have a blackish Head, and an Ash-coloured Body. They are about the bigness of our Lark, will fight a Crow, and many other Birds much larger than themselves. They are pretty good eating, but what Physical Virtues they may be endued with, are unknown.

The *Mocking-Birds,* so called, from their mocking all other Birds in their singing, for they have such diversity of Notes, that there is scarce a Bird in these parts, that they hear, but what they will imitate; and they certainly are one of the finest singing Birds in the World. There are two sorts of these Birds. The first has Feathers much of the Colour of our *Green-Plover,* with White in the Wings, like a *Magpye's*. This has a more melodious and soft Note than the latter, and is generally about the bigness of our *Thrush*. They are held

to

to be the Choristers amongst the Birds of *America,* as indeed they are, for they will sing with the greatest diversity of Notes that is possible for any Bird to change. They are fond of our Dwellings, and frequently resort thither; being bold and brisk Birds, yet seem to be of an extraordinary tender Constitution; for they neither sing in the *Winter,* nor in the midst of *Summer,* and it is with great difficulty that any of them that are brought over, will live in *England* or *Ireland.* They may be bred up tame, and will sing in Cages; yet the Planters seldom take them or their Young ones (except it be to sell to those trading to *Europe*) notwithstanding they make their Nests, and breed most commonly in the Orchards, and other places near the Dwelling Houses, because they have their Company as much as if in Cages, for they frequently sit on their Houses in the *Summer,* and sing all the Evening, and most part of the Night. They feed on *Mulberries,* and several other Berries and Fruit, especially the *Mechoacan-berry* which grows plentifully in these Parts.

The second sort is called the *Ground-mocking-Bird,* and is of a light Cinnamon colour, about the same bigness of the former. This Bird sings excellently well, but is not so common amongst us as the other, neither does it frequent or resort our dwellings, but delights to live amongst the *Myrtle Trees* (being of a wilder Nature than the first) where it breeds it's young Ones; and like the former, is never known to sing in *Winter.* Both these sorts of Birds continue here all the Year and are in great request amongst the Planters.

The *Red-birds,* so called from their beautiful Red colour, whereof there are two sorts, the Cocks of both sorts are of a pure Scarlet, and the Hens of a duskish Red. I distinguish them into two sorts; for the one has a fine Tuft or Topping of Scarlet Feathers on the Head, and the other is smooth

Feathered

Feathered. I never saw a Tufted Cock with a smooth-headed Hen; they generally resort Cock and Hen together, and always play in or near a Thicket, where the Boys set their Traps and catch, and sell them to Persons trading to *Europe.* They have strong and thick Bills, and are near as big as our *Black-Birds* in *Europe.* They are very hardy, and continue here all the Year. They Whistle and Sing like a Thrush, but are more melodious. They are good for turn-ing Cages with Bells, and if taught like the *Bull-Finch,* and other Birds, I do not doubt would prove very docile; 'tis pleasant to behold this Bird seeing it's own Image in a Look-ing-Glass, because it hath so many diverting and strange Gesticulations, either making a hissing Noise, or lowering it's Crest, setting up it's Tail, shaking it's Wings, striking at the Glass with it's Bill, with many more too tedious to Name. If they are taken at any time they will feed and become tame; yet it has been observed, that when they are shut up in Cages for some Years, they become Milk-white, and so stupid that they scarce know how to feed themselves, which is never known to happen whilst they are in the Woods and free from Confinement. They feed on *Indian* Corn and several sorts of Berries and Seeds, produced in this Country. These Birds and the former, eat much like our Thrushes.

The *Field-fair,* is much like those with us in *Ireland,* but are never to be seen in this Province but in *Winter,* they are then very fat, and excellent Food.

The *Thrushes* are the same in those parts of *America,* as with us, only they are Red under their Wings. They never appear amongst the Planters but in hard frosty Weather, and quickly leave us again; 'tis supposed they go to the Northward where they breed. They are fat in that Season, and the Flesh is of good Nourishment.

The

The *Throstles* are of the same bigness and Feather with those in *Europe,* but are not to be admired for their warbling Notes, as ours are, for I have seldom heard them sing. These Birds are very fat in the *Winter,* and are good eating. Being roasted with *Myrtle-berries,* they help most sorts of Fluxes. The *Throstle* is called in Latin, *Berbiacenfis,* from *Berbiacum,* a Village near *Verona* in *Italy,* being there first seen at the Battle between *Otho* and *Vitelus,* where the former was overcome.

The *Whipoo-will,* is a Bird so called, from it's frequent and exact repeating those Notes or Words. These Birds are about the bigness of a *Thrush,* and are hard to be seen, although they be heard never so plain, for they constantly run under Thickets and Bushes where they hide themselves, and call their Notes. They are scarce in this Province, and seldom to be met with to the Southward of it; but in *Virginia* and other Provinces to the Northward, they are very plenty in most of the Plantations, and are tolerable good eating.

The *Jays* are here very common, but more beautiful and finer Feathered than those in *Europe,* for these are Blue, where ours are Brown, and not above half as large, but have the same Cry, and sudden jetting Motion. They are mischievous in devouring the Fruits of the Country, and commonly spoil more than they eat. The Flesh of these Birds are much better Nourishment than any of the same sort in *Europe,* where they are commonly eaten by the poorer sort of People, and especially in *France,* but are seldom made use of in these parts of *America,* where large Fowl are so plenty.

The *Kill-Deer,* is a Bird in these parts, so called, from it's frequent repeating those Words. It is about the bigness of our *Redshank,* and of the same colour, and frequents the Banks and River sides, as the former. These Birds continue

here

here all the Year, are generally fat, excellent good Meat, and easily shot; but being a small Bird, are little regarded, or made use of.

The *Sand-Birds,* so called from their being always on the Sand-banks, and scarce any where else. They are about the bigness of a *Lark,* and of a gray and brown Colour. They are generally fat, and numerous in these Parts; they are a most delicious Morsel to eat, yet few spend their Time or Amunition to kill them.

The *Runners,* are Birds so called, from their continual running and feeding along the Sands. They will suffer one to run after them a long time, and even to throw a Stick at them, before they will get up or fly away; so that they are often driven together in great Numbers, and shot. They are about the bigness of a small *Snipe,* partly of that colour, and excellent good to eat.

The *Lark* is heeled, and coloured as those with us are, but the Breast is of a glittering fine Lemon colour, in shape like a Half Moon. These Birds frequent the Savannas, or Natural Meads, and green Marshes, and are as large as a *Field-fare,* and they have a soft Note. They breed twice a year, and are said to be troubled with the Epilepsy. They nourish very much, and are excellent good Meat. The Blood drank fresh, with Vinegar, helps the Stone in the Bladder.

The *Bunting-Larks,* whereof there are two sorts, though the Heels of these Birds are not so long as those in *Europe.* The first have an Orange colour on the tops of their Wings, and are good Meat. They frequently accompany the *Black-bird,* and sing as the *Bunting-Larks* do in *Europe,* differing very little in their Notes, and have much the same Virtues with them.

The second Sort is something less than the former, of a lighter colour, and differ nothing in Feathers or bigness from those with the Tuft or Crest on their Heads, that are commonly to be met with in *Ireland,* and many other parts of *Europe*, and their Flesh is good to eat.

The *Blue-Bird,* so called, from it's being all of a beautiful fine Blue-colour, except the Breast of the Cock, which is Red like the *Robin Red-brest.* They have an odd kind of Cry, or Whistle, very different from the former. These Birds hide themselves in the *Winter,* so that they are not to be seen all that Season, but are plenty in the *Summer.* They are but a small Bird, not so large as our *Buntings,* but are excellent good Meat.

The *Bull-finches* in these parts of *America,* are of the same size and bigness of those with us, but differ some small matter in their Feathers, from those in *Europe;* those in *Carolina* being more beautiful. But whether they are so docil as those with us, I cannot tell, never having seen any of them bred up in Cages. The Flesh of these are much the same with that of the *Sparrow.*

The *Nightingals* differ something in their Feathers from those in *Europe,* but have much the same Notes: They are as big as a *Goldfinch,* and always frequent low Grounds, especially amongst the Myrtle-berries, where they generally sing very prettily all Night; but in the *Winter* (like the *Swallow*) are neither to be heard or seen. They breed in *May,* and generally lay about four or five Eggs in a Nest, near which they seldom sing, for fear of being discovered. The Flesh is sweet and good Food, helping the *Cachexia,* and strengthning the Brain. The Gall mixed with Honey, helps Disorders in the Eyes.

The *Sparrows* differ in Feather from those in *Europe,* and are never known to resort or build their Nests in the Eaves of Houses, as ours do. There are several sorts of Birds called *Sparrows,* from their being so plenty all over this

Province;

Province; one kind of these *Sparrows* exactly resembles the Bird we call the *Corinthian Sparrow.* All the Species of *Sparrows* are extraordinary good Meat, and the Boys catch great numbers of them in Traps, especially in *Winter.*

The *Hedge-Sparrows* are here, though there are few Hedges, but what are made of Timber. They differ little in either Plume or Bigness; yet I never heard them Whistle as those in *Europe* do, and especially after Rain. These and the other *Sparrows* are nourishing, and prevalent in the decay of Nature.

The *Red-Sparrow,* so called, from the great resemblance it has to a *Sparrow* in it's Size and Bill, and being one of the most common small Birds in these Parts. They are striped with a brown, red, and Cinamon colour, and the Tail and Wings incline to black.

The *Titmouse,* or *Tom-tit,* is the very same as with us in *Europe,* differing in neither shape, size, or feather. These small Birds are in plenty all over this Province. They are found for the most part about Trees, and live chiefly upon Insects which they find there.

The *Snow-Birds,* (I take to be same with our *Hedge-Sparrow*) are so called, from the vast numbers of them that come into those Parts in hard Weather, and especially when there is any Snow, but are seldom or never to be met with at any other time. For the Weather no sooner changes, than they are gone to the more Northerly parts of *America,* where they are most numerous. They are a small Bird, about the bigness of the *Wheatear.* The Boys catch great quantities of them in Traps, during their abode in these parts. They are fat, nourishing, and good eating.

The *Yellow-wings* are small Birds, so called, from their beautiful yellow Wings. They are of the colour of a *Linnet* on the Back and Breast, but in size less, with Wings yellow

as

as Gold.  They frequent high up the fresh Water Rivers
and Creek sides, where they breed.  They hide themselves in
the thick Bushes, and are very difficult to be seen in the
Spring, but in Summer they appear and sing all the Season.
What other properties they may be indued with, is uncertain.

The *Weet* Birds are about the bigness of a *Sparrow,* and
of a greyish Colour, and are so called, from their *Weeting*
or cry before Rain.  These Birds frequent near the sides of
Rivers and Ponds of fresh Water, where they Breed.  What
physical Uses they may have is not known.

The *Goldfinches.*  There are a sort of Birds like these to
be met with here, variegated with *Orange* and *Yellow* Feathers, very specious and beautiful to behold; yet I never heard
them sing, as those in *Europe* are known to do.

The *Baltimore* Birds, so called from my Lord *Baltimore,*
being Proprietor of all *Mary-Land;* in which Province they
are very plenty.  They are about the bigness of a *Linnet,*
with yellow Wings and variety of other beautifull Colours.
They appear most commonly in this Province in the Winter
Season, at which time they are fat and good eating.

The *East India Bats,* or *Muskeetoe Hawks,* are so called
from their killing and feeding on *Muskeetoes,* and because
the same sort of Birds are found in the *East Indies.*  They
are as large as a *Cuckow,* and much of the same Colour, but
have short Legs, not discernible when they flie.  They appear
here only in the heat of the *Summer,* and at the approach of
cold Weather, leave us again.  They are never seen in the
Day time, but are scudding all Night, like our *Night Raven,*
in pursuit of *Muskeetoes, Gnats,* and other Insects, on which
they feed.  And though it is called a *Bat,* I see no reason for
it, because it bears no manner of Resemblance to the *Euro-*

*pean*

*pean Bat,* the *East India Bat* being a Fowl with Feathers, and the other bodied like a *Mouse,* with Leather Wings. I never knew any use made of these Birds, for the Planters never kill them; because they destroy those pernicious Insects the *Muskeetoes.*

The *Bats,* whereof there are two sorts, which I have already given a Description of amongst the Beasts, it bearing the greatest resemblance to that Species; for though it flies, yet it hath no Affinity to Birds, not so much as a flying Serpent, and notwithstanding it be not properly a *Quadruped,* it hath Claws in the Wings, which answer to fore Legs. These *Bats* are plenty in this Province, and differ only in being larger than those in *Europe.*

The *Swallows* are very plenty in the *Summer,* and differ nothing from those in *Europe.* The flesh of these Birds is no good Nourishment, yet often eaten, is said to help Dimness of sight, the falling-sickness, and many other Disorders. The Nest outwardly applied, is of excellent use in Quinsies, redness of the Eyes, &c. These Birds feed on Flies, Worms, and many other kinds of small Insects.

The *Swift,* or *Diveling,* has a great Head and Wide Mouth, but a small Bill. The colour of the Feathers of the whole Body is black, only under the Chin, is a Spot of white or Ash-colour; the Legs are short, but thick, and the Feet small. These Birds feed as the Swallows do, and have much the same Virtues.

The *Martin,* or *Martinet,* whereof there are two sorts.

The first is exactly the same as with us in feather and size, and have the same uses and virtues; but what becomes of these and some other Birds in the *Winter,* whether they flie into other Countries, or sleep in hollow Trees, Rocks, or other

secret

secret Places, *Natural Historians* are not agreed, nor can they
certainly determine. They constantly come to these parts
in the beginning of *March,* and one or two are generally seen
hovering in the Air for a Day or two before any large Flocks
of them appear.

The second sort is near as large as our *Black-bird,* they
have white Throats and Breasts, black Beaks and Wings.
The Planters are very fond of preserving them, and frequently tye a number of *Gourds* on long standing Poles near
their Dwellings, on purpose for them to breed in, because
they are a warlike Bird, and beat the *Crows,* and many other
kinds of Birds much larger than themselves from their Plantations. One morning, very early, I espied a Snake crawl-
ing up one of these Poles, with a design to destroy the
Young ones or Eggs in these *Gourds,* and it was surprizing
to see with what eagerness the *Martins* fought with the
Snake, which still approached nearer the *Gourds.* Seeing
the Birds in this Distracted manner endeavouring to preserve
their Species, I had the Curiosity to come near the Pole,
where I observed the approaches the Snake still made to
procure it's Prey. I immediately got a long hollow *Reed*
and killed the Snake (which was one of the *Chicken-Snakes,*
whereof I have already made mention) and placed it near the
Pole, which the *Martins* still attacked, and would not be
pacified 'till it was conveyed from the Place.

The *Wren* is scarce, and seldom to be met with, but is the
same in size, Feathers and Notes, as in *Europe.* This small
Bird builds it's Nest in the Moss on Trees, it lays Nine or
Ten, and sometimes more Eggs at a sitting: It is wonderful
strange, that a Bird with so small a Body, should cover such
a Number of Eggs, or that it should feed so many Young,
and not miss one of them. The Flesh is said to help the
stoppage of *Urine,* and to have the same Virtues with the
*Sparrow.*

                                                        The

The *Humming Bird* is the least of all Birds, yet well known in the World, and may properly be said to be the miracle of all Winged Animals, for it is Feather'd like a Bird and gets its living as the Bee does, by sucking the Honey from each Flower. They are of different Colours, but the Cocks are more beautiful than the Hens, with variety of Colours, such as Red, Green, Aurora, and several other beautiful Colours, which being exposed to the Sun Beams shines admirably. They have long Bills and Tails, considering their bigness, which is scarce equal to a *Spanish Olive.* In some of the larger sort of Flowers they very often bury themselves, so that they are quite covered, to suck the bottom of them, by which means the Children commonly catch them whilst they are thus feeding; and I have seen of them nourished and kept alive in Cages for six Weeks, on Honey. They fly very nimbly (but more like Insects than Birds) from Flower to Flower, to seek their Food and make a humming noise like a *Hornet* or *Bee,* hence it took it's Name in *English* of *Humming-bird.* They remain and breed here during the heat of the *Summer,* but what becomes of them in the *Winter* is not known, for they never appear at that time, *viz.* from *October* 'till *April.* They are so very small that I have frequently seen the *Butter-flies* chace them away from the Flowers. Their Nests are a great Curiosity, and may properly be said to be one of the greatest pieces of Workmanship the whole species of winged Animals can shew, for it commonly hangs on a single *Bryer* most artificially Woven like a round Ball, with a small Hole to go in and out, where it lays and Hatches its Eggs, which are very White, of an Oval figure, and for the most part but two in Number which are no bigger than a Small Pea. What virtues these small Birds may be indued with, is unknown.

The

The *Blue-Peters,* or *Water-Hens,* are very plenty, and differ from ours neither in size or Feathers, but are seldom or
never eaten (except it be by the *Indians* and *Negroes*) being
very hard of Digesting and ill tasted.

The *Marsh-Hen* is much the same as with us in *Europe* in
size and Feathers, but has a more different and shrill Note.
Their Flesh is seldom made use of except it be by the *Indians*
and *Negroes,* being Black and ill tasted.

The *Bitterns,* whereof there are three sorts. The first is
the very same as with us in its size, Feathers, and Notes.

The second sort is of a dark brown Colour, with a Yellowish white Throat and Breast, with a large Crest or Topping
of Feathers on its Head, but is not quite so large as the
former.

The third sort is no bigger than a *Wood-cock,* of the same
Colour with the first, and is accounted by many to be fine
eating, yet the Flesh of the former is of the nature of the
Stork and *Heron,* of no good nutriment. The Skin and
Feathers calcin'd, stop Bleeding. The Grease eases pains
of the Gout, helps Deafness, clears the sight, and is excellent
bait to catch Fish with.

The *Herons,* of these there are three sorts. The first or
common *Heron* is from the tip of the Bill to the end of the
Claws four Feet long to the end of the Tail about thirty eight
Inches. It hath a black Crest on the Head four Inches high,
and is in size, Colour and all other respects, exactly the same
as is to be met with in *Ireland.*

The second is larger than the former and is Feather'd much
like the *Spanish-Goose.*

The third is not near as large as any of the former, but is
of the same shape, and of a most beautiful white Colour, with
red Legs. These Birds are only to be met with in *Summer,*
and are the finest of that kind I have ever seen, and many in

these

these Parts would perswade me, that they become the same
Colour with the common *Heron,* when they are a Year old,
which I am not apt to believe, but look upon them as a distinct Species from any of the former. All these sorts are
plenty in these part of *America,* and have the same slow flight
as those with us. They feed on Fish, Frogs, *&c.,* and
like the *Rooks,* build their Nests in high Trees, and generally many together. Their Flesh is better than that of
the *Crane,* but best when young, and eaten by many. The
Bill in Powder, causeth Sleep, the Grease is Anodyne, eases
Pains, and has much the same Properties with the *Bitterns.*

The *Crane* is a large bodied Fowl, weighing sometimes
above ten Pounds. It's Neck and Legs are long, being five
Foot high when extended. The Head is black, with a fine
crimson Spot on the Crown of it, the rest of the Body is of
a Cream colour; they frequent the Savannas, Marshes, and
low Grounds, and though they are Water-fowl, yet it is
thought that they do not feed on Fish, but only on Herbs,
Grain, and several sorts of Seeds and Insects. They are
easily bred up tame, and are good in Gardens to destroy
Frogs, Worms, and other Vermine. The Inhabitants boil
their Flesh, which is tough and hard of Digestion, but makes
good Broath. Their Quills make good Pens, and the Feathers serve for other uses. The *Indians* eat their Eggs, which
have a strong smell, are hard of Digestion, and of an unpleasant taste. The Gall is good against Palsies, Consumptions,
Blindness and Deafness. The Fat or Grease helps all hardness, being of the Nature of Goose-grease. They flie with
the Wind, make a great Noise, run fast, and are said to live
about forty Years.

The *Storkes* are a larger Fowl than the former, and of the
same Shape, only their Necks are thicker and shorter, and

are

are of a dark grey Colour. They are frequently to be met with amongst the *Cranes,* they make a clattering Noise with their Bills, by the quick and frequent striking one Chap against the other. It is reported by several Persons whom I have conversed with, that they are to be found in no part of *America* but in this Province. They feed on *Frogs, Snails,* and many other sorts of Insects. The Flesh nourishes as that of the *Herons* and *Bitterns,* and the other Parts of this Fowl have the same Virtues with them.

The *Swans,* whereof there are two sorts. The first are called the *Trumpeters,* from a trumpeting sort of noise they make, and are the largest sort of *Swans* in these parts. They come here in the *Winter,* and remain with us 'till *February,* in such great Flocks, that I never saw more of any Waterfowl in all my Travels than of them, for at that Season, they are in such vast Numbers on each side of the fresh Water Rivers and Creeks, that at a distance it seems to be Land covered with Snow. About Christmas they are frequently so fat, that some of them are scarce able to fly. In *Spring* they go to the *Northern* Lakes to breed. I have several times eat of them, and do prefer them before any *Goose,* for the goodness and delicacy of their Meat, and especially a *Cygnet,* or last years *Swan.* These *Swans* are larger than any I have seen in *Europe.* Their Quills and Feathers are in great request amongst the Planters. As to their Flesh and Parts, they have the same Virtues with that of the *Geese.*

The *Hoopers* are a second sort of *Swans,* and are so called, from a hooping Noise they make. This sort are as numerous as the former, and come to these parts, and go at the same time that they do ; yet the latter abide more in the Salt Water

than

than the former, are not so large, but their Flesh and Feathers are as valuable. And it is observable, that neither these nor the other have the black piece of horny Flesh down the Head and Bill as those in *Europe* have. The Grease or Fat cleanses the Face from *Morphew,* and other Vices, and their Oil helps the *Gout.*

The *Wild Geese,* whereof there are three Sorts, but differ very little from each other, only in their Size, having black Heads and Necks. They are plenty here all the *Winter,* come and go with the *Swans,* and commonly feed with them; they eat as well as those in *Europe,* being nourishing, though hard of digestion, and are apt to breed Agues in cold weakly Constitutions; The Oil or Grease is exceeding hot, and of thin Parts, piercing and disolving. It cures Baldness, helps Deafness, pain and noise in the Ears, is good against Palsies, Lameness, Numbness, Cramps, pains and contractions of the Sinews, and many other Disorders. The Dung is used with success in the Jaundice, Scurvy, Dropsy, and Gout. The green Dung gathered in the *Spring,* and gently dried, is best.

The *Grey Barnets,* or *Barnacles,* are in shape like the *Wild Geese,* of an Ash and dark grey colour, something less than the common Goose, with which they agree in Nature and Virtues. They are very plenty in this Province all the *Winter,* at which time they are fat and eat extraordinary well; there is no difference between them and the *Barnacles* in *Europe.* Some writers assure us, that they breed unnaturally of the Leaves or Apples of certain Trees in the Islands in *Scotland;* others, on the contrary affirm, that they are produced from Eggs hatched after the same manner as Geese Eggs are, which we are intire Strangers to here, because they

are

are never to be seen in these Parts of *America* but in the *Winter* time, for they generally come and go with the Swans and Geese.

The *White Brants,* are something larger than the former, with which they agree in Nature and Virtues, and are very plenty in the *Winter* Season. These Birds are as white as Snow, except the tips of their Wings, which are Black. They feed on the Roots of Sedge and Grass in the Savannas and Marshes, which they tear and root up like Hogs. The Planters frequently set Fire to these Savannas and Marshes, and as soon as the Grass is burnt off, these Fowl will come in great Flocks to eat the Roots, by which means they shoot vast Numbers of them. They are as good Meat as the other, but their Feathers are stubbed and good for nothing.

The great *Grey-Gulls* are as large as a *Duck,* and very plenty in these parts, and accounted good Food. They lay Eggs as large as a House-Hen, which are found in great Quantities in the Months of *June* and *July,* on the Islands, in the Sounds, and near the Shoar. These and the Young ones, which are call'd *Squabs,* are good Food, and prove relief to Travellers by Water, that have spent their Provisions. The Grease of these, and the other *Gulls,* is good against the Gout, and hard swellings, strengthens the Nerves, and eases Pains in several parts of the Body.

The great *Pied-Gulls,* are also plenty here; they are a large Fowl with black and white Feathers, and their Heads beautifully adorned with a black-hood. They lay large Eggs, which are good to eat, so are their *Squabs* or Young ones in the Season; they are of the same Nature and Virtues with the former.

The

The little *Grey-Gulls* are likewise numerous near the Sea Shoar. They are of a curious grey Colour, about the bigness of a grey or *Whistling Plover,* and good Food, being nourishing and well tasted. Their Nature and Virtues are much the same with the former.

The *Old-wives,* but why so called, I know not, for they are a black and white pyed *Gull,* with extraordinary long Wings, their Feet and Bill of a fine Golden Colour. They make a strange and dismal Noise as they flie, and are frequently dipping their Bills in the Salt-Water, and are larger than the former, but seldom eaten, only by the *Indians* and *Negroes,* their Flesh being black, hard of digestion, and tastes Fishy.

The *Sea-Cock,* so called from it's Crowing at break of Day, and in the Morning, exactly like a *Dunghill-Cock;* it is another sort of *Gull,* of a light grey and white Colour. They are to be met with in great Numbers near the Sea-Shoar, and are larger than the former: Their Cry being so Domestick, hath deceived many, supposing some Inhabitants to be near them; yet it is very pleasant, especially to *Europeans,* in those wild and uninhabited places. Their Flesh is not good, therefore seldom or never made use of, except it be by the *Negroes* and *Indians.*

The *Gull, or Sea-mew* (this Bird is also called *Sea-cob*) is the same as in *Europe.* This Fowl is little regarded, because the Flesh is of an ill scent, and odious to be eaten; yet it is said to help the falling sickness; and the Ashes of the whole Bird, the Gravel in the Bladder and Kidnys.

The *Tropick Bird,* so called, being in great plenty under the Tropicks and thereabouts, but are scarce any where else.

They

They are a white *Mew,* with a forked Tail.   They are a swift
Fowl, and continually flying like the *Swallow.*   What uses or
virtues they may be indued with, is uncertain, because they
are seldom or never taken.

The *Duck* and *Mallard* are exactly of the same size and
Feather with those in *Europe,* they are very numerous, especially in *Winter,* but their Meat is not to be compared to our
tame *Ducks* for goodness, and are accounted one of the coursest
sort of Water-fowl in all this Province, so that they are little
regarded and seldom made use of except by the *Indians* and
*Negroes.*

The *Black-Duck,* so called, from it's black colour, is full
as large as the former, and is good Meat.   It stays here all
the *Summer,* and breeds.   They are pretty numerous, and
the Planters take their Eggs, and have them hatched at their
dwelling Houses, and they prove extraordinary good domestick Fowl.

The *Summer-Ducks,* so called, from their continuing here
all that Season.   They have a large Crest or Topping of
Feathers on their Head, are of a beautiful pied white and
black Colour, and are very plenty in these Parts.   They
generally build their Nests contrary to most web-footed Fowl,
in the Holes that *Wood peckers* make in large Trees, very
often sixty or seventy Foot from the Ground, where they
hatch their Eggs; they are an extraordinary good Fowl, and
eat well.

The *Whistling Duck,* so called, from it's Whistling when
it flies and feeds.   They are of a pretty white and black
Colour, but not so large as our Wild Duck.   They are to be
met with in great Flocks in several places of this Country,
and especially near the Mountains, and Hilly parts thereof,
where 'tis thought they breed; they are good Fowl, and excellent eating.

                                                          The

The *Whistlers,* are another Species of *Ducks,* and are so called, from the Whistling Noise they make as they fly. They are less than our wild Ducks, and very different in their Feathers from the *Whistling-Ducks,* and have a greater variety of beautiful Colours than the former. They are likewise good to eat.

The *Scarlet Eyed Duck,* so called, from their red Eyes, and a red Circle of Flesh for their Eye-lids. They are of various beautiful Colours, and are to be met with in several Places, but especially near the Mountains, and the Heads of Rivers. They are also good Meat.

The *Shell-Drakes,* are the same as in *Europe,* in Feather and Size. They are in great plenty here, and are very good Meat.

The *Bull-Necks,* so called from their thick Necks. They are a Species of Ducks, but as large as *Barnacles,* of a whitish Colour; and have the thickest Necks of any Fowl I have ever seen, of the same bigness. They come here about *Christmas* in great Flocks to the Creeks and Rivers. They are good Meat, but hard to kill, being a very wary Fowl; will dive as soon as you can shoot, and endure a great deal of Shot before they are kill'd.

The *Water Pheasant;* but for what reason so improperly call'd, I know not, for it has no manner of Resemblance of that Bird. It is a Species of Ducks, having a Crest or Topping of pretty Feathers on it's Head, which is very Ornamental. They are about the size of our *Wild Ducks,* of a light brown colour, they are in great Plenty, and fine eating.

The *Shovellers,* are another kind of Ducks, so called, from their broad and flat Bills. They are Grey, with black Heads, and something larger than our Wild Ducks. They are plenty in several parts, and are good Meat.

The

The *Blue-Wings,* are another Species of Ducks, and are so called, from their beautiful Blue-Wings. They are less than a Wild Duck, but excellent good Meat. These are the first Fowl that appear to us in the fall of the Leaf, at which time they come in large Flocks, as is supposed from *Canada,* and other great Lakes that lie to the *Northward* of us.

The *Red-heads,* are another Species of Ducks, so called from their Red-heads, and are less than the Bull-necks. They are very plenty in the Rivers and Creeks, are sweet Food, and very nourishing.

The *Swaddle-Bills,* are another Species of Ducks, of an Ash colour, and are so called, from their extraordinary broad Bills. They are excellent good Meat, but not so plenty in these parts, as the other Species of Ducks are.

The *Fishermen,* so called, from their Dexterity in Fishing. They are like a Duck, only they have narrow Bills, with sets of Teeth. They feed on small Fish and Fry, which they catch as they swim. They eat Fishy, therefore not in much request amongst the Planters. The best way in ordering them is, to take out their Fat and Guts, then bury them under Ground for five or six Hours, which will make them eat well, and take away their strong and fishy taste; as I have been credibly informed by many in these Parts.

The *Raft-Fowl,* includes several sorts of Ducks, *viz. Divers, Teals, Wigeons,* and various other Kinds, that go in *Rafts,* or great Flocks along the Shoar, which we know no Names for at present.

The *Divers,* whereof there are two sorts. The first are of a Grey Colour, the other Pied, White, and Black. They are both good Fowl, and eat well, but hard to shoot, because of

their

their dexterity in diving under Water, which they will do as quick as any one can shoot.

The *Wigeons* are the same as in *Europe,* and in great plenty in the Winter Season. They eat exceedingly well.

The *Teal,* whereof there are two sorts. The first is exactly the same as in *Europe,* and as good Eating, being more delicious than either *Divers* or *Wigeon.*

The second sort frequent the fresh Waters, and are always observed to be nodding their Heads when they are in the Water. These sorts are smaller than the former, but finer and more delicious. They are both very plenty here in the Winter Season.

The *Dipper,* or *Fisher;* these are small Birds about the bigness of a *Teal,* and much the same as those that are to be met with in the Islands of *Scilly,* and many other Islands in *Europe.* They are of a black and white Colour, and are so called, from their dexterity in Fishing and catching small Fish, on which they feed. They eat fishy, for which reason they are not in much Request amongst the Planters.

The *Black Flusterers;* some call these *Old Wives;* they are jet black, only the Cocks have white Faces, like the *Bald-Coots.* They always remain in the middle of the Rivers, and feed on Drift, Grass, Carvels, or Sea Nettle. They are the fattest Fowl in these Parts, and are sometimes so heavy that they cannot rise out of the Water. They make an odd sort of a Noise when they fly, and are something larger than a Duck; some call them the great *Bald Coot.* Their Flesh is not much admired, being of a strong and fishy taste, and hard of Digestion, but their Eggs (which are as large as those of Hens) are good Nourishment.

14     Dd     The

The *Bald-Faces,* or *White-Faces,* are almost as big as a Duck, and are an extraordinary Fowl and eat well. These Birds cannot Dive, and therefore are easy to be Shot.

The *Water-Witch,* or *Ware-Coots,* are a very strange Fowl, having all over them Down, and no Feathers, and neither fly nor go, but are so dexterous in Diving, that scarce any Fowler can hit or shoot them. They often get into the Fish-Wares, and are taken, because they cannot fly or get over the Rods or Poles, whereof the Fish-Wares are made. They are not much coveted or esteemed, by reason they eat fishy and are hard of Digestion.

The *King's-Fisher,* whereof there are two Sorts. The first is something larger than a *Jay,* with a long Bill, and large Crop, much of the shape and colour of the latter, though not altogether so curiously Feathered: These Birds most commonly frequent the Rivers, prey on small Fish, and build their Nests on the Shoar.

The second is much the same as with us in *Europe;* being a fine Bird, with red Feet, long Bill, and about the bigness of our *Bunting.* The Chin is white with a certain mixture of Red, and the upper part of the Belly is of the same Colour. The lower Belly under the Tail is of a deep red, so are the sides and Feathers under the Wings. The Breast is red, the utmost Borders of the Feathers being of a beautiful bleuish Green: From the Neck through the middle of the Back to the Tail is of a most lovely bright Purple or pale Blue, which by its splendour is apt to hurt the Eyes of those that look long and stedfastly upon it. These Birds, like the former, frequent the Rivers, and build their Nests on the Shoar. The Flesh roasted and eaten, is good in Convulsions

and

and Epilepsies, the Heart is sometimes dryed and hung about the Neck of Children for the same Disorders.

The *Pelican* in *Carolina* is a large Water-Fowl, being five Feet in length, from the point of the Bill to the end of the Tail, and almost equal in bigness to a *Swan.* It has a long thick Neck and Beak, and a great natural Wen or Pouch under the Throat, in which it keeps it's Prey of Fish, which it lives upon. This Pouch it will sometimes contract and draw up to the Bill, that it is scarce to be seen. It is a Web-footed Fowl, like a Goose, but shaped more like a Duck, and of a light grey Colour. The Flesh is seldom eaten, having a strong fishy taste, and hard of digestion; but being well boiled, maketh good Broth, and the Planters make handsom Tobacco-Pouches of it's Maw. They are plentifully to be met with in the *Winter* Season, especially near the Sounds and Sea Shoars. In *Spring* they go into the Woods to breed, and return again in *Autumn.* They have an odd kind of Note, much like the Braying of an *Ass,* and are reported to live to a great Age, *viz.* sixty Years or upwards. They are said to be white in *Guinea,* and St. *Jerom* saith, that there are two sorts of them in *Egypt, viz.* the Land and Water *Pelican.* The Gall of this Bird cleanses Silver.

The *Cormorants* are the same as in *Europe,* only those of this Province are larger. They are as numerous all over these Parts of *America,* as in any part of the World, especially at the run of the *Herrings,* which is in *March* and *April;* at which time they are seen sitting upon the Sand Banks, or Logs of Wood in the Rivers, and catch vast quantities of Fish, which is their only Food, and whereof they are very ravenous and greedy. They lay their Eggs in the beginning of the Spring, in the Islands, in the Sound, and near the

Sea

Sea Shoar in the Banks, and sometimes on high Trees, as the *Shags* do; they are very strengthning to the Stomach, and cure the Bloody Flux. The Flesh is black, and hard of digestion, therefore seldom made use of.

The *Shag* is somewhat like the *Cormorant,* but much less; it differs in the colour of the Belly, which in this is blackish, in the other white. It swims in the Sea with its Head erect, and it's Body almost covered in the Water. It is so dextrous in diving, that when a Gun is discharged at it, as soon as it sees the Fire flash, immediately it pops under Water, so that it is a hard matter to shoot them. I have never known or heard of any Webb-footed Birds but this, and the *Summer-* Ducks that sit upon Trees, and build their Nests in them. The Flesh is black, ill-tasted, and hard of digestion, being much of the same Nature with the *Cormorant.*

The *Gannet* is a very large white Fowl, having one part of it's Wings black. It lives on Fish, as the *Pelican* and *Cormorant* do; it is reported, that their Fat or Grease (which is as yellow as Saffron) is the best thing known to preserve Fire-Arms from Rust. The Flesh is of a bad Taste, and scarcely good for Food or Physick.

The *Shear-Water,* is a longer Fowl than a *Duck,* but has a much smaller Body. They are of a brownish Colour, and for the most part upon the Wing, like the *Swallow:* There are vast Quantities of them on several parts of these Sea Coasts (whilst others range the Seas all over) for they are sometimes met with five hundred Leagues from Land. I have frequently observed them to strike down upon a Sea-rack, or Weed that grows in the Gulf of *Florida,* which is plentifully to be met with in these Seas. It hath many winding Stalks,

which

which appear like *Coral,* whereon grow short Branches, set thick with narrow Leaves, amongst which are many round Berries, without either Seeds or Grains in them. I have often taken up of this Sea-wreck (which is a kind of narrow leaf'd Sea-lentil) wherein I found several sorts of small Shell-fish, which I am persuaded these Birds catch, and live upon. And it is the Opinion of many in these Parts, that these Birds never drink any Fresh Water, because they are never seen any where near the Freshes, or Rivers. Their Flesh is of an ill Scent, therefore not good to be eaten.

Thus have I finished the most exact Account that is yet known of the BIRDS that are to be met with in *North Carolina;* though doubtless there are many more different species of them, that we are entire Strangers to at present, which is chiefly owing to the want of Encouragement to a select number of travelling Gentlemen, whose Observations might tend to the Improvement of *Natural Knowledge.* For want of this, we are rendered incapable of being so well acquainted with this part of the World as the *French* and *Spaniards* are with theirs, who generally send abroad in Company with the *Missionaries* some of their young Gentlemen, with handsome Pensions for their support, who soon become acquainted with the Savages of *America,* and their Languages. These Gentlemen are likewise obliged to keep a strict Journal of all their Passages, whereby many considerable Discoveries have been made in a few Years. Such laudable Encouragements as these, would undoubtedly breed an honorable Emulation amongst the Gentlemen of our own Nation, to outdo one another even in all manner of Fatigues and Dangers, to be servicable to their King and Country. That Attempts of this

Nature

Nature may always be encouraged, I sincerely wish, for the Honour and Grandure of the *British* Throne.

I shall in the next place proceed to give an Account of the Inhabitants of the watry Elements, which at present can be but very imperfectly treated of, for want of Fishermen, and the fishing Trade going on in these Parts to perfection. Yet I am willing to satisfie the Curious with the best Account that is in my power, and leave the rest to Time (which perfects all Things) to discover. The Fishes in the salt and fresh Waters of *Carolina,* are as follows.

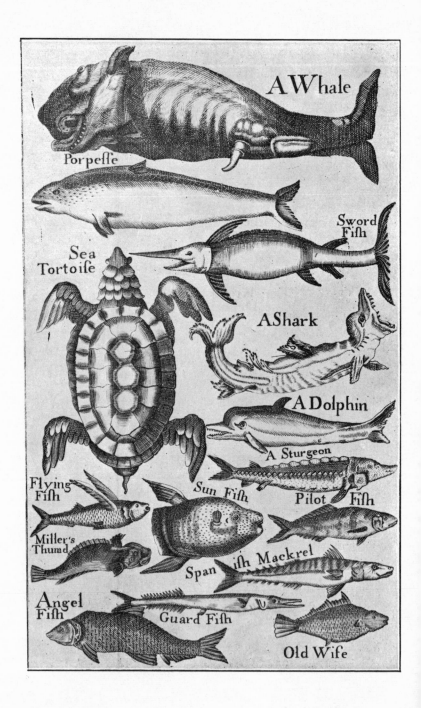

A Whale

Porpesse

Sword Fish

Sea Tortoise

A Shark

A Dolphin

A Sturgeon

Flying Fish

Sun Fish

Pilot Fish

Miller's Thumb

Span ish Mackrel

Angel Fish

Guard Fish

Old Wife

# OF THE FISH

## OF

# NORTH CAROLINA.

THE *Whales* differ from the *Fin-Fish* in their Fins. The *Fin-Fish* having a large Fin on the Back, where the *Whale* has none, but he has two behind his Eyes, covered with a thick black Skin, finely Marbled, with white Stroaks, and the representation of Houses, Trees, &c. With these two Fins and his Tail he swims and steers himself like a Boat with Oars. The Head of this Monster is somewhat flat, and slopes downwards like the Ridge of a House to the under Lip, which is broader than any part of his Body, and broadest in the middle behind the Bump, for between that and the Fins

are

are his Eyes, which are not much bigger than those of a Bullock, with Eye-lids and Hair like Men's.   The Chrystal of the Eye is not much bigger than a Pea, which in some is clear and transparent, and in others of a white or yellowish Colour. The Eyes lie low, almost at the end of the upper Lip.   The Head is the third part of the Fish, and in some more.   Their Lips are plain, somewhat bending like an S. and underneath the Eyes, before the two Fins, they are smooth, jet black, and round like the quarter of a Circle, but when they draw them together, they lock in one another.   Within the uppermost Lip is contained the *Whalebone,* (and not in the Fins, as some have imagined) which is of a brownish black and yellow Colour, with streaks of several other Colours, but the *Whalebone* of the young ones, is generally Blue.   The *Whalebone* hangs down on both sides within the Mouth, all hairy like a Horses Tail, and in some it is bended like a *Scymeter,* and in others like a half Moon.   In one side, in a Row, there are generally *Two hundred and fifty* Pieces of *Whalebone,* and as many on the other, besides the small Bone, which is not regarded, because they cannot well come at it to cut it out.   The middlemost is the greatest, and is sometimes eighteen or ninteen Foot long.   It lies in a flat row, one Piece by another, and is broadest at the top, where it sticks to the upper Lip, towards the Root it is covered with white Sinews, which when boiled, smell pleasantly.   There grows small *Whalebone* at the Root of the greater, whereof they make Boxes, Handles for Knives, walking Sticks, and the like.

The Tongue lies amongst the *Whalebone,* and is close fixed to the upper Chop, which is very large and white, with black Spots at the edges.   It has a soft spungy Fat, and cannot be easily cut, so that it is generally flung away, though it would

yield

yield seven or eight Barrels of train Oil. Upon his Head
there is a Bump, and before his Eyes and Fins at the top of
this Bump on each side, there is a spout hole, bended like an S.
out of which he blows the Water so fiercely, that it roars like
a great Wind. Just before in the under Lip, there is a Cavity
or Hole, which fits the upper as exactly as a sheath does a
Knife, and through this hole he draws the Water he spouts
out; when he is wounded, his blowing resembles the roaring
of the Sea in a great Storm. Neither does he hear when he
spouts the Water, and is easiest struck at that time. The
Belly and Back are quite Red in some, but under the Belly
they are sometimes White, and some of them Coal Black.
They look very beautiful when the Sun shines on them, and
the small clear Waves over them, glitter like Silver. The
outward Skin is thin like Parchment, and easily pulled off
when the Fish grows hot, which they frequently do by swiming, and then they stink.

The Yard is a strong Sinew, and from six to eight Feet
long, and where the Yard is fixed, the Skin is doubled, so that
it lies like a Knife in a Sheath. The *Pudenda* of the Female
is shaped like that of a large four footed Beast. They have
Breasts, with Nipples at the sides of it, like those of a Cow.
When they couple together, they stand upright, with their
Heads out of the Water, but how long they carry their Young,
is uncertain. Neither are they ever observed to have more
than two young ones at a time. When they are brought forth,
they are as big as an Hogshead; they suck their Dams, whose
Milk is very white and sweet, but tastes Fishy. The *Sperm,*
when fresh smells like wheaten Flower boild in Water, and
may be drawn out in Threads like hot Sealing Wax or Glew;
when cold, it turns to a Musk colour, smells strong, and is to

be

be kept sweet by no means.  At certain Seasons there may be whole Pails full of it taken out of the Water, for it swims upon the Sea like Fat, as does that of the *Sea-Horses* and *Seals,* the Sailors frequently make twisted Whips of the Sinews of the Yard.  The Bones are hard like those of a great four-footed Beast, but porous like a Spunge, and filled with Marrow, but when that is consumed, the Holes are as large as those of a Honey-Comb.  They have two large strong Bones which hold up the under Lip, and they lie opposite to each other in form of an half Moon, some of which are twenty Feet long of a side.  The Flesh is course and hard, like that of a Bull, mixed with many Sinews, and is very dry and lean when boiled, because their Fat lies wholy betwixt the Flesh and the Skin.  When the Sailors have a mind to eat of it, they cut great pieces off before the Tail, which is tenderest, and boil it.  Others report the Tongue to be good Food, and whenever they kill any of them eat part of it; some of the Flesh looks green and blue like powdered Beef.  The Fat is mixed with Sinews, which hold the Oil, as a Spunge does Water: The other strong Sinews are chiefly about the Tail, with which he turns and winds himself, as a Rudder does a Ship.  He swims as swift as a Bird flies, and makes a track in the Sea like a large Ship under sail.  Their Tails do not stand up as the Tails of most other Fishes do, but lie horizontally as those of the *Dolphin,* and are from three to four Fathom broad.

The middling *Whales* are about fifty or sixty Feet long, and commonly yield seventy, eighty, or ninty Barrels of Fat or Oil.  Besides the uppermost thin Skin, there is likewise another about an Inch thick, and of the same colour with the other, but both are so brittle, when dry that they are of no value; and the softness of the Skin is reckoned to be the cause

why

why the *Whale,* though the strongest and biggest of Fishes in the Water, cannot make much use of his strength. The Guts are of a flesh Colour, and the Dung within them yellow: Their Food is chiefly *Sea-Snails, Herrings,* and other small Fish; when they see a Man or a Long Boat, they dive and run away; but if they are wounded, or in danger, they value a Man no more than a Straw, and frequently beat the Long-Boat in pieces, but great Ships are too many for them, for when they strike against them with their Tails, they generally receive more Damage than they give. They sometimes run away with some thousand fathom of Rope-line (after they are struck with the *Harpoon* or *Sharp-Iron,* that is fixed to a Stick, and resembles a Dart) a great deal swifter than a Ship can sail, or a Bird flie, by which means the Lines are sometimes set on fire, when there is not proper Care taken to prevent them, by constantly throwing Water on them as they run out. They shift their Quarters, as is supposed, according to the Seasons. They have Ailments as well as other Beasts, and are strangely afflicted with Lice; they will sometimes leap out of the Water, as if they were in an Agony. Before a Tempest they beat the Water about with their Tails like Dust. They are observed to have the greatest Strength when they strike side-ways. If they escape, their Wounds are quickly healed up, because of their Fat; but the Wound always leaves a white Scar behind it.

These Monsters are very numerous on the Coasts of *North-Carolina,* and the Bone and Oil would be a great Advantage to the Inhabitants that live on the Sand-Banks along the Ocean, if they were as dexterous and industrious in Fishing for them as they are Northwards; but as I observed before, the People in these parts are not very much given to Industry, but wait upon Providence to throw those dead Monsters on

Shoar, which frequently happens to their great advantage and Profit. For which Reason abundance of Inhabitants dwell upon the Banks near the Sea for that Intent, and the benefit of Wrecks of Vessels which are sometimes driven in upon these Coasts. Not many Years ago there were two Boats that came from the Northward to *Ocacock* Island, to fish, and carried away that Season Three Hundred and Forty Barrels of Oil, beside the Bone, but these Fishermen going away without paying the Tenths to the Governor, they never appeared to fish on these Coasts afterwards, or any other that I ever could hear of. I only mention this to shew with what Advantage the Fishing for *Whales* might be carried on here, when only one Tryal carried off so rich and valuable a Cargoe.

There are four sorts of *Whales* in these parts: The first is the *Sperma-Ceti Whale,* from whence the *Sperma-Ceti* is taken, and is the most choice for its rich and valuable Commodities. These sort are sometimes found on this Coast, and are a rich Prize to those that are so fortunate as to find them. The other sorts are of a prodigious large size, and it is of these the Bone and Oil are made, the Oil being only the Blubber or Oily Flesh or Fat of this Fish boiled. These differ not only in Colour, some being all White, others pied, and others not, but likewise very much in Shape, one being called the *Bottle-Nose,* and the other the *Shovel-Nose,* which is as different as a *Salmon* from a *Sturgeon.*

These Fish are never found dead or floating to the Shoar with their Tongues in their Heads, for it is the opinion of many in these parts, that the *Thrashers* and *Sword-Fish,* (which are mortal Enemies to the *Whales* where ever they meet them) eat the Tongue out of their Head, as soon as they

have

have killed him; but whether this is done by the Fish above mentioned, or by others of the same voracious Nature, I will not take upon me to determine, but leave it to the determination of every judicious Reader.

There is another sort of these *Whales,* or great Fishes, though not commonly found on these Coasts, and are contrary to all the others in shape, that were ever found in these Parts, being about Sixty Feet in length, and not above four Feet and a half Diameter; I never saw but one of them. It is reported that some *Indians* in *America* will go out to Sea and get on the *Whale's* Back, and peg, and plug up his Spouts, and so kill him, which I can scarce believe, except they have some secret Spell to make them stupid, to treat them after that manner. It is very strange to see how they will throw up the Water with their Spouts, by which means they are seen or discovered at great distances. They cannot abide long under Water for want of Air, which is common to most large Fishes; so that they are frequently seen to rise with their Heads and Backs above the surface of the Water, and spouting it in the Air, after which it is said, they draw in a sufficient quantity of Air necessary for their supporting of Life.

The *Crampois,* is another large Fish, about twenty five or thirty Feet long, and is accounted by many to be a young *Whale,* by reason it has Spouts as the *Whale* has and produces as good Oil as the former.

The *Bottle-Noses,* are another Species of large Fishes, between the *Crampois* and the *Porpoise.* They are to be met with for the most part near the Soundings, and are never observed to Swim leisurely, as sometimes other Fishes do, but are continually in pursuit of their Prey, in great Shoals, like

wild

wild Horses, leaping now and then above the Water. Some make use of them, and especially the *French*, who esteem them good Food, and eat them both fresh and salt. These as well as the *Porpoise,* are often heard to puff and blow very strong, as they are Swimming.

I hope it will not be unpleasing to the Reader, to give an Account what I saw done by these Fishes, *viz.* In our Passage through *Pamticoe* Sound, we had very good Diversion with them, which were in great Numbers about the Ship; one of our Company shot amongst them, with a Brace of Balls, and happened to wound one of them, which we could plainly discover from some of it's Blood in the Water, the Weather being very calm; which was no sooner done, but all the rest left us in pursuit of the one that was wounded, and we could often see it leaping above the Water, for near half an Hour, still striving to avoid the rest, 'till at last it was quite spent, (as we supposed) for we could not perceive it any longer leaping out of the Water. The Master of the Vessel assured me, that the rest devoured it, which they always do with those wounded, still pursuing the Blood, like a Pack of Dogs after a Deer. They are very fat and produce good Oil.

The *Porpoise,* or *Sea-hog,* is large, being above four Feet long and two and a half thick, the Figure is somewhat long and round, continually tapering towards the Tail. It is covered with a slender thin Skin, of a blackish colour, and has only three Fins like the *Dolphin.* It has a large Head, small Eyes, and a forked Tail. They are frequently to be met with all over the Ocean and Rivers that are salt. We have a freshwater Lake in the great Sound of *North Carolina,* that has *Porpoises* in it, with several other sorts of unknown Fish (as the *Indians* report) that we are intire Strangers to. As to the

*Porpoises,*

*Porpoises,* they are generally very fat, and make good Oil. They prey on other Fish, such as *Drums* and *Mullets,* yet are seldom or never known to take the Bait, so as to be catched with a Hook. Some call these *Herring Hogs,* from their feeding on those Fish, and their Flesh being so very fat, like Pork. They are much fatter than a *Dolphin,* but not so good; the Gentry bake it as Venison, but it is not pleasant Food. They are always approaching the Shoars in great Numbers before Storms.

The *Thrashers* are likewise large, as I have been informed, and one of the mortal Enemies that pursue and kill the *Whale,* as I said before. They make good Oil, but are seldom found in these Parts.

The *Sword-Fish,* or *Saw-Fish,* has a long broad Bone fixed to his Nose, with sharp Teeth like a Saw, on each side of it. It has two Fins on the Back, that next the Tail is hollow like a Sickle. He has four underneath his Belly, *viz.* two on each side. The Tail is like a piece of Board, painted behind and underneath, but not divided, his Shape from Top to Tail, is like a Man's Arm. His Eyes stand high out of his Head; his Nostrils are oblong, and his Mouth is directly under his Eyes. They are from twelve to twenty Feet long, and are generally very fat on the Back, almost like a Hog. They are mortal Enemies to the *Whale,* about which they gather in great Numbers, and when they kill him, only eat out his Tongue, as is supposed, and then the *Whale* floats to Shoar, which is an extraordinary Prize to those that find him. They likewise joyn with the *Thrashers,* to kill them, and it is reported that they will singly attack a Whale. In calm Weather, the Fishers lye by till they kill the *Whale,* and upon the approach of the Boats, the *Sword-Fish* being frighted, retires. The Flesh is

dry

dry and solid, but it is said to nourish much, and as good as a Sturgeon.

The *Devil-Fish*, so called, from the large pair of Horns it has upon its Head, and as near as I could be informed; it is shaped like a *Scate* or *Stingray*. It is of a monstrous large Size and Strength, for it hath been known to weigh a Sloop's Anchor, and run away with the Vessel for a League or two, and to bring her back again almost to the same Place, against the Tide. This I have been informed of by several of the most credible and substantial Planters in these parts; and that this strange and wonderful Adventure has happened more than once. They are in most of our Inlets, but I never heard of any of them being killed or taken, therefore cannot inform the Reader what Uses they are of, but doubtless they would make good Oil as well as other large Fishes, if they could be taken to make the Experiment.

The *Shark*, whereof there are two sorts. The first is called the *Paracoda-Noses,* the other the *Shovel-Noses:* Both these are very large, bold, voracious and dangerous Fishes, especially to those that have the misfortune to fall over board. It is reported, that they will follow Ships for Hours together, and if either Man or Dog, or any other living Animal happen to fall into the Water, they immediately seize and snap in two, having exceeding sharp, and several Rows of Teeth in their Heads: Some of them are so large, that they are said to weigh about four thousand Weight. They are easily caught with a Bait, but can never take their Prey 'till they turn themselves on their Backs, wherefore some *Negroes* and others that can swim and dive well, go naked into the Waters with a Knife in their Hands, and fight them, and commonly kill, or wound him, so that he turns Tail and runs away. Their Flesh is eaten in time of scarcity, but is not very palatable,

having

having a strong fishy taste. Their Liver makes good Oil to dress Leather with, and the Bones found in their Head, are said to hasten the Birth, and ease the Stone, by bringing it away. Their Back-bone is of one entire thickness, having many Joints in it, whereof I have known Buttons made by the Sailors and others that live in those remote Places. *Gillius* says, that the People of *Marseilles* told him, that they had caught one of them, in which they found a Man armed with a Coat of Mail.

The following Relation, will in some measure corroborate the former Account of the *Negroes* killing them: *August* 1730, a Sloop sailed from *North Carolina,* bound to the Island in the *West Indies,* and after four Days sailing from the Bar, was most unfortunately overset, and all the Crew, except the Master, two Sailors, and one *Negroe,* were drowned, these being upon Deck at the time when this misfortune happened, and had the good providence to get upon the Keel of the Vessel, where they remained twenty one Days, and then were taken up by a Vessel trading to *Europe;* having neither Water or any other Necessaries to support Nature, but by Gods Providence, the *Negroe* killed a *Shark,* whereon they lived, and was the only support they had during the said time, which was confirmed by the Master in his Letter from *London,* to his Friends in *North Carolina.*

The *Pilot-Fish* is of a deep Blue, and the Belly of a lighter Colour than the Back or Sides. The Scales are smooth like a *Tench.* It's Back is speckled like a *Seal-skin.* When it is swimming, it appears much like a *Mackarel,* and looks as if it were painted Blue and White, like a *Barbers Pole.* It is reported, that the *Shark* is always attended by one or two of these Fishes, which he will not devour, though never so hun-

15           Ff           gry,

gry, because they find out the Prey for him. They are reckoned exceeding good to eat.

The *Dolphin,* is a large Fish, not much unlike a *Porpoise.* It has two strong Fins, which like the Arms of a Man, are joined to the Shoulder-blades, and is said to be of that swiftness, that it will easily overtake a Ship in full sail before the Wind. They generate like rational Animals, bringing forth their Young alive, not from Spawn but Seed, and have but one or two at a time. They go with young ten Months, breed only in the *Summer,* and are said to live two or three hundred Years. They sometimes swim in Shoals, and at other times only the Male and Female together. It is reported that when they are taken, they are observed to deplore their Condition by Groans, Lamentations, and a flood of Tears. It is also said to be a certain sign of a Storm shortly to follow, when they are seen sporting, and frequently moving their Bodies in the Water. They have a groaning Voice, sharp Sight, and are said to be lovers of Musick and Men. There are great numbers of them to be met with in these Seas, and are said to live out of the Water for two or three Days. They are much deceived who imagine *Dolphins* to be of the Figure they are usually represented on Signs; that Error being more owing to Painters, than any such thing in Fact, for they are straight and not crooked. Their Flesh is eaten by the *Dutch,* and is of good Account amongst the *French;* though according to the Accounts of some, it yields no very grateful Taste. The Liver is of a tender Substance, and very nourishing, so is the Tongue. The Bowels smell and taste like *Violets,* and help the Spleen. The Ashes of the whole Fish applied with Water, is good against the *Tettars, Ring-worms, Scruff* and *Leprosie.*

The

The *Flying-fish* is slender and long, the Eyes large, and the Tail forked. The Body is in shape like a Seal's, and in colour like one of our Mullets. It has two large Fins near the Head, which resembles a pair of Wings, one on the Back, and two underneath the Belly, with these Fins, it flies near a Gun-shot before it touches the Water, and when it hath wet it's Wings it will mount up again. They are constantly chased by the *Dolphins,* which swim so fast, that they are often catched by them as they drop into the Water. There are vast Shoals of them in these Seas, and when they rise out of the Water, at a distance, appear like a large flock of small Birds.

The *Dog-fish,* is a small sort of the *Shark* kind, but seldom exceeds twenty Pounds. They are frequently caught with the Hook and Line when they fish for *Drum.* They have a long tapering Body without Scales, but covered with a sharp hard Skin, that is made use of to polish fine Wood. Their Snout is a little long and round at the point, the Flesh is white, of easy concoction, but of no pleasant Taste, and is therefore best eaten with Mustard or some sharp Sauce. They are very numerous in these Parts, but little regarded or made use of, where there are so many delicate sorts to be had in such plenty. The Fat of these Fish, and the *Shark,* have much the same Virtues with the *Alligator.*

The *Spanish Mackarel,* they are in shape and colour like the common *Mackarel,* only these are much thicker, and generally about two Feet long; there are vast numbers of them in these Seas. They are caught with Hook and Line in the Inlets, and sometimes a small distance out at Sea, being a voracious Fish, greedily swallowing either Beat or Fish that comes in their way. They are a very fine hard Fish, and of good Taste. The Liver eaten, helps Obstruction of the Liver and Jaundice.

Ff ²                                    The

The *Cavallies* are about the bigness of a *Mackarel,* the Fins and Tail are partly like a *Dolphins.* They have large Eyes, and are of a brownish colour on their Backs, and their Bellies white; they have exceeding small Scales, and a very thick Skin. They are taken in the same places with the *Spanish-Mackarel,* and are one of the firmest Fishes known in these parts, and will therefore keep sweet (in the extremity of the hot Weather) two or three Days without Salt, when others will Stink in half a Day, if not Salted. Those that catch them, immediately take off their Scales, otherwise you must pull off the Skin and Scales when boiled; the Skin being the choicest part of the Fish. Their Meat is exceeding White, and very relishing when it is well Drest.

The *Boneto's* are very fine and palatable Fishes, and generally about a Yard long. They most commonly frequent the Inlets and Waters near the Ocean, and are kill'd with the *Harpoon* and *Fish-gig,* but seldom or never with the Hook and Line, though they are very plenty in several places on this Coast.

The *Blue-Fish,* so call'd, from their being of that colour, they are accounted one of the best sort of Fishes in these parts, being very fat. They have a forked Tail, and are partly shaped like a *Dolphin.* They are as large and as long as a Salmon, and as good. They come to these Coasts in the fall of the Year, and after there has been one black Frost, in great Shoals, so that the *Indians* and others who wade into the Waters strike and kill vast Numbers of them with their *Fish-gigs.* Sometimes many Cart loads of them are found dead and left dry on the Sea Shore; which is occasioned for the most part by their eager pursuit after the small Fish; by which means they and several other Fishes run themselves on Shoar, and the Tides leaving them on the dry Sands they

cannot

cannot recover the Water again and so dye; wherefore those that are disposed to get up early before the Fowl come to prey, may get what quantities they please of several sorts of Fishes all along these coasts. And notwithstanding these Blue-fish are accounted so extraordinary good, yet they sometimes occasion Sickness after eating them, *viz.* violent heats all over the Body with Shiverings, Head-ach, and the like, which is chiefly owing to the Gall being broke in some of them, which is very hurtful, as I found by giving it to a Dog.

The *Drum-fish,* whereof there are two sorts, *viz.* the Red and the Black. The Red is a large scaly Fish, much bigger than the *Blue-fish,* some of them being above four Feet long; the Body is excellent firm Meat, and extraordinary good nourishment; their Heads exceed in goodness all the Fish in these parts, being the most delicious Dish I ever met with. There are greater numbers of them to be met with in *Carolina,* than any other sort of Fish. Those that are disposed to fish for them, especially every new Flood, catch as many Barrels full as they please, with Hook and Line, for at that time they will catch them as fast as they can throw their Bait into the Water, which is generally a soft *Crab,* and so Salt them up and Transport them to other parts that are scarce of Provisions.

The *Black-Drums* are a thicker made Fish, and much fatter than the former; they are an excellent good Fish, but not so common here, as they are in the more *Northerly* parts of this Continent, they are taken after the same manner with the former, *viz.* with Hook and Line.

The *Angel-fish,* so called from it's beautiful Golden Colour, that shines all about it's Head and Belly; it is in shape exactly like the *Bream,* and is very good to eat. The same sort

of

of Fish is plentifully to be met with all along the Coast of
*Bermudas,* and is very much esteemed by the Inhabitants of
that Island.

The *Bass,* or *Rock-fish,* are to be met with both in the salt
and fresh Water; when they are young they very much resemble a *Grey-Ling,* but they grow to the size of the large
*Cod-fish.* They are a good, firm, and well tasted Fish, and
are in great plenty in these parts; they are good Food, especially the Heads of the large ones soused, make a choice Dish.

The *Mullets* are the same as with us in size and goodness,
and are in greater plenty here, than in most parts of *Europe,*
especially where the Waters are salt and brackish. They are
killed by striking them with the *Fish-gig,* or caught in *Nets,*
for they seldom or never take the Bait. I have frequently
known them at Night-time, to leap into the *Cannoes,* and
likewise vast numbers of them to be found dead on the dry
Sands or Shoars. They are much of the Nature of the *Pike.*
They strengthen the Stomach, and are good against the *Cholick, &c.*

The *Sheeps-head,* is a Fish, so called, from it's having
Teeth in it's Head like a Sheep. It is much about the bigness
of the *Angel-fish,* and partly shaped like him, being flat. It
has the vogue of being one of the choicest Fishes in this Province: Most certainly it is a delicate Fish, and well relished,
yet I think there are many others as good. It is taken with
the Hook and Line as the Drum. They are plenty in all our
Salt-water Rivers and Inlets, and generally weigh two to
three Pounds, and sometimes more.

The *Plaice* are here very large and plenty, being the same
as with us in *Europe,* they are of good nourishment, but more
watry than *Soals.* The best *Plaice* have the blackest Spots,
as the best *Flounders* have the reddest.

                                                          The

The *Soals* are found here, but not in such plenty as generally other Fish are, but are as good and as sweet here, as in any part of *Europe.* They are of the nature of the *Plaice* and *Flounder,* but a much better Fish, being more firm and solid, and afford more plenty of nourishment. The *Indians* and others kill vast quantities of these two sorts, and the *Flounders,* with their *Fish-gigs,* especially in the dark Nights, when the Weather is calm, with Lights.

The *Shads* are the same here as in *Europe;* they are pleasant, sweet, and nourishing, but are full of Bones, that it is dangerous to eat them without great care. They are to be met with in great plenty at some Seasons. They are said to be something Hypnotick in their Nature.

The *Fat-backs,* are so called, from being one of the fattest Fishes ever yet known, for when they are fryed in a Pan, they neither use Oil or Butter for that purpose. They are like the *Mullet,* but not so large, they are an excellent sweet Fish, eat well, and are very nourishing.

The *Guar,* or *Guard-fish,* whereof there are two sorts, *viz.* the White and the Green. The White is shaped almost like a *Pike,* but more slender. It's Mouth has a long small Bill, set with very sharp Teeth with which it catches it's prey which are several sorts of fry and small Fishes. They have strong large Scales so firmly knit together, that it is a hard matter to pierce through them with the sharpest Knife. When they dress them, they slit the Belly, where the Scales are not so strong or Armor-like, and take off their Skin, which they throw away as useless. The Meat is white and firm, and looks rather like Flesh than Fish. It is but very indifferent and course Food, therefore not much coveted by the Planters, though the *Indians* are very fond of them. The

Gall

Gall is very Green, and a most violent *Cathartick* if taken inwardly.

The *Green-guard,* is shaped in all respects like the other, only it is not so large, and it's Scales are Finer. The upper Jaw is the same as in the *Alligator,* moveable. It's Bones when fry'd or broyl'd, remain as green as Grass, though the Meat be of a white colour, and is but indifferent Food. The same sort of Fish is generally to be met with on the Coasts of *Ireland,* before the Season of the *Mackarel,* and seldom afterwards.

The *Scate,* or *Stingre,* is altogether of the nature of the *Thornback,* but stronger. They are the same here as are to be met with in several parts of *Europe,* and are very common; but the great plenty of other good Fish makes them little regarded, for few or none eat them in this Province (except the *Negroes* and *Indians*) though they are at every Planter's Door, as far as the salt Waters are. The Skin is used to polish *Ivory,* and fine Wood; it is said that they couple with the *Thornback,* and grow till they weigh One hundred and Sixty Pounds. The Oil of the Liver is good in hard Swellings, and the Ashes of the Skin help running Ulcers of the *Head* and *Baldness.*

The *Thornbacks* are the same here as in *Europe,* but not so plenty as the *Scate* and *Whip-Rays.* Their Flesh is moist, nourishes much, and restores in long and deep Consumptions, the Liver is sweet, and has the same virtues. The Gall cures Diseases of the Ears and Itch.

The *Conger,* or great *Sea-Eel,* always remains in the Salt Waters, it is white, fat, and sweet Flesh, which nourishes to excess, and is dangerous because of Surfeits: They are best when first boiled in Water, Salt, Sweet-Herbs, and Spices, then Broiled, or Collared, and then they are exceeding good

Meat.

Meat. These kind of Fish are better known to the *North-ward* of *America,* than in this Province.

The *Lamprey,* or *Lampron,* is not common in these Parts but plenty to the *Northward.* They are best in *March* and *April,* being then fattest; in *Summer* they are harder and leaner. They are about a Yard long, live in the Sea in Rocky places, and in the Mouths of Rivers, and weigh about twelve pound Weight: They eat Flesh, and when taken, are said to fly at the Fishers, and to be an Enemy to the *Conger.* They are sometimes taken in the Fish Wairs, but the *Indians* cannot endure them, neither will they eat them, though they are fond of most other sorts of Fish found in these Parts. *Pliny* reporteth, that they Spawn at all times of the Year, whereas all other Fish have certain Seasons. The Flesh is sweet and of good Nourishment, yet it is apt to cause Surfeits like the former, with which it agrees in Nature and Virtues.

The *Eels* are plenty in all our Rivers, and eat as well as in any part of the World. Their Flesh is very sweet, and yields much Nourishment, but apt to surfeit if much eaten. The Fat is good against blows and discolouring of the Skin, dropt into the Ears, helps old Pains and Deafness. The Gall is excellent against Suffusions of the Eyes, and the Blood warm with Wine helps the *Cholick.*

The *Sun-Fish* is very fat and rounder than a *Bream,* it's hinder part is invironed with a Circular Fin, which serves instead of a Tail, so that it may seem to be but the Head of a Fish, or a Fish in part rather than a whole one. They are plenty in these parts of *America,* and sometimes weigh a hundred Weight; they are commonly two or three Feet in length, they have no Scales, but are covered with a hard thick and

Gg                                                    sharp

sharp Skin, the colour whereof on the Back is black, and on the Belly a light silver grey. They are extreamly well tasted, therefore in great Esteem amongst the Inhabitants.

The *Toad-Fish*, or rather the *Sea Urchin*, because they are nothing but a Skin full of Prickles, and very few Bones. They are as ugly as a *Toad*, and of no manner of Use only to be preserved and hung up in Grottos to look at. Their manner of swimming is to rowl and tumble round like a Ball.

The *Sea Tench* is of a blackish colour, but exactly in shape like a *Tench*, except in the back Fins, which are like those of a *Perch*. They are as good if not better than the fresh-water *Tench;* they are taken by Angling with Hook and Line as the *Drum* and *Pearch*, near the Inlets, or a small distance out at Sea, where they are in great Plenty.

The *Salt-Water Trouts*, commonly called the *White Trouts*, are exactly shaped like the *Trouts* with us, only these have blackish and not Red Spots. They are in great plenty in the Sounds, near the Inlets, and Salt Waters; but they are not red within like some Trouts. They are excellent good, but so tender, that if they are in or near the fresh Waters, and a sudden Frost come on, they are so benumb'd, that they float as dead on the surface of the Water, at which Season they take Cannoes full of them, yet notwithstanding they are thus benumb'd they will recover again by the heat of the Sun, or put them into warm Water they will become brisk and lively. They are taken with the Bait, in or near the Salt Waters.

The *Crocus*, so called, from the croaking Noise it makes in ones Hand when it is taken with the Hook and Bait. They are in shape like a *Perch*, and in taste like a *Whiteing*, and are very plenty.

The

The *Smelts,* are the same here as I have observed in several parts of *Europe.* They are about eight or nine Inches long, and one broad; they smell like Violets, and are of the finest, lightest, softest, and best Juice, of most other Fish, especially in the *Winter,* and when full of Spawn. They lye down a great way in the Sound towards the Ocean, where they are very plenty, and vast numbers of them are taken at certain Seasons of the Year.

The *Sea-Bream* is thin, broad, and flat, exactly resembling our Fresh-water *Bream;* though there hath not been any such Fish discovered yet in the fresh Waters of *Carolina,* that I could ever learn. Their Flesh is white and solid, of good Juice and Nourishment, and easy of Digestion. They are very plenty in the Sound and Salt-Water.

The *Taylor* is about the bigness of a middling *Trout,* but of a blueish and green Colour, with a forked Tail like a *Mackarel.* They are excellent fine and delicious, Fishes, very plenty in the salt and brackish Waters, where they are caught with the Bait.

The *Herrings* are not quite so large as those with us in *Ireland,* and other parts of *Europe.* They come in such great Shoals to Spawn in the Months of *March* and *April,* that I have seen the *Christian* Inhabitants catch as many Barrels full as they pleased, or as long as their Salt lasted to preserve them, with Sieves and Shovels, instead of Nets; for at that Season they run up the Creeks and small Rivulets of Water in such Numbers, that the *Bears* take them out of the Water, as I have observed elsewhere. When they are fresh their Flesh is very white and more delicious than the *Herring* with us in *Europe,* but when they are Salted they become red, and if drest with Oil and Vinegar resemble an *Anchovy* very

much,

much, being far beyond any I have ever met with in *Europe,* when well Pickled, but if those Fish are eaten too greedily whilst fresh, are apt to breed Feavers. The Planters export several Barrels from hence to the Islands in the *West-Indies* and other parts that are scarce of Provisions.

THUS I have given you the most exact and Impartial account of the Salt-water Fish that came to my knowledge during my stay in those parts, though I have eat of several other sorts of Fish which I have omitted by reason that they are not distinguished by any certain English Names, that I cou'd learn, yet the *Indians* are well acquainted with them and have very uncouth Names for, which no doubt the *Christians* in time will discover, especially when this Colony is better inhabited and the Fishing Trade is well carry'd on. I shall therefore proceed to give an account of the FISH that are to be met with in the fresh Waters.

The *Sturgeon* is the first of these whereof we have great plenty, all the fresh parts of our Rivers being well stored with them. The upper parts of this fish are of a sordid Olive Colour, or betwixt a grey and a black: The Belly of a Silver Colour. They have a midling Head; very small Eyes, for the bulk of the Fish. The Snout is long, broad and sharp, and the Mouth without Teeth, they have no Chops, from whence it appears that they feed by sucking. They are a large Fish with a long Body, sixteen Fins and five rows of Scales; two on each side, and one on the back: The Scales of the upper row which are in the middle of the Back, being greater than the rest, rise higher; of these there are no certain Number; for it has been observed that some have Eleven some Twelve and others Thirteen; this row is extended from

the

the Head to the fin of the Back near the Tail. The Rows
on the sides extend from the Head to the very Tail; made
up with about thirty sharp Thorns or Prickles. The lower
row which begin at the first pair of the Fins and end at the
second, are each made up of Eleven, Twelve or Thirteen; all
the Scales of the rows in general, have on their Tops strong
sharp Prickles bending backwards. Besides these five rows,
they have only two Scales in the middle of the Belly, the
rest of the Belly being smooth. They have a large forked
Tail like that of the *Shark's,* the upper part whereof shoots
out beyond the lower a considerable way. These Fishes
sometimes frequent the Salt Waters like the *Salmon,* but
come to their greatest perfection in the Rivers, where they
are found twelve or fourteen Feet long, but those in the Sea
seldom exceed above a Foot and a half. They always are
observed to swim fastest against the Stream, and grow till
they weigh above two hundred pound Weight. In the Month
of *May* (at which time they are best in Season especially the
Females) they run up towards the Heads of the Rivers to
Spawn, where you shall see vast quantities of them in a Day
and especially before Rain, leaping at a great height out of
the Water. The *Indians* kill great Numbers of them with
their *Fish-gigs* and Nets, which they make and fix at the
ends of long Poles; for they are seldom or never taken with
Hooks. The *Indians* that live up towards the Heads of the
Rivers are fond of them, and frequently eat them, but those
near the salts and *Christians* will not make any use of them.
Their Bones serve indifferently for Rasps or Graters to grate
*Nut-megs, Bread,* and the like withall. The *Sturgeon* is an
excellent Fish when in Season, being strengthning, and is
esteemed as good as *Veal,* if not better; of their Eggs or
Spawn is made the *Caviary* so much esteemed amongst the

Quality.

Quality. The Liver is so sweet, that without some of the Gall, it causeth loathing. The Flesh is good against *hoarsness* and clears the *Voice,* the Fat cures the *Kibes,* and the Bones help the running *Gout.*

The *Jack, Pike,* or *Pickerel,* of these we have two sorts (one living in the fresh, and the other in the Salt Water) and are exactly of the same shape with those in *Europe,* but differ very much in size, for they are seldom found in these parts of *America,* above two Foot long, as far as I have yet seen. They are very plenty with us in this Province, all the fresh Water Rivers and Creeks abounding with them, and vast quantities are frequently taken in their Wairs at a time. The Flesh of this Fish is whiter and more excellent than that of the *Carp,* and is so harmless that it may be given to sick Persons. The Spawn or Row provoke both Vomit and Stool, and several other virtues are ascribed to them. Those of the Sea are a more delicate and better Fish than those of the fresh Water. They are said to live above two hundred Years, and that from their greediness of eating, they will often disgorge their Stomach of those Fishes they had taken in, and that they will sometimes swallow a Fish near as large as themselves, taking the Head in formost, the Tail hanging out of the Mouth, and so draw it in by little and little, till they compass the whole.

The *Trouts* are the same in *Carolina* as with us; but are not to be met with till you come up to the Heads of the Rivers, and where the Streams are swift and have Stony and gravelly Bottoms. These Fishes are equal in goodness to any Fish that live in the fresh Waters. The fat is very good for the *Hœmorrhoids* and clefts in the Fundament.

The *Gudgeons,* there are the same sorts found here, as in several parts of *Europe,* they are of the nature of the *Perch,*

and

and the whitest is the best, they are good pleasant food and of easy digestion, nourishing much, and increasing good Blood, and are good against the Cholick arising from cold or Tartarous humours, they help the Bloody flux, and other fluxes of the Belly, and being applied help the biting of Mad-dogs and *Serpents.*

The *Perch* whereof we have five sorts in *Carolina.* The first is the same as is to be met with in *Europe,* but is not quite so large. They are an excellent Fish and very whol-som, and good against Fevers, and the Stones in their Heads near the Back bone are accounted good against the Stone in the Reins.

The second sort of *Perch* is call'd the white *Perch* because it is of a Silver colour otherwise it is like the former or *English Perch* in shape and size. These are in very great plenty and preferable to the red ones in goodness.

The third sort which are commonly call'd *Welch-men,* are of a Brown colour and are the largest sort of *Perches* we have in these parts, some growing to be larger than any *Carp,* and are a very firm white and sweet Fish, and are very plenty in the Rivers and Creeks.

The fourth sort are vulgarly call'd *Irish-men,* these are a more flat Fish than any of the former, and much resembling a *Bream,* being all over freckled or mottled with Black and Blue spots, they are a very good Fish and are never taken any where but in the fresh Waters where they are very plenty.

The fifth sort are distinguished by the Name of round *Robins* and are the least sort of all, they are flat and very round shaped like a *Roach,* are beautifully mottled with red spots, and are as good Meat as any of the former, they are very easily taken with a Bait, as all the rest of the *Perches* are and are very numerous, each Creek and River of fresh Water abounding with them.

The

The *Roach* is here Likewise but is not as large as those in *Europe*. It is a good Fish but its being so full of small Bones makes it dangerous and Little regarded. It is reported to be a healthful Fish and not Subject to any diseases, whence comes the Proverb as sound as a *Roach*. The Flesh is said to excite Lust and cure Fevers.

The *Carp* is the same as in *Europe* but is not quite so large. It has a short Head without either Teeth or Tongue, but instead thereof a fleshy Palate that it may relish its food. The Fins are broad, the Tail forked and the Body covered with very large strong Scales. Its flesh is fat, soft, sweet, and nourishes very much, and is best in *March,* the Male being better than the Female, and the White than the Yellow. The fat cures diseases of the Nerves, the Stones about the Eyes are said to be good against the heat of Fevers, and likewise for the falling Sickness, and the Gall helps dimness of sight.

The *Dace* is the same here as in *Europe,* but is not so large or plentiful as with us. The flesh is soft, sweet in taste, and of good nourishment; and when pickled like *Anchovies* after the *Italian* manner, is Stomachical. They are best in *February, March* and *April,* and are excellent good food roasted and seasoned with Salt and Pepper. The fat helps pains in the Ears. The Gall mixt with the fat or Oil is good against Dimness of the Sight.

The *Flounders* are here in very great plenty and as large and good as any in *Europe*. Some of these Fish have Yellowish spots both on the Back and fins, and taste very much like a *Plaise*. The *Indians* and others kill vast quantities of them not only with the Bait but likewise with their *Fishgigs,* especially with Lights at Night. They are an excellent Fish and of good Nourishment, strengthen the Stomach, cause Appetite and help the Spleen.

The

The *Loche* is the same here as in *Europe*. The Flesh is very light and excellent nourishment, delicate in taste, wholsome, and good for Women with Child.

The *Sucking-Fish* are nearest in taste to a *Barble,* only they have no *Barbs,* they are about a Foot and a half long, and are a very soft and flabby Fish, and therefore are seldom or never made use of except by the *Negroes* and *Indians,* they are generally taken with the Bait and are very plenty in our Rivers and Creeks.

The *Cat-Fish,* so call'd, from the Whiskers or small fins they have about their Mouths. They are nearest in taste to *Eels* of any Fish I have ever met with. They are generally boild and made into Soop or Broath, which is the best way of dressing them. They are an excellent good Fish and nourish very much. There is another kind of *Cat-fish* which frequents the Salt Waters exactly like the former, both these sorts are very plenty in these parts, and are taken by angling with a Bait. They are a round blackish Fish with a great flat Head and wide Mouth, and like the *Eels* have no Scales.

The *Grindal,* are a long scaled Fish with small Eyes, and frequent Ponds, Lakes, and slow running Creeks and Swamps, but a very indiffrent soft fish, therefore not much coveted or made use of except by the *Negroes* or *Indians,* though some eat them, and report they are good Fish.

The *Old-wives,* these are bright scaly Fish which frequent the Swamps and fresh runs of Water, they have very small Mouths and large Eyes, with a great Fin on their Back, they seem to be between an *European Roach* and a *Bream,* and eat much like the latter, they are in great plenty up the Freshes. The *Indians* take abundance of these Fish and *Barbakue* them till they are Crisp, and so Transport them on wooden *Hurdles* to their Towns and Quarters.

The *Fountain-fish,* so call'd, from its frequenting the Fountains and clear running Streams of Water, where they breed and are to be met with and no where else. They are of a whitish colour and as large as a midling *Trout,* and by the clearness of the Water are very difficult to be taken, therefore I can't inform you how good they are, having never tasted any of them, but the *Indian*s say they are a fine fish.

The *Barbouts,* or *Miller's-Thumb,* are the very same here as those in *England* and other parts of *Europe.* They are about three or four Inches long, have no Scales, and the Back is Yellowish with a few little black Spots. The head is large, and the Mouth wide and round. Out of the Fins grow several sharp prickles or Thornes, especially in those near the Head. These fish are very plenty in Rivers and Creeks near the Sea Shoar where they feed on watry Insects.

This is the best Account I can give, or is yet known of the FISHES in the fresh Waters, few more being discovered, though I am satisfied, and may with Justice and safety say, that there is not one third part of them yet discovered, or made known to us, therefore shall omit many strange and uncouth shapes and sort of Fishes which we are told by the *Indians,* are to be found in the Rivers and Lakes, whereof I can give no certain Information to my Readers, having no farther account of them than only hearsay from those People, so shall proceed to treat of the *Shell-fish* which are found in the Salt Waters, as far as they are yet discovered.

The *OYSTERS,* whereof there are two Sorts, the great and the small, both these are in greater plenty here than

in

in most parts of the known World, for great Numbers of them are to be found in almost every Creek and Gut of Salt Water, and frequently hanging upon Boughs of Trees, as they bend into the Water, so that when the Tide is out you shall see them suspended in the Air, which would be a very uncommon sight in *Ireland,* to see Fish growing upon Trees. In the sound in several places there are such quantities of large *Oyster-banks*, that they are very troublesome to Vessels trading to these parts which happen to come in amongst them. They are of a different shape, from those with us, for those in *Carolina* are very long and large, and not round as ours are. They are excellent good, and nourish as much as any Fish whatever, and that without any manner of danger of Surfeiting. They strengthen the Stomach, cause an Appetite, and breed good Juices, being light and easy of digestion, and are good in Consumptions and several other disorders.

These *Oysters*, pickled, are well relished, excellent good for a Cold raw and squasy Stomach. The Shells in Powder cure Heartburnings, are good in Feavers and the like, and are the only Lime we have for building in this Country.

The *Spanish-Oysters,* are so call'd, from their great plenty in the *Spanish West-Indies;* they have a very thin Shell, and rough on the outside. They are excellent good *Shell-fish,* and so large that half a Dozen are sufficient to satisfie a hungry Stomach. From these *Oysters* come the Pearls that are so useful in Physick and so Ornamental.

The *Cockles,* whereof there are two sorts, the larger and the smaller, and first, the large *Cockles* are so very big that one of them is as large as five or six of those in *Ireland.* They are so very plenty in several parts, that they are often thrown upon the Sands on the sound side, where the *Gulls*

Hh 2                                    and

and other Birds are always ready to open and eat them. These as well as the former are great Strengtheners of the Stomach, and increase a good Appetite, provoke Urine, help the Cholick, restore in Consumptions, and in all decays of nature are very good.

The *Small Cockles* are about the bigness of our largest *Cockle,* and differ in nothing from them except in the Shells which are striped cross-ways, as well as long-ways, they are as good, and have the same virtues with the former.

The *Clams* are a kind of *Cockles,* only differing in the Shells, which are thicker, and not streaked or ribbed as the *Cockles* are. They are plenty in several places along the Sound-side, and Salt-water Ponds. They are very good Pickled, and their Meat tastes like other *Cockles;* they make excellent strong Broth, which strengthens the Stomach, is nourishing, breeds good Juices, is a Restorative in Consumptions, and other natural Decays.

The *Conchs,* some of these are very large, but the lesser sort are the best Meat; and that, in my Opinion, not extraordinary, notwithstanding several in these parts are fond of them, and extol them very much: The Fish within their Shells is shaped exactly like a Horse's Yard; of this Shell the *Indians* make their *Peak,* or *Wampum,* which is the richest, and most valuable Commodity they have amongst them. They breed in a kind of Substance shaped like a *Snake,* which contains a sort of Joints, in the hollowness whereof are thousands of small *Conchs,* no bigger than small Grains of Pepper. They are plenty along the sides of the Sounds and Salt-waters, but are not as large here as those found in the Islands in the *West-Indies.*

The *Musles* are much larger than those with us, their Shells being thicker, larger, and striped with Dents: they grow

by

by the sides of Ponds, and Creeks of Salt-waters, where may be had what quantity they please. They are very apt to give Surfeits, yet there are those who are fond of them, and prefer them to *Oysters.* Some boyl them, whereof they make Broth (which is the best way of dressing them) which is nourishing and purgeth the Reins, therefore good for those that have the Dropsie, Jaundice, Stone or Gout. They also eat well when they are Pickled.

The *Whale-Louse.* Their Head is like that of a *Louse,* with four Horns; the two short ones that stand out before have Knobs like the Sticks of Kettle-Drums. They have six plates on their Backs, and their Scales as hard as *Prauns.* Their foremost Legs are in shape like a half Moon, with sharp points, by which they fasten in the Skin of the *Whale,* and then bite pieces out of them. The *Whales* are mostly annoyed with them in warm Weather, and frequently at that time leap to some height out of the Waters in a rage.

There is a little small Fish in the fresh Waters in *Ireland,* something like the former, but has no Scales, which is very troublesome to the *Pike,* but whether it molests any other Fish, I cannot inform the Reader; but I have known the *Pike* to leap out of the Water upon dry Land with one of these sticking fast to his Belly; I have also been assured by those that fish, and dwell near the Rivers, that one of these will kill the largest *Pike,* by cutting a hole in his Belly.

The *Crabs* whereof there are two sorts, viz, the large stone *Crab* and the small flat *Crab.* The large stone *Crabs* are the same in *Carolina* as with us in *Ireland,* having black tips on the ends of their Claws, these sorts are plentifully to be met with near *Ceder-Island, Core Sound* and the south parts of this Province. The whole *Crab* is excellent against all sorts

of

of Fevers, Consumptions, Hecticks, Asthmas, the Stone in
the Reins and Bladder, pains and Stopage of Urine, and
many other disorders.

The smaller or flat *Crab,* in *North Carolina* is one of the
sweetest and best relished of any of that species I ever met
with in any part of *Europe,* when they are boyled their flesh
is very red and preferable in goodness to any *Lobster,* they
are as large as a Man's Hand, or rather larger. These are
innumerable, lying in great quantities all over the Salts; I
have known the little Boys take Bushels full of them in a few
Hours. They are taken, not only to be eaten, but are one of
the best Baits for all manner of Fish that take the Hook.
They are very mischievous to those that set Night Hooks to
catch Fish, for they generally take away all the Bait; both
these sorts cast their Shells every Year, at which time they
make Holes in the Sand, and cover themselves, or those with
hard Shells lye on them 'till their Shells harden, otherwise
they would be destroyed by other Fish. These sort have the
same Virtues with the former.

The *Fiddlers,* are a sort of small *Crab* that lie in Holes in
low, wet, and marshy Ground. The *Racoons* are very fond
of them, hunt for them in those places, and eat them. I
never knew any of them eat by the *Christians,* so cannot
inform you whether they are good or no.

The *Runners* or *Spirits,* so called, because they are apt to
pinch and bite Peoples Legs in the Night, as they walk near
the Shoar, and likewise from their running so fast. They
are a kind of a whitish *Crab,* and though they are so small,
they will run as fast as a Man; and are good for nothing but
to look at. They live chiefly on the Sand Breaches, where
they have their Holes. But will frequently run into the Sea

when

when pursued. I take this to be the *Hippœe,* or *Hippeis,* represented by *Pliny.*

The *Soldier,* is a kind of Shell-fish, so called, but for what reason I know not, except it be for their often changing their Houses, or Quarters, from one hollow *Conch shell* to another; for they are observed to be still changing their Habitations as they grow larger, having no Shell of their own. They have Claws like a *Crab,* and may be reckoned a Species of them, but of the smallest kind. They are good when well dressed, very nourishing, and create a good Appetite.

The *Wilks,* or *Periwinkle,* are not so large as they are in many parts of *Europe,* but as sweet and good, or rather better, being good Food and Nourishment; they are restorative in Consumptions and Hecticks, being sodden in their own Sea-water, or boiled in Milk.

The *Skallops* are pretty good, if well dressed, but if only roasted, without any other Addition, are too luscious to be made use of, and are apt to surfeit, but otherwise they are nourishing, and comfortable to the Stomach.

The *Man of Noses* are *Shell-fish,* commonly found in these parts, and are much valued and esteemed for increasing vigour in Men, and preventing barreness in Women, which is a thing seldom attends the Females here; for generally they are fruitful enough, without the benefit of these Fishes. But most certain it is, that they are very nourishing, and create good Juice in the Blood.

The *Flatings* so called from their flat shape. They are inclosed in a broad thin Shell, the whole fish being flat. They are a very good and delicious Fish and inferior to no Shell-fish this Country affords.

The Sea *Snail Horn* is exactly shaped like as other *Snail Horns* are. They are a large and very good Shell-Fish and

their

their Meat is very nourishing and communicates good Juices to the Blood.

The *Finger-fish,* so called, from their being about the length of a Man's Finger, they are very plenty in this Province, but generally lye at the bottom of the Waters about one or two feet deep, and are an extraordinary good Shell-Fish.

The *Shrimps* are very plentiful in *North Carolina,* and vast quantities of them are taken by the Boys and Girls with a small bow Net. They are very restorative and good in Consumptions, Hecticks and Asthmas, and are an excellent good Bait to catch *Mullets, Pikes,* and several other sorts of Fish that are caught by angling with the Bait.

The *Sea-Nettles* (by some called *Carvels*) whereof there are great plenty in the Western-Seas and Salt Waters on the coast of *America.* They seem to be nothing else but Slime, or a lump of *Jelly,* with a cast of red, blue and green colours in it, they Swim like a *Bladder* above the Water, but downwards there are long Fibrous Strings, some of which are near half a Yard long; some will have this *Jelly* to be a sort of Sea-plant, and the Strings its roots growing in the Sea as *Duck-weed* does in Ponds, but the Query is, if they be not a certain Species of Spawn for when they are taken out of the Water, or any thing touches them (though they scarce seem to have Life) yet they will very suddenly change their colours, which they quickly recover again. They may be reckoned amongst Potential Cauteries, because they are apt to blister the Hands or any other part of the Skin (like *Nettles*) where ever they touch. I am persuaded that they are of so venemous a Nature that few Fish prey upon them, otherwise they wou'd not be so numerous as they are, notwithstanding I have known some of them taken out of the Guts of the

*Hawks-billed*

*Hawks-billed Turtle.* They are called *Sea-Nettles,* from the stinging and blistering quality they have like *Nettles,* occasioning burning Pains to whatever part of the Skin they happen to touch.

The fresh-water *Shell-fish* are the *Mussels* and *Craw-fish.* The *Mussels* are here plenty in several parts of the Freshes, and are much the same as in *Europe;* they are only made use of by the *Indians,* who eat them after five or six Hours boiling to make them tender; there are valuable Pearls found in some of them, the whitest are the best, being the wholsomest. The Broth is opening, and therefore good in the *Dropsie, Jaundice,* and *Gout.*

The *Craw-fish* are very plenty in the Brooks and small Rivers of Water amongst the *Indians,* and at the heads of the Rivers near the Mountains; they are as delicious and good here as in any part of the World. They are shaped like a *Scorpion,* and the Stones in the Head are accounted good against the *Jaundice* and *Stone* in the *Reins.* The Black are much better than the White; they nourish and strengthen the Body, and the Soop made of them is in very great Value and Esteem amongst the Quality.

Having thus given a Description of several Species, or Kinds of Fishes that are to be met with, and already known in *North Carolina;* I shall in the next place proceed to what remains of the *Present State,* having already accounted for the *Animals* and *Vegetables,* as far as this Volume would allow of, and whatever remains may be easily guessed at by any ingenious Man who considers what Latitude *Carolina* lies in, which reaches from 29 to 36 Degrees 30 Minutes of *North* Latitude, as I have already observed: Most part of

this

this spacious Country being waste and uninhabited, at present, except by wild Beasts and Savage *Indians,* from whom we can have but very imperfect Accounts, they being a People of little or no Speculation, nor any way Curious.

# FURTHER

# OBSERVATIONS

## ON THE PRESENT STATE OF

## NORTH CAROLINA.

AS to the AIR, I don't know what fault it has, except what I have said before of it's being sometimes extreamly hot, at other times subtile, and piercing; and I am persuaded, it enters a Man's Body easier than that in *Ireland;* yet I think that much of the Mortality that happens among Strangers, is owing in a great measure to the ill government of themselves, for they eat but little, having destroyed their Stomachs by Surfeits of Fruit, or excessive Drinking hot Spirituous Liquours; and if any rather chuse the cold, his Stomach is chilled, and he is immediately in danger of a Flux, or extream Looseness. There is another thing to be observed, Men guard themselves less from the Air here, than in most

Ii ₂                                    other

other Place, trusting to the heat of the Climate, and receive
the cool of the Evenings with only a Shirt. I think that the
Air, though not so cold, is much more subtle and piercing
here than in *Ireland,* it corrodes Iron much more, not by
Moisture, for it is not so moist; and besides it does it in the
dry Weather.

Notwithstanding this Country is as fertil and pleasant as
any in the World (in the same Latitude) for the produce of
Minerals, Fruit, Grain, Wine, and several other rich Commodities, that are frequently to be met with in it. All the
Experiments that have been already made of the Fertility
and natural Advantages of the Country, have answered beyond expectation, as affording some Commodities, which
other Places in the same Latitude do not.

As for *Minerals,* they being subterraneous Products, so
in all New Countries, they are the last Species that are generally discovered, and will most certainly be so, where the
*Indians* never look for any thing lower than the superficies
of the Earth, being a race of Men, the least addicted to search
into the Bowels of the Earth, of any in the World, that inhabit so fine a Country as *Carolina;* and I am satisfied, that
there are as good and rich Mines here, that lie full to the
Westward of us, as any the *Spaniards* possess in *America.*
The Lands near the Heads of the Rivers being Mountainous,
and no doubt, have as rich *Minerals* in them as any of those
parts that are already discovered to be so rich.

I shall say no more on this Subject at present, but give you
some general Observations concerning *North-Carolina;* which
are, That it lies as convenient for Trade as any Province in
*America,* abounding with several rich and valuable Commodities, such as *Tar, Turpentine, Pitch, Rosin, Masts, Yards,
Planks, Boards, Staves, Lumber, Timber* of many sorts, fit

for

for any uses; Skins of *Deers, Beeves, Buffelo's, Elks, Bears, Panthers,* and several other Beasts. The Furrs of *Beavers, Racoons,* and many other wild Beasts, which are in great Plenty here; as also *Rice, Wheat, Indian Corn, Barley, Oats, Buck-wheat,* and sundry sorts of *Pulse, Potatoes,* and variety of fine Fruits, *Flax, Beef, Pork, Tallow, Hides, Horses, Whale-bone, Oil, Bees-wax, Myrtle-wax, Honey, Cheese, Butter, Cotton, Tobacco, Indico, Coffee,* and no doubt would produce good *Silk, Oil,* and *Wine,* the Soil of this Country being as proper as any in the World for that purpose.

This Country is likewise adorned with pleasant Savannas or Meadows, Rivers, Mountains, Vallies, Hills, and rich Pastures for Cattle, and blessed with a wholsome pure Air, especially a little backwards from the Sea, where only wild Beasts inhabit at present, few of which are so voracious as to kill Men, Horses or Cows, for there cannot be a richer Soil, no place abounding more in Flesh and Fowl, both wild and tame, besides vast numbers of excellent Fish, Grain, Cyder, and many other pleasant Liquors, together with most Necessaries convenient for Life, that are daily found out, to the great Benefit and Advantage of those that are already settled here.

The *Stone* or *Gout* seldom or never afflict the *Christian* Inhabitants, and the *Europeans* that have been afflicted with the Stone and Gravel, find present Ease, by drinking *Yaupan* Tea.

The *Consumption* we are entire Strangers to, no Country affording a better Remedy for that Distemper than the pureness of the Air; neither has the *small Pox* ever visited this Country but once, and that in the late *Indian War,* which destroyed most of those Savages that were seized with it.

As

As for Trade, we lie so near *Virginia,* that we might have the advantage of their Convoys, if there were occasion for them, as also Letters from thence in two or three Days, and from some places in a few Hours. The great numbers of ships that come to *New-England, New-York, Pensilvania, Mary-Land,* and *Virginia,* make the Provisions scarce in those Places, so that they are frequently obliged to *North-Carolina* for those Necessaries, where Provisions and Naval Stores never fail of a good Market. Besides where these are produced and raised in such plenty, there appears good House-keeping, and plenty of all manner of delicate Eatables.

The *Porke* is excellent good, from their *Hogs* feeding on *Straw-berries, Wall-nuts, Peaches, Maiz,* and several other sorts of delicate Fruits, which, are the natural produce of this Country, and make them the sweetest Meat the World can afford; as is well known to all Strangers that have been in that Country. And as for their *Beef,* it proves extraordinary good, being fat and well relished. We have not only Provisions very plenty, but Cloaths of our own Manufacture, which are made and daily increase in these parts; such as *Cotton, Wool, Hemp* and *Flax,* being all the growth of this Country. But the women do not over burthen themselves with care and Industry; otherwise there would not be such continual calls for those necessarys from *Europe.* But this Climate being visited with so mild and short Winters, save abundance of Cloaths. We likewise can go out with our Commodities to any part of the *West-Indeas,* or elsewhere in the depth of Winter, whereas those in *New-England, New-York,* and *Pensilvania,* and those Colonies to the *Northward* of us, cannot stir for *Ice,* but are fast locked into their Harbours all that Season.

We

We have no frontier Town in *North-Carolina,* which is an advantage in not being so continually alarm'd by the Enemy, and what has been accounted a detriment to us, proves one of the greatest advantages any People cou'd wish or desire. This Country being Fenced with a Sound near ten Leagues over in some Places, through which, although there be Water enough for as large Ships to come in at, as any part hitherto seated in both *Carolinas;* yet the difficulty of that Sound to Strangers hinders them from Hostilities against us, so that this natural Bull-work proves very advantagious to us in securing us from our Enemies.

Our distance from the Sea likewise rids us from two curses or Plagues which attend most other parts of *America,* viz. the *Musketo's,* and the water *Wood-worms,* that eat Ships bottoms. Whereas at *Bath* and *Eden-town,* there is no such thing known, and as for *Musketo's* we are very little troubled with them, except it be in low Marshes, and near the Salt-waters, which are only habitations for wild Beasts, Birds, and Snakes of various kinds. The vast quantities likewise of Fish that this great Sound or Water supplies us with, when ever we take the pains to Fish for them, is another considerable advantage not to be met with so commodiously in any part of *America* as in this Province.

As for the *Climate* (as I observed) we generally enjoy a very wholesome and serene Sky, and a pure and thin Air, the Wether seldom proving so overcast or Cloudy but we have the blessing of the warm Sun, except it be in *Winter,* and then as soon as the South and West-winds begin to blow, the Horizon immediately clears up and restores the light of the Sun. The Weather in *Summer* is very pleasant, being continually refreshed with cool reviving Breezes from all Quarters except the South, which is very sultry.

The

The *Spring* here is as pleasant and as beautiful as in any place I have ever been in, and the *Winter* generally proves so mild that it is rather like an *Autumn,* except the Winds blow North-west, at which time it is peircing and cold, but proper enough for our constitutions, and very wholesome, freeing these parts from many dangerous distempers that a continual *Summer* afflicts them with, nothing being wanting as to the natural Ornaments or blessings of a Country to the making reasonable Men happy.

As for the Constitution of this Government, it is so mild and easy in all respects, to the Liberties and Properties of the Subject, that it is the best established Government in the World, and a Place where a Man may peaceably enjoy his own without being invaded by another; rank and superiority always giving place to Justice and Equity, which is the foundation that every government ought to be built upon, and regulated by.

Besides this Province has been settled and continued the most free from the insults and barbarities of the *Indians* of any Colony in *America,* which was one of the greatest blessings that cou'd attend such a small number of People as they were, and how I regularly settled first, and at what distance they are from each other, and yet how undisturbed they have remained and free from any Foreign danger or loss, to what most of the other Colonys have been exposed to, not only by the *Indians,* but their own Slaves the *Negroes.* And what may well deserve Admiration is, that their Prisons are never crowded with *Malefactors* or *Debtors;* as to *Malefactors* I never knew but one that was guilty of death, for Murder, which happened as follows; two Persons well known to each other, being at the *Tavern,* one of them was falling

asleep,

asleep, his Friend importuned him to go home along with him, which the other refusing to do, his Friend told him, that he would leave him, which he had no sooner said, but the other Stab'd him with his Knife, whereof he instantly died; the Murderer was immediately apprehended, tried, and condemned to die, he confest that before he left *Europe* he had murdered two, and notwithstanding his Condemnation, he found means to make his escape out of Prison some few Days before the Execution.

As for *Debtors,* few or none are confin'd in Prison above four and twenty Hours, for the *Sherriff* generally takes them Home to his House, or takes their Word for their Appearance at the next Court, to be held, in any of their precincts or Barronies, where they Judge him a Servant to the Creditor for as long time as they imagine the Debt deserves, but if the Person has been a Planter and by misfortunes has contracted Debts, or an aged Person they frequently at these Courts make a Collection amongst themselves, by which means they discharge the Debt, or satisfie the Creditor; so that by these methods none are kept in confinement.

It is likewise enacted by the Laws of the Country, that no Person shall be liable to pay above forty Shillings of their Country Money for any publick-House Scores for Liquors, let the Persons that keep such Houses trust them what they please, yet by Law they can recover no more: This is done chiefly to prevent People, if possible, running in Debt, or spending their Time idly after that manner, especially in a Country where Industry is so much wanting. Notwithstanding this Law, some will owe above One hundred Pounds at these Taverns, or publick Houses, which they will justly and honestly pay, looking upon it as the greatest Scandal in Nature to make use of this Law; neither would the Country much regard them afterwards if they did. Yet there are some that are not so scrupulous, or so strictly bound up to Principles of Justice, that have taken the advantage of this Law, to defraud their Creditors, when they had an Opportunity.

There are several other good Laws in this Province, and particularly, that no Vagabond, or inferiour Person is suffered to travel through the Country without a Pass from the Governor, or some of the Justices of the Peace, this is done to prevent Transports from *Europe* running away from their Masters.

They have no Frontier Towns, as I before observed, neither have they any Army, except their Militia, which are both of Horse and Foot, having proper Officers, who are Commissioned, or Nominated by the Governor, although they are seldom obliged to Muster (as they are in most of the other *English* Provinces in *America*) except it be to apprehend Offenders that will not submit themselves to the Law, or be taken by the Authority of their Justices of Peace's Warrant; in such cases, they generally raise the *Posse* or *Militia,* to seize and bring them to Justice; Yet instances of this Nature are but seldom, for I never knew but two whilst I was in the Country.

But to return to the Subject in Hand, there are made throughout this Settlement, as good Bricks as any I have ever met with in *Europe:* All sorts of Handy-crafts, such as *Carpenters, Joyners, Coopers, Bricklayers, Plaisterers, Shoemakers, Tanners, Curriers, Taylors, Weavers,* and most other sorts of Tradesmen, may with small Beginnings, and good Industry, soon thrive well in this Place, and provide good Estates, and all manner of Necessaries for their Families,

Lands

Lands being sold at a cheaper rate here than in most parts of *America.*

The Farmers that go thither (for which sort of People it is a very thriving place) shou'd bring with them several sorts of Seeds of *Grass,* as *Trefoil, Clover-Grass,* all sorts of *Sanfoin,* and common *Grass,* and especially those that have arose and sprung in a warm Climate, that will endure the heat of the Sun; likewise several *Garden-Seeds,* and choice *Fruit-Trees,* and *European-grain,* for increase and hardness, and especially *Olive-Trees* and several sorts of *European-Grapes.* The necessarys for Husbandry I need not acquaint the Husbandman withal, but *Hoes,* of all sorts, and *Axes* must be had, *Saws, Wedges, Augurs, Nails, Hammers,* and what other things may be necessary to build with Timber and Brick. For whoever reads this Treatise with attention, must needs be acquainted with the nature of the Country, and therefore cannot but be Judges what will be chiefly wanting in it.

Whoever goes to this Province need not complain for want of Lands for taking up, even in places most delightfully seated on navigable Rivers and Creeks, without being driven to remote parts of the Country for settlements, as at present they are forced to do in *New-England,* and several other *English* provinces in *America,* which are already become so populous, that a new comer cannot get a beneficial and comodious seat, unless he purchases it at a very dear rate.

Another great advantage here is, that there is liberty of Conscience (as I said before) allowed to all. These things being duly weighed, any rational Man that has a mind to purchase Lands for a Settlement for himself and Family, will soon discover the advantages that attend the settlers and purchasers of Lands here above all the other Provinces in the *English* Dominions in *America,* for Ease, Pleasure, Satisfaction, and all necessaries of Life.

And as several parts of *Europe* may be admired for its artificial, so may *Carolina* for its natural Beauty; for the Country in general is level, except some Hills near the *Cherokee* and *Appelapean* Mountains, and most agreeably diversified with fine arable Lands, producing vast increase, and two Crops in one Season, with large and spacious Savannes or Meadows, most beautifully adorn'd with variety of Odoriferous and fine Flowers, intermixt with plenty of good Grass for Pasture for Cattle. The large Woods and Forests with their Lofty Trees and spreading Vines of various sorts, affording not only refreshing, but most pleasant shades to sit under in the extremity of the hot Weather, and likewise abounding with various kinds of wild Beasts and Birds, which are preserved in them, not only for diversion of Hunting, but likewise convenient and profitable for the support of Man.

And Lastly, the large and Navigable Rivers and Creeks that are to be met with watring and adorning this Country, well stored with vast quantities of Fish and Water-Fowl. These ornaments and many advantages which it enjoys, makes it one of the pleasantest places in the World to live in, *Sed, Nescio qua natale solum dulcedine capto ducit & Immemores non sinit esse sui.* They make very necessary Vessels for carriage of their Commodities by Water, which are called in these parts *Periaugers* and *Canoes,* which are the Boats made use of in this Country, and are generally made out of one peice of large Timber, and that most commonly of the *Cypress* kind, which they make hollow and shaped like a Boat, with Masts, Oars, and Padles, according to their size and bigness. Some of these *Periaugers,* are so large that they are capable of carrying forty or fifty Barrels of

*Pitch*

*Pitch* or *Tar*. In these Vessels likewise they carry Goods, Horses, and other Cattle from one Plantation to another over large and spacious Rivers; they frequently trade in them to *Virginia* and other places on this continent, no Vessel of the same Burthen made after the *European* manner is able to out Sail one of these *Periaugers*.

The *Canoes* are of less Burthen than the former, some will carry two or three Horses over these large Rivers, and others so small that they will carry only two or three Men. These are more ticklish than Boats, but no Boat in the World is capable to be rowed as fast as they are, and when they are full of Water they will not sink, and not only the *Indians* but even the *Christians* are very dexterous in managing of them.

Before the arrival of the *Christians* in these parts (as I have been credibly inform'd) the *Indians* had no other Method in making these *Periaugers* and *Canoes,* but by Fire, burning them hollow with Gums and Rosins, and scraping them with sharp Stones or Shells, prepared for that use, according to the shape and size they proposed to make them, having neither Handsaws, Axes, Adds, Chizel, or any other Instruments made of Iron or Steel, wherewith to fashion or make them; but at present they have all manner of Instruments proper for such uses, which they have purchased from the *Christians*. It is most certain, that no People in the World are more handy and dexterous in managing their *Periaugers,* and *Canoes,* with either Sail, Oar, or Paddle, than they are; and when ever it happens that their *Canoes* are full of Water, they will very nimbly leap out, and holding the *Canoe* with one Hand, throw out the Water with a *Gourd* with the other, and so proceed on their intended Voyage. They likewise very often set their *Periaugers* and *Canoes,* along the Shoar with long Poles.

The

The Land Carriages are much after the same manner as those with us; there being not only plenty of Horses, but likewise of Carts and Waggons, and several other Necessaries convenient for Carrying all manner of Commodities by Land from one place to another.

The Roads are as good as in most parts of the World, and the travelling as pleasant, especially the Road from *Edentown* to *Virginia,* being made broad and convenient, for all sorts of Carriages, such as Coaches, Chaises, Waggons and Carts, and especially for Horsemen, these Lands lying so level, and the beautiful and delightful Objects they are entertained with in their Journey, render it both amusing and diverting. What is remarkable is, that traveling from *Edentown* to *Virginia,* there is a Post set up in the Division between those two Provinces, with *North Carolina* on the South, and *Virginia* on the North, in large Capital Letters, to shew to all Travellers the Bounds between those two Colonies.

In other parts the Roads are more like Paths than any publick Road, only that they are made broad enough for Coach, Chaises, and all manner of Carriages. But this is a general Rule to be observed throughout all *America,* that wherever you meet any of those Paths like Roads, with the Trees marked or notched on each side, it is a sure sign that it is the publick Road from one *Christian* Town to another. Notwithstanding there are several Paths of Horses, Cows, and other Beasts in the Woods, as large as the former, which are to be avoided, by reason that the Trees are not marked as above; neither do the *Indians* ever use this Method in making their Roads, having some secret Knowledge to guide them through these large Woods, which we are entire Strangers to; so that several Christians not knowing, or regardless of these Marks, have been for several Days lost in the Woods,

before

before they could come to any Planters House, or meet with any Person to inform them which way to go; yet I never heard of any perish for want of Provisions, under these misfortunes, there being not only great Plenty of several good Fruits to be met with, all over the Woods most parts of the year, but likewise variety of Birds and Beasts, necessary for the support of Life; but I have known some lost for eight, others for fourteen Days, before they could meet with any human Creature to inform them what part of the Province they were in.

The *Negroes* sometimes make use of these Advantages in the Woods, where they will stay for Months together before they can be found out by their Masters, or any other Person; and great Numbers of them would act after the same manner (which would be detrimental to the Planters) were they not so much afraid of the *Indians,* who have such a natural aversion to the *Blacks,* that they commonly shoot them when ever they find them in the Woods or solitary parts of the Country.

There are no Wind-Mills in this Province at present, and not above two or three Water-Mills, which are for the most part continually grinding their Wheat; for the small *Sloops* and *Periaugers* are continually coming and going with Corn and Flower: But the common method that the Planters use to grind their Corn is with Hand-Mills, which almost every one of them has. The Stones for these Mills are got up the River *Neus,* which are very soft when dug out of the Earth, but grow exceeding hard and durable after they are some time in the Air, and are serviceable upon these occasions. These Stones seem more like a parcel of *Oyster-shells* petrified, than any natural Stone, for through the whole Grain of this Stone there is no other appearance, but the exact shape

of

of the *Oystershells*.  Of this kind of Stone there are several
Quarries and Rocks to be met with towards the Heads of the
Rivers; notwithstanding there is plenty of Free-Stone near
the Mountains, and most kinds of Greet proper to make
Millstones, yet the former being so easily acquired, are only
made use of at present, except some few brought from *England,* for their Water-Mills.  The Proprietors of these Mills
take most commonly every other Barrel as Toll, for grinding;
but the Laws of the Country allow only every sixth.

There are abundance of excellent good Springs to be met
with in several parts of this Province, abounding with as
sweet and fresh Waters as any in *Europe,* and especially
near the Mountains, in which there can be none better.  The
Lands near these parts being for the most part very rich,
with an extraordinary black Mold, some of a Copper colour,
and both very good.  Here are likewise great quantities of
Iron Mine, several sorts of Stone, divers kinds of Spaws,
and *chalibeat* Springs, the Water whereof being drank, make
the Excrements as black as Ink by its *chalibeat* Quality.

It is very remarkable, at certain seasons of the Year, but
especially in *Winter,* as Persons travel up near the Mountains, they hear at Night the most hideous and strange Noise,
that ever pierced mortals Ear, which at first was very frightful to us, 'till such time as we were informed by our *Indian*
Guides, that this Noise is customary in those parts there
being innumerable numbers of *Panthers, Tygers, Wolves,*
and other Beasts of Prey, going in whole droves to hunt the
*Deer,* making this frightful Noise all the Night, until Day
appears, or that a Shot or two is fired, then all will be still
and quiet.  There are several large Swamps to be met with
here, which are the Habitation of those wild Beasts, where

they

they make their abode in the Day, at which time they are not to be seen or heard in the Woods.

But these kind of wild Beasts are not very plenty (except the *Wolves*) near the Settlements, the Planters continually destroying them as they hunt and travel in the Woods, and in process of time will be lessened as this Country begins to be better Inhabited. This Country affords many and large Swamps, which are generally overflowed or under Water in the *Winter,* yet I never met with any Bogs, but plenty of good Pit Coal in many places, of which they make no manner of use at present, all kind of Timber being so plenty, and proper for fireing; so that all other kinds of Fuel are disregarded and made no use of by the Inhabitants of this Province.

It will not be improper, in this place, to give an account how the *Turpentine, Tar, Pitch,* and *Rosin* are made, being all the produce of one Tree, and a very good Stable Commodity in these parts. The Planters make their Servants or *Negroes* cut large Cavities on each side of the *Pitch-Pine* Tree (which they term *Boxing of the Tree*) wherein the *Turpentine* runs, and the *Negroes* with Ladles take it out and put it into Barrels: These Trees continue thus running most commonly for three Years, and then decay, but in process of time fall to the Ground, which is what they call *Light-Wood,* of which their *Pitch* and *Tar* is made. (*viz.*)

The Planters at certain Seasons of the Year, and especially in *Winter,* make their *Negroes* gather great quantities of this *Light-wood,* which they split about the thickness of the small of a Man's Leg, and two or three Feet in length; when they have got a sufficient quantity of it in readiness, they set their Kilns on some rising Ground or Earth thrown up for that purpose, in the center whereof they make a hollow

Ll place,

place, from whence they draw a Funnel some distance from the Kiln. Then they take the *Light-wood* which they pile up with the ends of each, placed slanting towards the center of the Kiln, which is generally made taper from the Ground, afterwards they cover it very secure with Clay, Earth, or Sods, to keep in the Flames, after this is done they set it on fire at the Top, the Weather permitting, which must be neither too dry nor too wet. By this means the *Tar* runs into the center, and from thence into the Funnel, where they attend Night and Day (with Ladles to put it into Barrels prepared for that purpose) till the Kiln is quite burnt out, which is generally in eight and forty Hours or less, according to the dimensions of the Kiln. It sometimes happens through ill management, and especially in too dry Weather, that these Kilns are blown up as if a train of Gun-powder had been laid under them by which Accident their *Negroes* have been very much burnt or scalded. The Planters generally know very near what quantity of *Tar* each of their Kilns will produce, according to their dimensions, for which reason they are always provided with a sufficient Number of Barrels for that end.

The *Pitch* is made of the *Tar,* which is done in the following manner. They have large Furnaces made in several parts, and more now than ever, by reason of a late act of Parliament made in the Reign of his present Majesty, which obliges every Person or Persons that burn *Tar-kilns* in his Majesties dominions in America to make half of the first running into *Tar,* and the other half into *Pitch,* the penalty being a forfeture of the whole. With this second running they fill their furnaces, and so place a fire underneath it till such time as it begins to boyl, then they set it on fire and burn it to the consistence of *Pitch.*

The

The *Rosin* is very scarce in these parts, few giving themselves the trouble; but when made, it is done after the following manner, *viz.* Take *Turpentine,* as much as you think proper, put it into an *Alembick* or a *Copper Vesica,* with four times its weight of fair Water, and distil it, which will produce a thin and clear Oil like Water, and at the bottom of the Vessel will remain the *Rosin.* The *Indians* never make either *Pitch, Tar* or *Turpentine,* ranging and hunting continually through the Woods, being all the Industry they are given to, except they plant some small quantity of *Indian* Corn or *Maiz,* and dress their *Deer-Skins,* being as well satisfied with this way of living as any among us, who by his Industry has acquired immense Treasure.

I will in the next place give an account of those that are Transported to these parts from *Europe,* and the many advantages that attend them in this Province, according to their good behaviour. These are indented for such a limitation of time, as appears by each of their *Indentures,* and are disposed and made Servants of during that time, each of them being more or less regarded according to their good or bad behaviour, and the reason of their being Transported. Neither can any Servant give a second *Indenture* on himself before he is out of his Apprentiship, and a Free-man in the Country; then he is at his Liberty to make what bargain he pleases, but before that time all contracts made by him are void and of no effect. For by only applying to any of their Courts, he is immediately discharged and set free, notwithstanding he has received a gratuity (from the Planter who claims him) for so doing. This being an established law of the Country to prevent Masters taking advantage of their Servants before they have obtained their freedom. As soon

as

as they have fullfill'd the Obligation of their *Indentures,*
and are become Free-men, their Masters are obliged on their
parts to give each Man Servant a new Suit of Cloaths, a Gun,
Powder, Shot, Ball and ten Bushels of *Indian* Corn, and by
the Laws of the Country, they are entitled to fifty Acres of
Land, which they seldom take up, but dispose of for Trifles,
this quantity of Land being too small for large Stocks of
Cattle (which most Planters here are possessed of) or to
make *Pitch* and *Tar* on, which is another Staple of this
Country, so that an Instance of this Nature is not to be met
with in this Province.

Thus they appear after they have served their time and
have obtained their freedom, having no other visible Fortune to depend upon or support them except their Industry.
The Question then may be reasonably asked, how it is possible for them to live, or make Fortunes from such small and
despicable beginnings? Concerning which Objection, I shall
thus endeavour to satisfie the Reader.

Those that are thus made Free-men, their former Masters
generally give a Character of them, according to their good
or bad behaviour during their Apprentiship, and those that
have acted with prudence, care, and good conduct, whilst
they were Servants never are at a loss to meet with the best
usage from their Masters, who recommend them to other
planters (if they have no Imployment for them) to be their
*Stewards,* or overseers of their Plantations (several of the
Planters of this Country having many) wherein are generally great Stocks of Cattle, Horses, and Swine.

The overseer being thus employ'd, his business is to mark
all the *Calves, Foles,* and young *Pigs,* with the Planters
Mark or Brand, every Planter having his Brand or Mark
recorded in proper Books, kept for that purpose in each Pre-

cinct

cinct or Barony throughout this Province. This is done to prevent the Planters having any disputes about any of these Beasts, each Planter claiming by these marks nothing but what is justly his own, and if there be any *Negroes,* to see them perform whatever Work the Planter requires to be done; this being chiefly what the Overseer is employed in, for which Service he is allowed every seventh *Calf,* seventh *Fole,* and half of all the young Hogs that are bred during his Stewardship, and likewise the seventh part of all sorts of *Grain* and *Tobacco* that is produced on the said Plantation. Whatever quantity of *Corn, Rice* or *Tobacco* he plants by his own Industry, is all his own Property, the Master having nothing to do with it. Thus in three or four Years time, with good management, he has a sufficient Stock of Cattle, Grain, Money, and all other Necessaries proper to purchase a Plantation, by which means many are become as wealthy and substantial Planters, as any in the Government. But I must confess, that few are such good Proficients in this way of Industry, notwithstanding there are such considerable advantages to be acquired thereby. But on the contrary, those of ill behaviour, and such as have been negligent in their Apprentiship, are not thus recommended, but generally get their livelyhood by the sweat of their Brow, yet live after a very loose and indolent manner; for if they work two Days in the Week, they generally drink and are idle all the rest (Provisions and Liquors being so very cheap) and are rather greater Slaves when made free, than they were during their Apprentiship, never making any advantage of their Time. Thus, I hope I have satisfied the Reader as to this Point.

I shall only mention one particular in regard to these Servants or Transports, which I had like to have omitted; which is, that they run away from their Masters, to prevent

which

which there is a Law made in this Country, whereby those that run away are obliged (if apprehended and taken, as they generally are) to serve double the time they are absent from their Masters; this they are obliged to perform after the expiration of their *Indentures,* which is done to prevent their running away before they have served their time, which so deters them, that they are not so guilty of this kind of Practice of late, as formerly.

Few Masters of Ships will venture to carry on board their Vessels any of these Servants or Debtors from this, or any other of the Provinces, without their giving sufficient security that they are not in Debt, and Freemen, or publish an *Advertisement* sometime before their departure out of the Province; wherein they require all Person that they are indebted to, *To come, and they will pay them what they can make appear to be justly due.* And likewise, *That all Persons indebted to them, are desired to come and pay them before they quit the Country, in such or such a Ship.* This being the Substance of this *Advertisement,* which is fixed on their Court-House Door, for all Persons to peruse. These Obligations being thus performed, they are at their Liberty to go where they please, and the Masters liable to no Penalty; but if they should act contrary to the Laws (and they be discovered) both their Persons and Ships are liable to be arrested, and subject to pay whatever the Creditors can make appear due to them, or any other Losses they have sustained thereby. Notwithstanding all these Laws, some of them run away, and when they are taken, like the *Negroes,* have Neck-yoaks put on them, which they constantly wear, 'till they give sufficient Testimonies of their good behaviour to the contrary. Several Instances of this Nature I have been Eye-witness to during my stay in that Country.

There

There is an Office here which is worth our Notice, *viz.* the *Gunpowder-Office,* which hath continued ever since the last War with the *Indians,* at which time there was a Law made, by which all Vessels trading to those Parts were liable to pay three Shillings and four Pence, *Carolina* Money *per* Ton, or the Value in *Gun Powder,* except the said Vessel was built in the Country, or that the Merchant had a Plantation there, then the Vessels were liable to pay half Fees, or one Shilling and eight Pence *per* Ton to the *Powder-Office.* The lessening of these Fees was to encourage Merchants to build and settle in this Country. They nominated at their General Assemblies such Persons as they judged proper in each County to receive the said Fees, which were to be laid out in a sufficient Magazine or Store of *Gunpowder,* which was to be always in readiness for the use of the *Christians* against the *Indians,* whenever they made any Attempts, which there is no danger of their ever doing for the future; yet this Office continued 'till the Year 1733, being about that time laid aside as unnecessary, as I have been informed since my return from those parts.

The Planters are very Hospitable and Charitable to each other, and especially if any have had the misfortune to have their Houses burnt, or any other grievous Affliction befall them. On these occasions they readily contribute to make up the loss of the Sufferers, whereby they generally become more wealthy than they were before this misfortune happened.

Thus have I given an Account of the Advantages and Disadvantages that attend the *Christian* Inhabitants of this Province; having nothing more in view than to satisfie my Readers with the best Account I could learn (during my Residence there) I shall proceed to give a short Account of

the

the *Negroes* or *Blacks,* together with a Description of the *Indians,* and the Laws and Customs now in force and use amongst them.

The *NEGROES* are sold on the Coast of *Guinea,* to Merchants trading to those Parts, are brought from thence to *Carolina, Virginia,* and other Provinces in the hands of the *English,* are daily increasing in this Country, and generally afford a good Price, *viz.* more or less according to their Goodness and Age, and are always sure Commodities for Gold or Silver, most other things being purchased with their Paper Money. Some of them are sold at *sixteen, twenty five,* or *twenty six* Pounds *sterl.* each, and are looked upon as the greatest Riches in these Parts. There are great Numbers of them born here, which prove more industrious, honest, and better Slaves than any brought from *Guinea;* this is particularly owing to their Education amongst the *Christians,* which very much polishes and refines them from their barbarous and stubborn Natures that they are most commonly endued with. I have frequently seen them whipt to that degree, that large pieces of their Skin have been hanging down their Backs; yet I never observed one of them shed a Tear, which plainly shews them to be a People of very harsh and stubborn Dispositions.

There are several Laws made against them in this Province to keep them in Subjection, and particularly one, *viz,* That if a *Negroe* cut or wound his Master or a Christian with any unlawful Weapon, such as a *Sword, Scymiter,* or even a *Knife,* and there is Blood-shed, if it is known amongst the Planters, they immediately meet and order him to be hanged, which is always performed by another *Negroe,* and generally the Planters bring most of their *Negroes* with them

to

to behold their fellow *Negroe* suffer, to deter them from the like vile Practice. This Law may seem to be too harsh amongst us, to put a Man to death for Blood-shed only, yet if the severest Laws were not strictly put in execution against these People, they would soon overcome the *Christians* in this and most of the other Provinces in the Hands of the *English*.

Notwithstanding the many severe Laws in force against them, yet they sometimes rise and Rebel against their Masters and Planters, and do a great deal of mischief, being both treacherous and cruel in their Natures, so that mild Laws would be of no use against them when any favourable Opportunity offered of executing their barbarities upon the *Christians,* as hath been too well experienced in *Virginia,* and other Places, where they have rebelled and destroyed many Families.

When they have been guilty of these barbarous and disobedient Proceedings, they generally fly to the Woods, but as soon as the *Indians* have Notice from the *Christians* of their being there, they disperse them; killing some, others flying for Mercy to the *Christians* (whom they have injured) rather than fall into the others Hands, who have a natural aversion to the *Blacks,* and put them to death with the most exquisite Tortures they can invent, whenever they catch them.

When any of these *Negroes* are put to death by the Laws of the Country, the Planters suffer little or nothing by it, for the Province is obliged to pay the full value they judge them worth to the Owner; this is the common Custom or Law in this Province, to prevent the Planters being ruined by the loss of their Slaves, whom they have purchased at so dear a rate; neither is this too burthensom, for I never knew but one put to death here for wounding, and after attempting to kill his Master, who used all Means he could to save his Life, but to no purpose, for the Country insisted on having the Law put in execution against him.

The *Negroes* that most commonly rebel, are those brought from *Guinea*, who have been inured to War and Hardship all their lives; few born here, or in the other Provinces have been guilty of these vile Practices, except over-persuaded by the former, whose Designs they have sometimes discovered to the *Christians;* some of whom have been rewarded with their Freedom for their good Services; but the Reader must observe, that they are not allowed to be Witnesses in any Cases whatever, only against one another.

There are some *Christians* so charitable as to have the *Negroes* born in the Country, baptized and instructed in the *Christian Faith* in their Infancy, which gives them an ab-horance of the Temper and Practice of those who are brought from *Guinea*. This Freedom does not in the least exempt them from their Master's Servitude, whatever others may imagine to the contrary, who believe them to be at their own Liberty as soon as they have received Baptism. The Plan-ters call these *Negroes* thus Baptized, by any whimsical Name their Fancy suggests, as *Jupiter, Mars, Venus, Diana, Strawberry, Violet, Drunkard, Readdy Money, Piper, Fid-ler, &c.*

Their *Marriages* are generally performed amongst them-selves, there being very little ceremony used upon that Head; for the Man makes the Woman a Present, such as a *Brass Ring* or some other Toy, which if she accepts of, becomes his Wife; but if ever they part from each other, which fre-quently happens, upon any little Disgust, she returns his Present: These kind of Contracts no longer binding them, than the Woman keeps the Pledge given her. It frequently

happens,

happens, when these Women have no Children by the first Husband, after being a Year or two cohabiting together, the Planters oblige them to take a second, third, fourth, fifth, or more Husbands or Bedfellows; a fruitful Woman amongst them being very much valued by the Planters, and a numerous Issue esteemed the greatest Riches in this Country. The Children all go with the Mother, and are the Property of the Planter to whom she belongs. And though they have no other Ceremony in their *Marriages* than what I have represented, yet they seem to be Jealously inclined, and fight most desperately amongst themselves when they Rival each other, which they commonly do.

Their Children are carefully brought up, and provided for by the Planters, 'till they are able to work in the Plantations, where they have convenient Houses built for them, and they are allowed to plant a sufficient quantity of *Tobacco* for their own use, a part of which they sell, and likewise on *Sundays,* they gather *Snake-Root,* otherwise it would be excessive dear if the *Christians* were to gather it; with this and the *Tobacco* they buy Hats, and other Necessaries for themselves, as *Linnen, Bracelets, Ribbons,* and several other Toys for their Wives and Mistresses.

There are abundance of them given to Theft, and frequently steal from each other, and sometimes from the *Christians,* especially *Rum,* with which they entertain their Wives and Mistresses at Night, but are often detected and punished for it.

There are several *Blacks* born here that can Read and Write, others that are bred to Trades, and prove good Artists in many of them. Others are bred to no Trades, but are very industrious and laborious in improving their Plantations, planting abundance of *Corn, Rice* and *Tobacco,* and

making

making vast Quantities of *Turpentine, Tar,* and *Pitch,* being better able to undergo fatigues in the extremity of the hot Weather than any *Europeans.*

The *Children* of both Sexes wear little or no Cloaths, except in the *Winter,* and many of the young Men and Women work stark naked in the Plantations in the hot Season, except a piece of Cloath (out of decency) to cover their Nakedness; upon which Account they are not very expensive to the Planters for their Cloathing. The Planters at their Death used to make some of their favourite *Negroes* free, but there is now an established Law (especially in *Virginia*) that if they do not quit the Province in about Eleven Days after their Freedom, whoever takes them they become his Property; but before the expiration of that time they either go to another Province, or sell themselves to the *Christians.* The Planters seeing the Inconveniencies that might attend these kind of Priviledges to the *Negroes,* have this and all other Laws against them continually put in practice, to prevent all Opportunities they might lay hold of to make themselves formidable.

**AN**

## AN ACCOUNT OF THE

# INDIANS

## OF NORTH CAROLINA.

THE *Indians,* it's well known were the Natives and Inhabitants of *America* before the *Spaniards* and *Europeans* made any discoveries of several parts of that Country. Amongst whom are several different Nations and Kings to this Day. What is very surprizing and strange is, that scarce any two Nations to be met with, spake the same Language, though they live ever so near to each other, this being a common thing all over this new World, as far as ever I cou'd be Informed. What shou'd occasion such a Diversity of Languages or Speeches amongst the *Savages,* is what most writers can hardly account for. But to return, the *Indians* of *North-Carolina,* are a well shaped clean made People, of

different

different Statures as the *Europeans* are, but chiefly inclined to be tall, are very streight and neat limb'd as are to be met with in any part of the World, they never bend forwards or stoop in the Shoulders, except they are much over powered with old Age, as for their Legs and Feet they are as well proportioned and as handsome, as any in the World. They are of a strong hale Constitution, and their Bodies very streight, but a little flat, which is occasioned by their being laced or tyed hard down upon a board in their Infancy, this being all their *Cradle,* which I shall describe in another place.

Their Eyes are full and Manly, and of a black or dark Hazel colour, the White marbled with Red Strakes, which is always common amongst these People, unless they have either a white Father or Mother.

Their Colour is Tawny, which wou'd not be so dark did they not daub themselves so often with *Bear's-Oil,* and a Colour like *Burnt-Cork,* which they practice from their Infancy, and continue so to do most part of their lives, it fills up the pores, and enables them the better to endure the Weather, and prevents most sorts of Insects and Vermin to be any wise troublesome to them. They are never to be met with Heads bald, though very Old, which I am perswaded is occasioned by their Heads being always uncovered, and greasing their Hair and other Parts so often as the do with *Bear's-fat,* which undoubtedly is a great nourisher of the Hair, and causeth it to grow so very fast. Amongst the *Bear's Oil* (when they intend to be fine) they mix a certain red Powder that is produced from a kind of *Scarlet* Root that they get in the Hilly Country, near the foot of the great ridge of Mountains, and as it is reported by them, is no where else to be found. They have this *Scarlet Root* in great Esteem, and sell it at a great Price one to another, and the

Reason

Reason of it's being so very valuable is, because they not only go a great way for it, but are likewise in great Danger of the *Sinegars,* or *Iroquois,* who are mortal Enemies to all our civilized *Indians,* and are very often by them or others before their return from this Voyage, made their Captives or killed.

The *Tuskeruros* and other *Indians,* have frequently brought the Seeds of this Plant from the Mountains, but it would never grow in our Land, delighting no where but in the Hilly and Mountainous parts; with this and the *Bear's-grease* they anoint their Heads and Temples, which is esteemed as Ornamental as *Oil* and *sweet Powder,* or any other thing we can use to our Hair; besides it has the Virtues to kill *Lice,* and suffer none to abide in their Heads. For want of this Root, they sometimes use a Root called *Pecoon,* which is of a Crimson colour, but apt to die the Hair of an ugly Hue, they likewise make use of an Herb called *Wasebur,* and small Roots called *Chappacor,* and the Bark of a Tree called *Tango-mockonominge;* all these are Dyes for several sorts of Reds, which the *Indians* use to paint their Faces, Matts and Baskets with, but whether they would prove good in Cloath, is not yet known. This, I am certain of, that one of our civilized *Indians* brought me a handful of dryed Flowers and desired me to put them in a large Sausepan filled with Water, and boil them with a piece of Linnen Cloath, which made it have such a deep Purple Colour, that the same could not be discharged by any Method used, but the oftner it was washed, the more beautiful and lively it appeared; the *Indian* would by no means discover the plants the said Flower grew upon, but assured me, that he would procure any Person what quantity they pleased, if they would but satisfie him for his Trouble. They not only paint themselves *Red*, but with

many

many other Colours, such as *Black, Green, Blue,* and *White,* by which they represent all the Affairs in Life, such as *War, Peace, Feasts, Death,* and the like.

They generally let the Hair on their Heads grow very long, which is lank, thick, and the strongest of any People I have ever met with, and as black as Jet. They always travel bare-headed, having neither Hats, or any artificial Covering for those Parts, except it be their civilized Kings and War Captains, who of late wear Hats, especially when they visit the *Christians.* Those who have represented the *Savages* as rough as Beasts, have never had the Opportunity of seeing them, for they have naturally but little or no Beards, or Hairs on their Faces, and very seldome under their Arm-pits, which 'tis said they continually pluck out by the Root as it begins to grow. Neither have they any upon their Privities, except some few that wear Brieeches or Tail-clouts, however, though these People are generally smooth and free from Hair, yet I have known some that were old, hairy down their Backs, and those Hairs very long: It is to be observed, that the Head of the *Penis* is covered through-out the whole Nations of the *Indians* that I ever saw; I am credibly informed, that this is common with all, both old and younng in *America.* They have extraordinary good Teeth, but generally of a yellowish Colour, occasioned by their smoaking *Tobacco,* which they are very much addicted to; this Plant they report to have had, many ages before the arrival of the *Christians* amongst them.

They never cut or pair their Nails, but let them grow very long, saying, that that is the use they were made for, and laugh at the *Europeans* for pairing theirs, long Nails being always esteemed amongst them as a Beauty, which the Dancers at their Feasts generally have, who rather represent

the

the figure of *Harpies* than Men, with these kind of Ornaments. They have long and taper Fingers as any People
whatsoever, and it is to be admired how dexterous and steady
they are in their Hands and Feet, for they will walk over
deep Brooks and Creeks on the smallest Poles, and that without any Fear or Concern, which no People in these Parts
can perform but themselves. I have seen an *Indian* walk on
the ridge of a House without any manner of fear, and look
from off the Gable, and spit down as unconcerned as if he
had been walking on *Terra Firma;* as for Running, Leaping,
or any such like Exercise, their Legs seldom fail or miscarry,
so as to give them a fall; as for letting any thing fall out of
their Hands, I never knew an Example. Their Gate is very
upright and majestick, neither are they ever seen to walk
backwards and forwards as we do, or contemplate on the
Affairs of Loss and Gain, and many other things which daily
perplex us. It is this steadiness in their Limbs (which are
as well proportioned and as handsom as any in the World)
that makes them so dexterous at the Gun, for it is remarkable
that these People generally shoot and kill their Game with
one single Ball, and the Boys with their Bows and Arrows
are so well experienced in that kind of Exercise, that they
will kill a Bird flying, or a Deer running, with as much certainty, as others with a Gun, of which I have been an Eye-
witness.

They have no manner of Musical Instruments, such as
*Pipe, Fiddle,* or any other Arts, Sciences, or Trades, worth
mentioning, amongst them, which may be owing to their
careless way of living, taking little or no Pains to provide
for the Necessaries of Life, as the *Europeans* do. They will
learn any thing very soon, and seem to be indued with very
good Genius's, for I have seen several Guns Stocked by

Nn                                          them,

them, better than most of our *Joyners,* having no Instrument
or Tool to work with only a short Knife: I have likewise
known several of them that were taken Prisoners in the last
War, and made Slaves to the *English,* learn handycraft
Trades well and speedily.

I never saw a Dwarf amongst them, and only one that was
Hump-back'd. Though the *Indians* are a tall People, yet
they are not of so robust and strong Bodies as to lift great
Burthens, to endure hard Labour, or slavish Work, as the
*Europeans* do, yet some that are Slaves prove very industrious and laborious. Amongst themselves they never work,
taking little or no care or pains, but what is absolutely necessary to support Life, the Grandure and Riches of this
World being utterly despised by them.

The *Indians* in *North Carolina* that live near the Planters,
are but few (as I observed before) not exceeding *Fifteen* or
*Sixteen* hundred Men, Women and Children, and those in
good harmony with the *English,* with whom they constantly
trade; yet near the Mountains they are very numerous and
powerful, but have little or no fire Arms amongst them, so
that the three following Kings are not so much in dread or
fear of those near the Mountains as they formerly were,
since they have furnished themselves with Fire-Arms from
the *Europeans,* because they can kill at greater distances with
their Guns, than the other can with their Bows and Arrows.

They have three *Paricossy's,* or *Indian Kings* in this Province, who are civilized, *viz.* King *Blunt,* King *Durant,* and
King *Highter;* but they may rather be compared to Heads
of Clans than Kings, according to their Appearances. I
have frequently seen and conversed with these three Kings,
whose Dresses were as follows:

King

King *Blunt* appeared before the Governour to pay his Tribute, which he, as well as the rest, generally do once or twice every Year; and this Tribute is a quantity of *Deer-Skins,* dressed after the *Indian* manner.

Complements being passed between him and the Governour (which I shall describe in another place) they were desired to sit down and dine with his Excellency, which all of them generally do, whenever they come to Town, where the Governour is: Several Discourses past between them, and amongst other things, that they were afraid of the *Sinagars,* or *Irequois Indians* (who are not in subjection to the *English*) coming to invade them, and desiring the Assistance of the Governour, if there should be any Occasion, which he assured them of. Dinner being ended, the Glass went round very merrily, and whenever they drank to the Governour, they always stiled him by the Name of *Brother.* These three Kings speak *English* tolerably well, and are very wary and cunning in their Discourses, and you would be surprised to hear what subtile and witty Answers they made to each Question proposed to them, notwithstanding they are in general Illiterate People, having no Letters or Learning to improve them.

King *Blunt* being the most powerful of these I have mentioned, had a Suit of *English* Broadcloth on, and a pair of Women's Stockings, of a blue Colour, with white Clocks, a tolerable good Shirt, Cravat, Shoes, Hat, &c.

King *Durant* had on an old Blue Livery, the Wastecoat having some remains of Silver Lace, with all other Necessaries fit for wearing Apparel such as Shirt, Stockings, Shoes, &c. made after the *English* manner.

King *Highter* had on a Soldiers red Coat, Wastecoat, and Breeches, with all other conveniences for wearing Apparel,

like

like the former: And it is to be observed, that after their
return home to their Towns, that they never wear these
Cloaths till they make the next State Visit amongst the
*Christians.*

After this manner appeared the three civilized Kings,
with each of them his *Queen, Children, Physician, Captains
of War,* and his *Guards.* After Dinner was over, the Governour ordered *Rum* for the Queens, and the rest of the Retinue, who remained at some distance from the Governours
House during the time the Kings were in Company with
him. In a few Hours after they all withdrew from the
Governours House, and went into Town to dispose of their
*Deer-Skins* that were remaining, for *Blankets, Guns, Powder, Shot, Ball,* and other Necessaries they had occasion for,
and especially *Rum,* whereof they are very fond.

What is worthy of Observation amongst the whole Retinue, is this, That you shall not see two but what have some
Mark to distinguish them from each other; sometimes very
long black Hair, with several bits of Stuff, such as *Green,
Blue, Red, White,* and *Yellow,* tied in it; others with their
Hair cut close, only a Circle left on the Head, the Hair
whereof is about half an Inch longer than the rest. Others
with several Marks in different parts of their Bodies and
Faces, as if they had been marked with *Gun-Powder,* so that
if you see an hundred of them, you shall always observe some
difference in each of them, either in their Painting, Tonsure
of their Hair, or the marks made in their Skins. All these
Guards were well Armed, with each Man a Gun, good store
of Powder and Ball, and a *Tamahawk* by his side, which is
a kind of small *Hatchet.* It is likewise to be observed, that
scarce any of the whole Retinue, except the *War Captains,*
had any Cloathing, only *Tail-Clouts* (for decency) to cover

their

their Nakedness, and some few with a *Blanket,* or some such like piece of Cloth about their Shoulders.

As soon as they have sold their *Deer-Skins* for those Necessaries they had occasion for, and had drank what quantity of *Rum* they were allowed, or thought fit to make use of, they came out into the Street, to act the *Indian War,* which to any one bred in *Europe,* seemed rather like a Scene of Madness, than a Warlike Exercise, for one while they were Hooping and Hollowing, another while stamping altogether like Madmen, another time creeping, as if they were surprizing their Enemies, and many other antick Postures and Gestures, too tedious to name. Though these Kings may seem despicable and meane to us, yet are they most absolute, putting to death those they judge worthy of it; therefore it may not be amiss to give some Instances, because they seem cruel and barbarous, if compared with our Laws for punishing Offenders, as may appear by the following Account, *viz.*

An *Indian* came to a Planters House in this Province, and finding no body at home but a Servant Maid, he attempted to lie with her, but she not complying with his Desires, he was so provoked, that to be revenged, he shot the Planters Dog as he was going away. The Planter complained to the Governour of the injury the *Indian* had done him, in order to have him punished for the offence. A Messenger is immediately dispatched to their King to demand Satisfaction for the trespass the *Indian* had been guilty of. The Messenger coming late that Evening to the *Indian-town* the King courteously received him and prevailed upon him to stay all Night, and that the next Day when the Sun was up, at such a height (as he expressed it) he would deliver him the Offender. Accordingly he remained there all

Night,

Night, in hopes to have the *Indian* brought before the Governour, in order to be punished according to the *English* Law; but at the time appointed, the King desired the Messenger to walk with him into the Plantation, where to his great astonishment, he found the *Indian* dead, and hanging upon a Tree. The Messenger complained to the King, of the rashness and cruelty of this Proceeding, adding, that he did not deserve Death, and that he was sorry he had been the Messenger, or occasion to have a Person put to death, for so small a Crime, which only deserved Whipping, or some such kind of Punishment; that he only came in order to have him brought before the Governour, to have him punished. But the King replied, That he might then take him where he pleased, but he had put it out of his power ever afterwards to be guilty of doing any roguish Tricks. But to return: Their Queens, Sons, and Daughters, are never permitted to dine at the Governour's Table with the Kings, but remain with their Children and Guards at some distance from the House.

The first of these Queens was drest with a Peticoat made after the *European* manner, and had her Hair, which is generally long, thick, and Black, tyed full of bits of Stuff, such as Red, Green, Yellow, and variety of other Colours, so that to an *European* she rather seemed like a Woman out of *Bedlam,* than a Queen. She likewise had a large Belt about her full of their *Peack,* or *wampum,* which is their Money, and what they value above *Gold* or *Silver,* but to me it seem'd no better than our common *Snails,* or other ordinary Shells; the other parts of the Body from the Waste upwards were all naked. The other two Queens were drest much after the same manner, but none like the first, having not such rich Belts of Money about their Bodies, which to us in *Europe* woud not be worth one Farthing.

The

The *Indian Women,* as well as the Men, are swarthy, but their features are very agreeable and fine as any People you shall meet with, and few have better and sharper Eyes than they have. Neither did I ever see but one Blind Man amongst them, and they never would give me any account how he became blind, though I importun'd them to know the reason. This blind Man was led about with a Boy or Girl by a string, so they put what burthens they pleas'd on his Back, and made him serviceable after that manner upon several Occasions.

The firing they chiefly burn is *Pich-Pine,* that does not only strengthen the Eyes, but preserves them, which I do not doubt but it does, because the Smoak never offends the Eyes though you should hold your Face over a great Fire thereof, which is occasioned by the Volatile parts of the *Turpentine,* which rises with the Smoak, being of so friendly and Balsamick nature to them, that they are much relieved thereby, for the Ashes of the *Pine-tree* afford little or no fixt Salt.

The *Indians* in general are great Smoakers of *Tobacco* (in their Language *Uppowoc*) which they tell us they had before the *Europeans* made any discoveries of that Country. It differs in Leaf from the *sweet scented* and *Oroonoko,* which are the plants we raise and cultivate in *America.* Theirs likewise differs very much in the smell when it is Green from our *Tobacco* before it is cured, neither do they use the same method in curing it as we do, therefore the difference must be very considerable in taste and smell, for all Men (that know *Tobacco*) must allow, that it is the ordering thereof that gives a hogo to the Weed, rather than any natural relish it possesses when Green. They make the heads of their Pipes very large, which are generally cut out of Stones, the Shanks whereof are made of hollow Cane, and although they are great Smoakers, yet they are

never

never known to chew, or make it into *Snuff,* but will very freely take a pinch of Snuff out of an *European's* Box.

The *Indians* are Strangers to such delicacies as are in vogue amongst yet they have plenty of several kinds of Food, as *Buffeloes, Venison,* and *Fawns* in the Bags of the Does Bellys, *Bears, Beavers, Panthers, Pole-Cats, Wild-Cats, Raccoons, Possums, Hares, Squirrels,* roasted with their Guts in, wild *Bull's Beef, Mutton,* and *Pork,* which two latter they have from the *Christians.* The Deer, which is so highly esteemed in European Countries, for the delicacie of It's Flesh, is little valued amongst these Savages, only for the plunder of his Skin. All manner of wild Fowl that are eatable, *viz. Swans, Geese, Brants, Ducks, Turkeys, Pigeons,* and several other sorts of Fowl that are to be met with in *Carolina.*

*Fishes* of all sorts, both in the fresh and salt Waters, and all manner of shell-fish, as *Tortoises, Terebins, Oysters, Clams,* and the *Sting-ray,* or *Scate,* dryed and most other sort of Fishes that are known in these parts, except the *Conger, Lamprey-Eel,* and *Sturgeon,* our civiliz'd *Indians* that live near the Salt-Water will not touch, though those up the Freshes eat them. And as for *Snakes,* they scarce either kill or eat them, yet some of the *Savages* near the Mountains are said to do both. All manner of Wild Fruits that are palatable, some of which they dry and keep against the *Winter,* such as *Huckle Berries,* and several other sorts of *Berries, Wall-nuts, Chesnuts, Hazel-Nuts, Chinkapins, Acorns,* and many other Fruits, as *Peaches* which they dry and make *Quidonies* and *Cakes* of, that are very pleasant, grateful, and cooling, but a little Tartish.

*Rockahomine-Meal,* which is made of their *Maze,* or *Indian-Corn* parched or pounded, and made into several

sorts

sorts of Bread, Ears of *Corn* roasted in the *Summer,* and preserved against *Winter.* *Ground-Nuts,* or *Wild Potatoes, Oil of Acorns* and Wild *Pigeons,* which they make use of as we do *Butter,* and several other things that are to be met with in great plenty amongst them. They eat young *Wasps* when they are white in the Combs, before they can fly, which is esteemed a very great dainty amongst them, as likewise *Gourds, Mellons, Cucumbers, Squashes, Semblens,* and *Pulse* of all sorts. Tho' their Grounds be very fertile and able to produce much more than they do; yet they are contented to live upon a little, and what small quantity of *Indian-Corn* they have is brought forth by the Industry of their Wives, who instead of *Ploughs* (of which they have none, nor Creatures fit for tillage) cultivate and dig the Ground with *Wooden Spades* and *Hoes* made after their own Fashion, the Men's minds being wholly taken up in Hunting, especially till they are about 50 Years of Age.

The *Victuals* are common throughout the whole kindred and relations, and often to the whole Town, and especially when they are in their Hunting Quarters, then they all fare alike, there being little or no distinction observed amongst them in their eating. It is very strange to see in all the Places where they have been formerly settled, or had their Towns near the Salt Waters, what vast quantities of *Oyster-shells* are to be met with on the Banks of the Rivers, in such heaps, that it is surprizing to behold them: One might reasonably imagine (by such great quantities as are there) that they scarce lived upon any thing else, or that they must have been settled many hundred Years in one Place, which is not common amongst them, being a People always shifting from one place to another, as their Fancies lead them.

19                          Oo                          These

These *Savages* live in *Wigwams,* or *Cabins,* built with Poles and the Bark of Trees; their Houses are made oval, or round like an *Oven,* to prevent any Damage by hard gales of Wind, which are common in this Country. They make the Fire in the middle of the House, and have a Hole at the top of the Roof, right above the Fire, to let out the Smoak. These Dwellings are as hot as Stoves, where they sweat and sleep all Night; the Floors are never paved or swept, so that the Earth is always loose, much resembling the poor Cabbins that are to be met with in several parts of *Ireland,* only the *Indians* having such plenty of Wood, make no earthen Walls to theirs. The Bark they generally make their Cabbins with is *Cypress,* or *red* or *white Cedar;* sometimes when they are a great way distant from any of the Woods, they make use of the *Pine Bark,* which is the worst sort to cover their Houses with. In building these Houses they get long Poles of *Pine, Cedar, Ash, Hickery,* or any Wood that will bend; these Poles are generally about the thickness of a Man's Leg at the thickest end, stript of the Bark, and well warmed in the Fire, which makes them tough and pliable. Then they make sharp points on the thickest ends, and stick them fast in the Ground, about two yards asunder, in a circular Form, the distance they design the Cabin, then they bend the tops and bring them together, after which they bind their Ends with Bark of Trees, that is proper for that use, such as *Elm,* or the long black Moss that grows on Trees, which seldom rots; then they brace them with other Poles to make them strong and firm; lastly, they cover them all over with Barks of Trees (except a hole to let out the Smoak) that they are warm and tight, and will keep firm against Wind and Weather. These are all the kind of Dwellings that are to be met with throughout all

the

the Nations of the *Indians,* in these parts of *America,* except the civilized Kings, who of late have Houses fashioned and built after the manner that the *Christians* build theirs.

These Dwelling-Houses have Benches all round, except where the Door stands, whereon they lay Beasts Skins and Mats made of *Rushes,* on which they sleep and loll, having no other Beds but these. In one of these Houses several Families commonly live together, all related to one another, for these *Savages* do not seem so very careful of their Females as the *Europeans,* having no Bars or Partitions to keep the Men at a distance from the Women. They have other sorts of Cabins made without Windows or Holes at the top, which are their Granaries, where they keep their Corn and Fruit for *Winter,* or Store-Houses for their *Deer* or *Bever* Skins, and all other kind of Merchandize that they deal in. They have Cabbins of another kind made like a Shead, being only covered over head, the rest left open to the Air; these have Reed Hurdles like Tables to lie and sit on in *Summer,* and serve for pleasant Banqueting Houses in the extremity of the hot Weather.

As for *Liquors* they have little or none made amongst them, neither were they acquainted with any kind of intoxicating Liquors before the arrival of the *Christians;* contenting themselves with the pure Element, but they are now become very great Drinkers of *Rum,* and will part with any thing they have to purchase it; when they are a little mellow, they are the most impatient Creatures living, 'till they have enough to make them quite drunk, and then they are often the most miserable Spectacles in Nature, frequently tumbling into the Fire, and burning their Arms and Legs to that degree, that the Sinews are contracted, and they become Cripples all their Lives after; besides several other misfor-

tunes

tunes which attend them during their Drunkenness, as breaking their Bones and Joints, with many other melancholly Accidents, yet none sufficient to deter them from this Practice. *Drunkenness* is a Vice so common amongst them (if they can obtain strong Liquors) that they drop down and lie quite naked, in such brutish Postures as are not fit to be named. These base Dispositions are principally owing to the meanness of their Education, being strangers to all Arts and Sciences, and the Knowledge of other Countries, which renders them insensible of that Virtue and Decency which other Nations value at so high a Rate.

The chief and only Liquor they admire is *Rum,* which they generally drink without any mixture; this the *Europeans* bring in amongst them, and buy *Deer-Skins, Furrs,* and other Commodities with; they will freely sell or part with any thing they have in the World (except their Wives and Children) rather than not accomplish their Designs. They sometimes commit such brutalities and enormous Vices, as are not fit to be mentioned; yet there are some few amongst them that will not drink any strong Liquors.

In the Year 1708, the Governour summoned all the *Indian* Kings and Rulers in *North-Carolina* to meet, in order to make a firm and lasting Peace between the *Christians* and *Indians*: At which publick Meeting, the *Indian* Kings and Rulers desired, that in the conclusion of this Peace, it might be enacted that no *Rum* shou'd be Sold to them, which was accordingly granted, and a Law made by the *English,* which inflicted a penalty on any white Men that sold *Rum* to the *Indians*. But this Law was never strictly observed or put in force, because the young *Indians* were so disgusted at that Article, that they threatn'd to kill the *Indians* that had a Hand in making it, unless it were speedily laid aside, and

that

that they might have *Rum* sold them as usual when they went to the *Christians* Houses to buy it.

They likewise often times in their Drunken frolicks cut off their Hair and sell it to the *Christians,* which is looked upon amongst them as the greatest disgrace imaginable; and the only affront that can be offered them is to desire them to sell their Hair, when they are sober and free from Liquors.

The *Indians* are very revengful, notwithstanding they always conceal their resentments, but never forget an injury done, till they have received Satisfaction; yet they are the freest People from Heats and passions (which so frequently possess the *Europeans*) of any People I have ever seen or heard of. They never call any one to an Account for what they do when they are Drunk, but say it was the Drink that caused his misbehaviour, therefore he ought to be forgiven: Neither will they frequent any *Christians* House that is given to Passion, nor will ever buy or sell with him, if they can get the same commodities they have occasion for from any other Person; for they say such kind of People are mad *Wolves* and no Men. They seldom or never fight with one another, unless when they are Drunk, nor shall you ever hear any Scolding amongst them. For they say the *Europeans* are always rangling and uneasy with each other, and wonder they do not go out of this World, since they are so uneasy and discontented in it. Neither do they shew the least sign of being dejected or cast down at the greatest calamities that can attend them, except it be the loss of Friends. For it is remarkable, that all other losses and misfortunes end in Laughter, for if their Cabbins should take Fire, and all their Goods be burnt therein (notwithstanding all will strive to save what they can whilst there is any possibility, and prevent any farther damage) yet such a misfortune

tune generally ends in a hearty fit of Laughter. But if any of their kinsfolks have lost their Lives in the Flames, it is then the Case is altered, and they become very pensive and mourn for a considerable time, which always bears Proportion to the dignity of the Person deceased, and the number of Relations he had near him, who make a horrid howling during that time.

The *Indian* Women are never known to scold, and it is a thing impossible to hear them make use of that unruly Member the Tongue, with such Rage and Malice as our *European* Dames are subject to, whom I could wish would set these *Indians* for a Pattern, by which means there would be more Quietness and better Harmony in most Families, than at present is to be met with. For when these *Indian* Women are provoked or affronted by their Husbands, or any other Persons, they resent the Indignity offered them in Silence, Tears, or by refusing their Meat; these being always certain Signs that they have been injured and Affronted.

Neither are the Men Passionate, or over hasty to act any Affair with too much haste or impetuosity, never determining any Business of Moment without the greatest Deliberation and Wariness imaginable, being more content with common Accidents and Misfortunes incident to human Nature (such as Losses, contrary Winds, bad Weather, Poverty and the like) than People of more civilized Nations. I never felt any ill or unsavoury smell in their Cabins, whereas should we live in our Houses as they do, we should be poisoned with our own Nastiness; which confirms these *Indians* to be, as they certainly are, some of the sweetest People in the World.

Their Women when they are young, and at Maturity, are fine shaped Creatures (take them in general) as any in the Universe; and though they are of a tawny Complexion

(which

(which is very much occasioned by their being so much exposed to the Weather, and their continual daubing and painting themselves with *Bear's Oil,* and other Ingredients mixed
with it) yet their Features are very good, their Eyes Black
and Amorous, and their Smiles afford the finest composure
a Face can possess.

Their Hands are of the finest make, with small long taper
Fingers, and as soft as their Cheeks, the whole Body being
of a smooth Nature, with Limbs of the most exquisite shape.
They are Mercenary, except the Married Women, who sometimes bestow their Favours on whom they like best, in their
Husbands absence, for which they never take any Reward:
As for the report that some might have heard of them, that
they are never found inconstant like the *European* Women,
it is intirely false; for were the old World and the New, put
into a pair of Scales (in point of Constancy and Chastity) it
would be a hard matter to descern which was the heavier.
As for the *Trading Girls,* which are those designed to get
Money by Prostitution, these are easily known, by a particular Tonsure, or cut of their Hair, differing from all others
of that Nation, who are not of their Profession; which
Method is to prevent Mistakes, for these *Savages* are desirous (if possible) to keep their Wives to themselves, as well
as those in other Parts of the World.

When any Addresses are made to one of these Girls, she
immediately acquaints her Parents therewith, and they tell
the King of it (provided he that courts her for a Bedfellow
be a stranger) his Majesty being most commonly principle
Baud of the Nation he rules over, there being seldom any
of these Love-bargains made or concluded without his Royal
Assent.  He likewise advises her what Bargain to make with
her Gallant, who shews some Toys he has to present her
with:  But if it happens to be an *Indian* Trader, that wants

one

one of them for a Bedfellow, and has got *Rum* to sell, he always fees the King with a large Dram, to confirm the Match.

When any such Question is proposed to these *Savages,* they will debate the Matter amongst themselves with all the sobriety and seriousness imaginable, every one of the Girls Relations arguing the Advantage or Disadvantage that may ensue from such a Nights Encounter, all which is done with as much steadiness and reality, as if it were the greatest Concern in the World, not so much as one Person shall be seen to smile so long as the Debate lasts, making no manner of difference betwixt an Agreement of this Nature, and any other Bargain. If they comply with the Men's desire, then a particular Bed is provided for them either in a *Cabin* by themselves, or else all the young People turn out to another Lodging, that they might not spoil sport betwixt these Lovers, and if the old People are in the same *Cabin* along with them all Night, they lye as unconcern'd as if they were so many Statues or logs of Wood, in nowise offering to disturb them, and that the Man may have the Satisfaction of his new purchase, which pleasure is sometimes bought at too dear a rate. If it be an *Indian* of their own Town or Neighbourhood that wants a Mistress, he comes to none but the Girl who receives what presents she thinks fit to ask, and so lyes with him all Night without the knowledge or previous consent of her Parents or Relations. This familiarity so kindles lust, that the young Men will likewise go in the Night time from one House to another to visit the young Women, after which rambling manner they frequently spend the whole Night. In their adresses they find no delays, for if she is willing to entertain the Man, she gives him encouragement, and grants him admittance, otherwise she withdraws her Face

from

from him and says, *I cannot see you, either you or I must leave this* Cabin *and sleep some where else this Night.* This repulse makes him immediately withdraw, and address himself to some more kind Mistress, that will accept of his favours. Neither doth it displease the Parents, that their Daughters are thus acquainted, knowing by these Means that they can command the young Men to help them in any Work or Business they have occasion to use them in.

They set apart the youngest and prittiest Faces for trading Girls, who are remarkably known by a particular Tonsure in their Hair (as I said before) which distinguishes them from those engaged to Husbands; for what is accounted amongst us as most Criminal, are taken for slender Trespasses amongst them; for if a young Man can get a Favour of his Neighbour's Daughter, it is looked upon as a slight Offence, because they are not permitted to Marry without the King's Approbation, which is seldom before they are twenty Years of age.

These Girls are generally very Mercenary, and whoever make use of them, engages them with some gratuity or other, the principal part whereof is for the King's use, exercising his prerogative over all the Stews of his Nation, his own Cabbin being very often the chief Brothel House. As they grow in Years, the hot assaults of Love grow cooler, and then they become more staid and constant to their Husbands. if engaged; many of them after their Engagement or Marriage, are so reserved, that they will admit of no other to their Embraces but their Husbands.

These trading Girls, after they have led that course of Life several Years, in which time they scarce ever have a Child, for it is supposed that they have some particular Secret, or

Pp

Method

Method (with Herbs) by which they prevent Conception, 'till they are married, and then never fail to be fruitful. But if it should happen, that she brings forth a Child whilst she follows this lewd course of Life, she is not only accounted a Fool, but her Reputation is very much lessened thereby, at last they grow weary of the Address of so many Men, and betake themselves to a married State, or to the Company of one Man; neither does their having been common to so many, occasion any Blemish in their Reputation, or hinderance to a Husband, but rather a Promotion; for they say, *That a Woman living otherwise, is not worth a Man's acceptance, and never makes a good Wife.*

The Men are never to boast of Intrigues with the Women, if they do, none of the Girls will admit of their Company to their Beds, or have any regard for them afterwards. This is not out of any tender Regard they have for their Reputations, for there is no such thing (on that Account) known amongst them; although we may reckon them the greatest Libertines in the pursuit of their Pleasures, and most extravagant in their Embraces, yet they retain and possess a modesty that requires those Passions never to be revailed, or made known to the World.

The Woman is not punished for Adultery (this and Fornication being not so much as looked upon as a Sin amongst them) but the Gallant is obliged to make the injured Husband Satisfaction, which is the Law of Nations, and practiced amongst all the *Indians;* the Gallant that strives to evade such Satisfaction as the Husband demands, lives daily in danger of his Life: But when those Reparations are made him, that he is satisfied, with all Animosities cease, and he is laughed at by the whole Nation, for carrying on

his

his Intrigue with no better Conduct, than to be discovered, and pay so dear for his Pleasure.

The *Indians* say, that a Woman is a weak Creature, and easily drawn away by the Man's persuasion; for which reason they seldom or never lay any blame on the Woman, but the Man (that ought to be Master of his Passions) for persuading her to it.

They are of very hale sound Constitutions, and their Breath as sweet as the Air they breath in: The Women are of so tender a Composition, that they seem rather designed for the Bed than Bondage; yet their Love is never of that extensive force or continuance, that any of them run mad or make away with themselves on that score. They never love beyond retrieving their first indifferency, and when slighted, are as ready to untie the Knot at one end, as you are at the other.

I knew an *European Man* that lived many Years amongst the *Indians,* and had a Child by one of their Women, having bought her as they do their Wives, and afterwards married a *Christian.* Sometimes after he came to the *Indian* Town, not only to buy *Deer-Skins,* but likewise to pass away a Night with his former Mistress as usual, but she made answer, *That she then had forgot that she ever knew him, and that she never lay with another Woman's Husband;* so fell a crying, took up the Child she had by him, and went out of the Cabin in great Disorder, although he used all possible means to pacifie her, by offering her Presents of several *Toys* and *Rum,* but all to no purpose, for she would never see him afterwards, or be reconciled.

There are several *Europeans* and other Traders which travel and abide amongst them for a long space of Time, sometimes a Year, two or three, and those Men commonly have their *Indian* Wives or Mistresses, whereby they soon

learn

learn the *Indian* Tongue, and keep in good Friendship with
them, besides the satisfaction they have of a Bedfellow, they
find these Girls very serviceable to them upon several occasions; especially in dressing their Victuals, and instructing
them in the Affairs and Customs of the Country; moreover
they get a great Trade amongst them; but the Person that is
reserved, and doth not thus converse with their Women, it is
difficult for him to accomplish his Designs amongst the Natives.

One great misfortune that generally attend the *Christians*
that converse with these Women as Husbands, is, that they
get Children by them, which are seldom otherwise brought
up or educated than in the wretched state of *Infidelity;* for
it is a certain Rule and Custom amongst all the *Savages* in
*America* (as far as I could learn) to let all the Children fall
to the Woman's Lot; for it frequently happens, that two
*Indians,* that have lived together as Man and Wife for many
Years, in which time they have had several Children, if they
part, and another takes her to be his Wife, all the Children go
along with the Mother; and therefore on this Account it is a
difficult matter for the *Christians* ever to get the Children they
have had by these *Indian* Women away from them, to bring
them up in the Knowledge of the true God, and the Principles
of the *Christian Faith,* that they live in a miserable state of
Darkness and Infidelity all the Days of their lives. It is very
surprizing, that several *Christians* that are accustomed to the
Conversation of these Women and their way of living, have
been so infatuated and allured with that careless sort of life,
as to continue with their *Indian* Wife, and her Relations so
long as they lived, without ever desiring to return again
among the *Christians,* though they had several Opportunities,

ties, and considerable Advantages offered them. Of these lost and unfortunate sort of People (as I may properly term them) there are some living amongst the *Savage Indians* of *Carolina* to this Day, with whom I have frequently conversed, and exhorted them to return to the *Christians,* from the *Indians,* and their abominable Practices, and likewise reminding them of what our Saviour JESUS CHRIST said, *That where two or three are gathered together in his Name, he will grant their Request,* which they would not accept, but voluntary remained amongst them. I likewise urged many other Reasons and Texts of Scripture, but all to no purpose, neither could I have any satisfactory Answer from them for their obstinate and dangerous way of living.

The *Indians* being of several Nations, have as different Customs amongst them, and he that is the greatest Warrior, or the best Hunter, is sure to be the greatest favorite amongst the Women. The prettiest Girls are always bestowed upon the chief Men, and ugliest upon the lazy and useless Lubbers, as to the Ceremony of Marriage they have none amongst them, for the Girls at Twelve or Fourteen years of Age, or as soon as Nature prompts them, freely bestow their favours on some Youth about the same Age, and so continues them to whom she likes best, changing her Mate as often as she pleases; for few or none of them are constant to one, 'till the greater number of Years has made her capable of managing her Domestick Affairs; and that she hath try'd the vigour of most of the Nation she belongs to; for the multiplicity of Gallants beforehand are no objection or stain to a Females Reputation, or hindrance to her advancement, for the more she hath followed that course of Life, the more she is valued and respected, and coveted by those of the first Rank amongst

them

them to make a Wife of: So that a Virgin, so much esteemed and coveted by the *Europeans,* is in little value or request amongst them.

When a Man or Woman is arrived at a certain age of Maturity, and has passed the Ceremonies practiced by their Nation, and other Graduations and Qualifications amongst them, and are allowed to be Housekeepers, it is then he makes his Addresses to one or other of these for a Wife: When he has obtained her consent, the Parents of both Parties (with the consent of the King), agree about the matter, making a promise of their Daughter to the Man that requires her for a Wife; and it often happens that they converse and travel together several Moons before they are acknowledged as Man and Wife, or the Marriage published openly, these being Customs allowed amongst them in all parts. After this, the Man upon the least disgust or dislike may turn her away, and take another: But if she should disapprove of his Company, a Price is set upon her, and whoever takes her, is obliged to pay the Fine to the former Husband, then she becomes free from him, and is the latters Wife.

Sometimes their Captains of War and great Men keep three or four of these Girls for their own use, when at the same time they are so impotent and old as to be incapable to make use of one of them, but these will always have their Due, if there be either *European* or *Indian* that will accept of their Favours.

The Husband is never so displeas'd or enrag'd with the Adulteress, as to put her to Death, or even to inflict any grievous punishments on her, though she be caught in the very fact. But the rival becomes Debtor to the cornuted Husband in some few trifles of little value amongst the *Europeans* (yet much esteemed amongst them) which when paid,

all

all animosities cease, and are laid aside between the Husband and the Wife's gallant, otherwise they are a treacherous generation when thus injurd.

They will even sometimes let out their Wives for a Night or two for a gratuity, and sometimes to oblige their Neighbours or intimate Friends, especially their great Men, nor do they reckon their Wives Whores for lying with those that are as good or better then themselves, and sometimes to gratifie their Wives Inclinations. A custom much like this we read of amongst the *Britains,* which was a Society of Wives among certain Numbers, and by common consent. Every Man married a single Woman, who was always after, and alone, esteem'd his Wife. But it was usual for 5. 6. 10. 12. or more either Brothers or Friends as they coud agree to have all their Wives in common, so that encounters happen'd amongst them as they were invited by desire, or favoured by opportunity. Yet every Woman's Children was attributed to him that had Married her, but all had a share in the care and defence of the whole Society, since no Man knew which were his own. Such were the People and the customs of the *Britons* when the Romans invaded their Island under the Ensignes of *Julius Cæsar.*

But to return, when a young *Indian* has a mind for such a Girl for his Wife, he, or some one for him goes (as I before observed) to the young Woman's Father or Mother, if living, if not, to the nearest Relations, where he or they make offers of the Match betwixt them; the Relations reply, *they will consider of it:* This serves for a sufficient Answer, 'till there be a second meeting about it, where they seriously debate the Affair amongst themselves, the King being commonly present, and most of the great Men, who all give their Opinion about it, which if they agree upon, the Woman is imme-

diately

diately called to know how she approves of the Man (for as it is reported, they never give their Children in Marriage without their consent) for a Husband; if she approves and is satisfied, the Man pays so much for his Wife, and the handsomer she is, bears the greater price. It sometimes happens that the Man has not Effects enough to pay the Purchase for her; but if he be known to be a good Hunter, that he can raise and pay the Fine agreed upon in so many Moons, or such a limited Time as they propose, she is obliged to go along with him as betrothed, but he is not to have carnal Knowledge of her 'till all the Obligation or Payment is discharged. This is punctually observed, and then she is his Wife.

Thus they live together under one covering for several Months (till the obligation is fulfill'd) and the Woman remains the same as she was when she first came to him, as I have been inform'd by the *Indians* themselves. I am perswaded that there are but few of the *Europeans* but what wou'd break through these customs, if they had the same opportunities and Liberties allowed them. But the *Indians* are not so vigorous and impetient in the pursuit of Love, and gratifying their desires as the *Europeans* are, yet the Women are quite contrary; and those *Indian* Girls that have frequently conversed with the *Europeans,* never much care for the conversation of their own Country-men afterwards. They never marry so near as a first Cousin, yet they are allowed to marry two Sisters, or his Brothers Wife; and although there is nothing more coveted amongst them than to marry a Woman of their own tribe or Nation, which consists of very few People, so that they are all of them related to one another, yet they are obliged to look out for Husbands and Wives amongst strangers and People of another Nation. If an *Indian* should lie with his own Sister (and

that

that she proves with Child, or it is otherwise known) or any other near Relations, his Body is immediately Burnt, and the Ashes thereof thrown into the River, as unworthey to remain upon the Earth. Neither is Sodomy, that Beastly Action known amongst them, nor have they a Name for that abominable Sin in all their Languages.

These Marriages amongst them are no longer binding than the Man and Woman agree together, for either have liberty to leave each other upon any frivolous excuse. Both Men and Women commonly marry four or five times before they can settle to their Content; for when they thus marry, they do not intend to bind themselves for as long time as they shall live, but for as long only as they shall agree together and love each other: If they grow weary or discontented with each other, they may separate, which is equally allowed to both Parties. Thus they part without any clamour or noise, and perfectly indifferent to each other afterwards, and take no more Notice when they meet, than if they had never seen one another, and wonder that the *Europeans* do not follow the same course: But whoever takes the Woman that was another Man's before, and bought by him (as they all are) must certainly pay to her former Husband whatsoever he gave for her: But if he sends her away without any Cause, she keeps the Presents given her before Marriage: If she be a Widow, and her Husband died in Debt, whoever takes her to be his Wife, pays all her late Husband's Obligations, be they never so many; for the Woman is not required or obliged to pay any thing (unless she is willing so to do) that was owing from her Husband, so long as she lives single. But if a Man courts her for a Nights Lodging, and obtains it, if the Creditors have knowledge of it, they will make him

20 Qq pay

pay the Husband's Debts, then he may if he pleases, take her to be his Wife, or sell her to another for his own or a less Purchase.

There are several of these kind of Bargains made in a Day amongst them (the Women never living the worse for this kind of Traffick) for the Men will sell their Wives at their publick Meetings, as Men do *Horses* and other Cattle at a Fair or Market with us: A Man is not only allowed to change as often as he pleases, but likewise to have as many Wives as he is able to maintain, though they are seldom known to live with more than one at a time, except it be their great Men, such as *War-Captains, &c.* The Women have very easy travail with their Children; sometime they bring forth Twins, and are frequently brought to Bed by themselves, when taken at a disadvantage; not but that they have *Midwives* as well as *Doctors* amongst them, who make it their Profession (for Gain) to assist and deliver Women: Some of these *Midwives* are very knowing in several Medecins that the Country naturally produces, which most certainly expedite and make easy Births, besides they are unacquainted with those severe Pains that follow the Birth in *European* Women. Their Remedies are a great cause of this easiness in that state, for the Women will run up and down their Plantations the same Day they are delivered, without any sign of Pain or Sickness; yet they look very meager and thin, not but that we must allow a great deal to be owing to the Climate, and the natural Constitution of the Women, whose Courses of Nature never visit them in such quantities as the *European* Women have; although they always have plenty of Milk, I never saw an *Indian* Woman have large Breasts, which is common amongst the *Blacks* or *Negroe* Women, they having the largest and ugliest of any that are

to

to be met with; neither does the youngest Wife amongst the *Indians* ever fail of proving so good a Nurse, as to bring up her Child free from the *Rickets,* and disasters that proceed from the *Teeth,* with many other Distempers which are frequent amongst the Children in *Europe.*

They let their Children (amongst whom are many *Olive* Beauties) suck 'till they are well grown, unless they prove big with Child sooner than usual. They always nurse their own Children themselves, unless Sickness or Death prevents them. I only once saw a *Nurse* hired to give Suck to an *Indian* Woman's Child, the Mother happening to have a fit of sickness not long after her delivery; by which not only her Strength was much impaired, but likewise the Milk in her Breasts. As soon as the Child is born, they wash it in cold Water in the next Stream or River, then anoint or bedaub it all over with *Bear's Grease* and other Ingredients, as I have before observed; after their Delivery they wash themselves in the Waters, and absent themselves from the Company of Men for forty Days. The Husband takes care to provide a *Cradle,* which is soon made, consisting only of a piece of flat Wood that they hew with their *Hatchets* to the likeness of a Board, about two Feet long and a Foot broad, to this they brace and tie the Child very close, having near the middle a Stick fastned about two Inches from the Board, for the Child's Breech to rest on, under this they put a Wad of *Moss* that receives the Child's Excrements, by which means they can very readily shift the *Moss,* and keep all clean and sweet. They are apt to have the Bodies and Heads of their Children flat, which is owing to these kind of Cradles, yet they are the most portable things that can be invented, there being a String from one corner of the Board to the other, whereby

the

the Mother slings the Child on her Back, so that the Infant's Back is towards hers, and it's Face to the Sky; if it rains, she throws her *Leather* or *Woolen Match-coat* over her Head, which covers her all over, and secures her and the Child from the injury of the Weather. These being the only kind of *Cradles* that are common throughout all *America*.

The Women quit all manner of Company, neither do they dress their own Victuals during their Purgation; after they have had several Children, they grow strangely out of Shape in their Bodies; as for Barreness it is seldom or never known amongst them, their Women most commonly proving very fruitful, especially after Marriage, every *Cabin* being full of Children, who are taught as soon as they grow up to *Fish,* and *Hunt* in the Woods, and to do what is necessary about their Houses, *viz.* to beat *Indian Corn,* and the like, for they do not take the least Care of their Education, being strangers to all Arts and Sciences, so that they lead a very idle Life.

They name their Children according to their own Fancies, which is quite different to either the Father or Mother's Name. This Name they keep (if a Boy) 'till they arrive to the Age of a *Hunter,* or a *Warrior,* which is commonly at sixteen or seventeen Years, then they take a Name to themselves as they think proper, some being called *Eagle, Tyger, Panther, Alligator,* or some such wild Creature, esteeming nothing on Earth worthy to give them a Name, but such kind of Wildfowl or Beasts. Some likewise take the Names of some *Fish,* which they keep as long as they live.

They number their Age by *Moons* or *Winters,* and say a Woman or a Man is so many *Moons* or *Winters* old, and so they do with all memorable Actions in life, accounting it to

be

be so many *Moons* or *Winters* since such or such a thing happened. They likewise can guess tollerably well at the time of the Day by the height of the *Sun.* Though they have no different Names for *Sun* or *Moon,* yet they understand the latters Age, having no other Computation of Time but after this manner.

They have no *Sabbath,* or certain Days of Rest appointed for Devotion amongst them, that I ever could observe, except we will allow of their Feasts to be their festival Days, set appart for that purpose. However those that are frequently amongst the *Christians,* and speak the *English* Tongue, know very well when it is *Sunday,* or the *English Man's Gods Day,* as they term it. In these Parts they have likewise a particular and distinct Name for *Christmas,* which they call *Winick-keshuse,* or the *English-Man's Gods Moon.*

They name the Months according to what mostly is produced or taken in each of them, as one is called *Herring-month,* which is *March,* another the *Strawberry-month,* which is *April,* another the *Mulberry-month,* or *May;* others name them by Trees that bud or blossom at particular Seasons of the Year, such as the *Dogwood-tree, Tulip-tree,* and many others. Others again make out their Seasons from the flight of Birds, such as *Swans,* and many other Fowl, and some from the Gobling of *Turkey Cocks,* which is in *March,* and *April;* for when they are out in their Hunting matches they say they will returne Home when the *Turkey Cock* begin to Gobble.

The *Indians* are not Jealous like the *Spaniards* and other *European* Nations, neither do they know what Jealousy is, because they never think their Wives unconstant unless they are Eye witnesses thereof. They are generally bashful, especially the young Maids, who when they come into a

strange

strange *Cabin* where they are not acquainted, never ask for any thing, though they be ever so Hungry or Thirsty, but sit down without speaking a Word, till some of the House ask them some Questions, or fall into discourse with the Stranger.

The Women (as I observ'd before) never Scold with each other, and no People in the World more tender and Indulgent of their Children, so that they seldom or never correct or chastise them, which I am perswaded is a very great reason that they are not given to Scold (like the *Europeans*) when they come to Men and Women's Estate.

They have few or no complements amongst them, except shaking of Hands, and scratching on the shoulder, which are the greatest marks of affection and sincerity that can be shewed amongst them, not only to Strangers but to each other. And it is worthy of observation, to see when the *War Captains* (who are Men of the greatest esteem amongst them, next the King) come to the *Cabins* of the inferior *Indians,* that at his departure they scratch his shoulder, which is look'd upon amongst them, as the greatest honour, Complement, or marke of distinction they can confer on so great a Man.

They do not express *Fare you well,* but when they leave the House or Company will say, *I go straight away,* which is to intimate their departure, and if the Man of the House has any Message to send by the Person going he may acquaint them therewith. Neither does their Language allow them to say, *Sir, I am your Servant,* because they have little or no Degrees of Quality or Titles for Man, only *King, War Captain, Old-man,* or *Young-Man,* which respect the stations and Circumstances, that Men are employed in or arrived to, and not Ceremony. Neither is the Name of Master so much as known amongst them. And as for Servant, they have no

such

such thing, except Slave, for their *Dogs, Cats, Wild* and *Do-mestick Beasts* and *Birds* are call'd by the same Name, for the *Indian-word* for Slave includes them all; so when an *Indian* tells you, *he has got a Slave for you,* it may (in general terms as they use) be a young *Eagle,* a *Dog, Possam, Ottor,* or any other thing of that Nature, which is obsequiously to depend on the Master for its Sustenance.

When the *Europeans* come in amongst them to their Towns, though perhaps the *Indians* are well acquainted with some of them, yet not one of them will speak to them, till the King pays the first complement, which is shaking of Hands, and biding them welcome, after him the *War Captains, Doctors* or *Priests* so on gradually from high to low, not one of all these speaking to the *European* till his superior has ended his Salutation. After all this Ceremony is over then every *Indian* has liberty to speak and converse with his *European* acquaintance, this being an honour due to the King and his great Men, which is most strictly observed amongst them.

It is common amongst the *European* traders who trafick with the *Indians,* if they find no Body at Home, to make use of their *Huts,* or *Cabins* and other necessaries that they find in them, such as *Indian Corn, Peas, Beans, Chinkapin, Nuts, Wall-nuts,* and several other *Nuts,* and Fruits, *Pigeon's,-Oil, Barbacu'd Venison, Peaches,* and *Peach-Bread,* these *Peaches* are likewise made into a *Quiddony,* and then into Loaves like *Barley* Cakes, which cut into thin Slices and disolved in Water, make a very greatful and cooling Drink, all which they allow the *Christian* Traders to do, in lieu whereof they most commonly leave some small gratuity such as *Tobacco, Beads,* or some other Trifles of this Nature, (which are kindly received and acknowledged by them) and then proceed on their intended Journey.

The

The Women's dress in severe and cold Weather are Peti-
coats, Blankets, or Tail-clouts (which of late they have purchased from the *Europeans*) or a *Hairy Match-coat* made in
the nature of a Plad of the Skins of several wild Beasts,
which keeps out the Cold, and (as I said before) defends
their Children from the prejudices of the Weather, at other
times they have only a kind of flap or Apron containing two
Yards in length, and better than half a Yard deep, to cover
the Privities, which is done only for decency, both Men and
Women being accustomed from their infancy to an entire
Nakedness, for they go with their Feet, Body, and Head
bear, all seasons of the Year.  Others wear Blue or Red
Flaps made of Bays and Plains, which they buy from the
*Europeans,* both of which they tuck in at the Corners, to
fasten that kind of Garment, and at other times they make
it fast with a Belt: Sometimes they wear *Meggizons* or
*Indian Shoes* made of *Deer-Skins,* after the manner as the
Men's are.  Some of them likewise have in *Winter* Blue or
Red Stuff fastned about their Legs instead of *Stockins.*

The Hair of their Head is made into a long Roll like a
*Horses-tail,* and adorned or bound round with *Ronoak* or
*Procelan* a kind of Beads they make of *Conk-shells,* which
is the Money the *Indians* make use of in these parts.  Others
that have not this, make a Leather string or some pieces of
Green or Red Stuff serve, others adorne their Hair with
Beautiful Flowers and Feathers of several Birds: After
this manner they make their appearance, when they come
along with their Husbands amongst the *Christians.*

The Men have *Match-coats* of *Hair, Furs, Feathers,* or
*Cloth,* and their Hair rolled upon each Ear as the Women's,
only much shorter, and frequently a Roll on the Crown of
their Head and Temples, as they fancy, there being no great

nicety

nicety or strictness in their Dress. They make their Stockins of pieces of *Blue* or *Red* Cloath, which they fasten about their Legs with small Splinters made of bits of the *Pitch pine-wood,* or any other Wood. Others fasten them on with Strings on the out side of the Leg like *Buskins.* Sometimes they wear great Bobs in their Ears, others in the holes thereof put *Eagles* and other Birds Feathers for a Trophy; when they kill any Fowl, they commonly pluck of the downy Feathers and stick them all over their Heads, which make them appear more frightful than Ornamental, and more like People distracted than in their Senses: At other times both Men and Women wear great Belts and Necklaces of their Money made of *Conk-shells,* and often times Bracelets made of *Brass* and *Iron-wire,* and several other Toys which they purchase from the *Christians.*

Others have their Hair made up in long rolls, wherein are tied several bits of Stuff of various colours, such as *Yellow, Green,* and *Red,* and the like, as the Women do. Betwixt their Legs comes a piece of Cloth that is tuck'd in like a Belt both before and behind; this is contrived to hide their Nakedness, of which Decency they are strict observers, though never practiced before the *Christians* came amongst them. Some wear *Shoes* of *Buck* or *Bear Skins,* which they will tan in an Hour or two with the Bark of Trees boiled, wherein they put the *Leather* whilst hot, and let it remain a short time, whereby it becomes so qualified, as to endure Water and Dirt without growing hard. These *Moggizons* or *Shoes* have no Heels, but are made as fit for the Feet, as a Glove for the Hand, and easie to travel in when one is a little used to them.

The *Feather Match-coats* are exceedingly pretty, some of which are beautifully wrought with variety of Colours and

Rr                                        Figures,

Figures, which seem at a distance like a fine flowred *Silk-shag,* when new and fresh, they serve a Bed instead of a Quilt.  Some *Match-coats* are made of *Hair,* as *Racoons, Beavers,* or *Squirrell's Skins,* which are very warm.  Others again are made of the green part of the Skin of the *Mallards* head, and other Fowls which they stitch or sow perfectly well together, their Thread being either the Sinews of a *Deer* divided very small, or *Silk-grass,* when these are finished they look most beautifuly, though they must needs be very troublesome and tedious to make.  But those that have plenty of *Deer Skins* frequently buy the *English* made *Coats, Blankets, &c.* yet few  are ever known to buy or wear Breeches (except their Kings and great Men) saying they are too much confined in them, and prevents their speed in running, leaping, and other exercises.

There was formerly a Nation of *Indians* called the *Pasquotank Indians,* who kept Cattle and made Butter, but at present there is no such thing to be found amongst them or any other Nation in these Parts; had these inclinations in those poor *Savages* met with that encouragement (from the *English* and other *Europeans* settled in *North-Carolina)* which in justice, Piety and Virtue (ought to be the practice of every *Christian)* I do not doubt but that they wou'd soon be converted, and with joy embrace the *Christian-faith,* and belive us to be a more worthy race of People than themselves, by our good Actions and Morals.  But on the contrary, they have been formerly defrauded of the Lands allotted them, which was the occasion of a long and vexatious War to the Christians, and it frequently happens (at this Day) that the *Europeans* (which I am sorry I have occasion to mention) meet those poor *Indians* in the Woods, and not only beat and abuse them, but commonly rob them of their

*Furs,*

*Furs, Deer Skins,* and other commodities which they have acquired with so much pains and fatigue. I have known several complaints to the Governor of such usage during my abode in that Country, which shews the greatest ingratitude in Nature, when we consider how ready these poor Creatures are to serve and oblige us, in what ever assistance we want from them. And that in most of the Colonies already well Peopl'd with *Christians,* it would be impossible for them to live (for their own Slaves the *Negroes* wou'd destroy them) only for them who upon all occasions are ready to suppress them when they Rebel against their Masters, which they frequently do in *Virginia* and many other parts of *America* belonging to the Crown of *England.*

Their dresses are as different as the Nations to whom they belong, so that it is impossible to recount all the whimsical Figures that they commonly make by their Antick dresses. Besides *Carolina* is a warm Country, and very mild in its *Winters* to what *Mary-Land, Pensilvania, New-York,* the *Jersies,* or *New-England* are, wherefore our *Indian* Habits differ very much from the dresses that are used by the *Savages* that inhabit those cold Countries; in regard their chiefest cloathing for the *Winter* Season is made of the Furs of *Bevers, Raccoons,* and other *Northren-Furs,* as the *Monack-Moor, Marten, Black-Fox,* and many other Beasts that are to be met with to the *Northward,* that we are unacquainted with here.

Their dress in Peace and War are quite different from some Nations before they go to War, the Women comb out their Hair and anoint it with *Bears-grease,* and the *Red Root,* and likewise adorn it with Feathers of various beautiful colours, besides *Copper, Iron* Rings, and sometimes *Wampum* or *Peak* in their Ears. Moreover they buy red Colours of the *Indian* Traders, wherewith they Paint their

Faces

Faces all over as red as *Vermillion,* and commonly make a circle of Black about one Eye, and another circle of White about the others, whilst other bedaub their Faces with *Tobacco pipe Clay, Lamp black, Black Lead,* and divers others colours, such as *Green, Blue,* and the like, these they make with several sorts of *Herbs, Minerals,* and Earths, that they get in different parts of the Country where they Hunt and Travel. When these People are thus Painted they make the most frightful Figures that can be imitated by Men, and seem more like Devils out of Hell than any human Creature upon Earth, the reason why they thus Paint themselves is because they believe it adds to their Courage and strikes a terror in their Enemies.

It is worthy of Observation, that whenever you meet them thus disguis'd or Painted, you may be sure that they are about some mischief or other, for in all Hostilities that have ever been acted against the *Christians* at any time in several of the Plantations of *America,* these *Savages* always appear'd in these disguises, whereby they might never after be discovered or known by the *Christians* that shoud happen to see them after they had made their escape; for it is impossible ever to know an *Indian* under these Colours, although he had been ever so often at your House, and you were most intimatly acquainted with him before he put on this disguise.

As for the Women, they seldom or never use any Paint on their Faces, except *Bear's-Grease,* or *Lamp-black,* when they mourn for their dead; neither do they carry their Women along with them into the Field of Battle, or when they intend any Expedition (as they do in many parts of the *Eastren* Country) but always leave them at home with the old Men and Children, to provide all manner of Necessaries for them. By their different way of Painting, they

represent

represent most of the Actions in Life, such as *War, Peace, Feasts, Death,* and the like, using different Colours or Paintings suitable to each occasion. When they are thus Painted, they go to Battle in the following manner: Each Man takes his Gun, and a sufficient quantity of Powder and Ball, or if he has not these, his Bow (which is about an Ell long) and arrows, about eighteen Inches, made of small *Canes,* some of them are very artificially headed with sharp *Stones, Shells, Teeth* of *Fish,* or hardned after their manner, the other End being Feathered with two Feathers, and tied with the Guts of some Beast when green and moist; each of them has likewise a *Tamahawk* or small *Hatchet,* and *Cutlashes,* when they can get them purchased by any means from the *Europeans.* They also use Clubs or long Poles (in the ends whereof they fasten very artificially sharp *Stones,* or the *Horns* of Beasts) and wooden Swords, hardened after their manner; sometimes they have wooden Breast-plates for their defence; these being all the Weapons that are made use of amongst the civilized, and *Savage Indians* in these parts.

The way of waging War is so harsh, that one must have a Body of Steel to bear the Fatigues they are obliged to undergo. They give but little Quarters, and if they are taken Prisoners, they are never exchanged: When one Nation is engaged in War with another, there is little Valour used, though they accomplish notable Exploits by Craft and Stratagem, for they do not attack each other by open Force, but dividing themselves into small Parties, twenty five or thirty Men lie in Ambush near the Village they design to attack, 'till Night, then they set upon the Huts that lie dispersed in the open Country, if they meet with any aged Men they kill them, cut off their Heads, Hands, and Feet, nay, if they

have

have time, cut them all into small pieces, that every one may take along with him a part, as a signal of his Bravery: But if the Enemy are alarmed, they are glad to be contented with the Head alone, or perhaps a Lock of the Hair, which they carry home in triumph, as an undoubted sign of their Bravery. When they intend to do a bold Exploit, they enter a Village at Night, force open a House, kill all they meet with, and then betake themselves to their Heels, for fear of being pursued by their Enemies. If they engage in the open Field, their chief Design is to draw one another into an Ambush; but the death of one or two Men commonly decides the Quarrel, that Party which has lost them, returning immediately.

When they go to War, they carry their *Idol* with them, of whom they tell incredible Stories, and ask Council, as the Antients were wont to do with the *Oracle* of *Apollo,* and then proceed upon their intended Expedition, with their *Kings* or *War Captains,* who march first, with a *Club* in one Hand, and a *Bow* in the other, with a Quiver full of *Arrows,* all the rest follow him towards the Battle, with such Weapons as they can conveniently get, singing Songs instead of Drums and Trumpets, and whilst they fight, there is nothing to be heard but Skreeches and Cries amongst them, and it is accounted a great Battle amongst them where three or four are killed, or made Captives.

They are a People that never forget Injuries done by their Enemies, and seldom cease 'till they have Satisfaction, but before they go upon any Expedition, they often assemble in Council together, and there debate the Matter in hand, and take those Resolutions that they judge most advisable to be done, being a People never over hasty in what they do.

They

They make great Feasts after they have obtained a Victory over their Enemies, for several Days together, where they drink great quantities of *Yaupan Tea,* and whatever Trophies they obtain in Battle, they carefully bring home to their Towns, and place them all together, round which they Dance for several Hours, shewing all the signs of Joy imaginable, their young Men and Wives singing Songs of Praise to their *War Captains* and great Men, for their late Conquest over their Enemies; they likewise make the most antient Women of the Country Dance, holding the Hair of their Enemies in their Hands.

Their manner of War amongst themselves, is either by suddenly surprizing each other, which is most commonly done about the dawning of the Day, Moon-light, or by Ambushes; set Battles being very rare, except it be where there are many Trees, to have a place of Refuge or Defence after every Shot, or the delivery of their Arrows, by leaping behind them, or some other shelter.

When they go to War or their Hunting Matches, the Victuals which they generally carry with them is *Bread, Indian Corn, dried Fruits,* of several sorts, *Honey,* and *Meal* made of *Maiz* parched in the Fire, this they can preserve for a long time without receiving any damage; they likewise carry dried *Fish* upon these occasions, and these are most commonly all the Provisions they take with them.

The Cruelty they use to their Prisoners of War, is scarce to be paralel'd, because they strive to invent the most inhuman and barbarous Butcheries for these miserable Wretches that happen in their power, that is possible for themselves or Devils to invent. These *Savages* esteem Death to be no Punishment, but an advancement to him that is taken out of the World into another; therefore they inflict on them

these

these cruel Torments, in prolonging Life in that miserable
state, as long as they can, and never miss *Sculping* of these
Wretches (as they call it) which is to cut off the Skin from
the Temples, and take the whole Head of Hair along with
it from the Scull, like a Cap; this they hang at their Belts,
and carry to their Towns for their Wives and Children to be
spectators of.  They sometimes take the top of the Scull
along with it, all which they preserve and carefully keep by
them to shew their Conquest, and Victory over their Enemies.  Some of them keep their Enemies Teeth, which are
taken in War; whilst others split the *Pitch-Pine* and stick
the Prisoners Bodies (whilst alive) full of them, which they
set fire to, and burn like so many Toarches:   In this manner
they make him dance round a great Fire, every one buffeting
and deriding him 'till he expires; then every one present
strive to get a Bone or some other Relick of this unfortunate
Captive.  Whatever Weapons they kill or wound their Enemies with, they let the Blood remain on it as a Trophy of
their Victory.

It is remarkable, that if any of the young Fellows who
have been at the Wars, and had the fortune to take a Captive, returns the proudest Creature upon Earth, and sets
such a Value on himself, that he scarce knows how to contain
in his Senses.  In all their Wars they never destroy the
Women or Children that they make Captives, but carefully
preserve them.

The *Iroquois,* or *Sannagers,* and *Cherokees,* are the most
powerful and warlike *Indian*s that we know of in these Parts,
being always at War, and not to be persuaded from that way
of living by any Arguments or Persuasions whatsoever.
They live near the Mountains, and there has been several
Methods used by the *Christians* to perswade them to live

peaceably

peaceably with the *Tuskeruros* (who are one of the Civilized Nations, amongst the *English* that live near the Sea) notwithstanding these *Indians* very much desire to make Peace, and woud submit to the former, yet their answer is, that they cannot live without War, which they have ever been accustomed to, and that if peace be made with them or any other Nation they War withal, they must find out some others to wage War against. But for them to live in peace is to live out of their element, War, Conquest, and Murder, being what they always delight in, and value themselves for. Yet they have not molested the *Tuskeruros,* of late Years, and it is supposed that they are now at War with the *Indians* on the other side of the Mountains, and though they may seem such a Barbarous People, yet they are very fond of the *Christians,* and use them with all manner of civility when they meet them in the Mountains where they constantly trade with each other.

When they take a Prisoner, and intend to keep him as a Slave to Work in their Fields, they flea the Skin from the setting on of his Toes to the middle of his Foot, cut of one half of his Feet, wraping the Skin over the Wounds and then healing them. By this cruel and Barbarous method the *Indian* captive is hindred from making his escape, for he can neither run fast or go any where but his feet or Stumps are more easily traced and discovered, yet I have seen some that made their escape from their Enemies though they were disabled after this manner.

The *Indians* ground their Wars chiefly on Enmity, not on Interest, as the *Europeans* generally do, for the loss of the meanest Person in the Nation, they will go to War and lay all at Stake, and prosecute their design to the utmost, till the Nation they were injured by be wholly destroyed, or make them that satisfaction which they demand.

They maintain continual Wars one Nation against another, which sometimes hold for Ages, killing and making captive all they can, till they become so weak that they are often forced to make peace for want of a sufficient number of Recruits to supply their Wars; so that by these continual Wars, and the art they have and often practice of Poysoning one another, which they do with a large white Spongy Root that grows in their fresh Marshes, many numerous and form-idable Nations are dwindled away to a handful of Men in comparison to what they were sixty Years ago, and it's strange to imagine how many hundred Miles they come to make War on each other; without any visible view of Inter-est in Lands, or Riches, which are the chief motives of all *European Princes,* waging War against each other.

They are very Politick in waging and carrying on their War, first by advising with all the antient Men of conduct and reason that belong to their Nation; such as superanuated *War Captains,* and those that have been Counsellors amongst them for many Years, whose Advice has succeeded well. They have likewise their *Field Counsellors,* who are accus-tomed to Ambuscades and Surprizes, which methods are commonly used by them in these parts, for you shall seldom hear of a Field or set Battle fought amongst them.

Yet before they undertake any enterprizes, they meet several Mornings together in their State-Houses, where the King repaireth, and is placed on a seat which is generally higher than any of his Retinue's, where all of them salute him; as soon as the Salutation is over, every one sits down according to their Degrees or Seniority, and if there be any thing to be debated, the King calls his Priests and the most

antient

antient Men of his Nation and asks their Advice. After-wards he commands *Cassena* to be brought, and when he has drank a Cup full of the Liquor (which holds about a Pint and a half) they all, one after another drink the same pro-portion out of the same Cup.

This drink is in such great request amongst them, that no Man is permitted to taste thereof in this publick Assembly unless he has signalized himself in the Wars against his Ene-mies; Valour being highly esteemed amongst them: They drink this Tea very warm, which makes them sweat plenti-fully, and has the virtue to take away Hunger and Thirst for twenty four Hours.

These *Indians* exercise their young Men very much in Shooting with their Bows, and Arrows, the Strings whereof are made of the Guts of the Stag, or of a Stag's Skin, which they know how to dress as well as any People in *Europe,* and with as different sorts of Colours; there being plenty of several beautiful Dies in this Country, which they are well acquainted with, they likewise take great pleasure in Hunt-ing and Fishing, wherein they are very expert.

I will give you some few Instances of their Politicks and Expeditions, which are worth mentioning. The first was thus, two Nations were at War with each other, and both Parties were in the Woods or Forrest ranging to see what Enemies they coud take or destroy. The lesser Number found they were discovered by the greater, and that they cou'd not well get over a River (that lay betwixt them and their Home) without engaging the other party, whose Num-bers were much superior, they immediately called a Council, which being met, and having weighed and debated their pres-ent circumstances, with many arguments for a considerable time, and found their Enemies advantage, and that they

could

could not possibly expect any success in engaging such an
unequal Number. They at last concluded on this Stratagem, which in my opinion carried a great deal of policy
along with it. It was, that the same Night they should
make a great Fire, which they were certain would be discover'd by the adverse party, and there dress up Logs of Wood
in their Cloaths, and make them exactly seem like *Indians*
that were fast asleep by the Fire-side (which is their way
when they are Hunting or otherwise in the Woods) so said
they, our Enemies will fire upon these Images, supposing
them to be Men, while we lye in Ambuscade, and after their
Guns are unloaded we shall deal well enough with them.

This result was immediately put in execution, and the
Fire was made by the side of a Vally where they lay perdue,
very advantageously all Night. Thus a little before
break of Day they came down to the Fire, and at once fired
in upon these Logs in the *Indian* Cloaths and run up to them
expecting they had kill'd every Man dead upon the Spot,
but they soon found themselves to be mistaken, for then the
other *Indians* who had lain all the Night stark-naked, attacked them with their loaded Pieces, which so surpriz'd
them, that every Man was taken Prisoner and brought in
bound to their Town, some of whom were sold to the *English*
for Slaves.

There was another extraordinary Instance of this Nature
that happen'd betwixt the *Machapunga Indians* and the
*Coranines,* living on the Sand-banks near *Machapunga River,*
which carries a great deal of Treachery and Barbarity in it,
and is as follows. The *Machapungas* were invited to a feast
by the *Coranines* (which two Nations had been a long time
at War together, but had lately concluded a Peace) there-
upon the *Machapunga Indians* took the advantage of coming

to

to the *Coranines* feast, and to avoid all suspicion, and that
there was a good harmony and understanding now amongst
them; the *Machapunga* King who though of a Savage nature,
was a great Politician, and very stout, order'd all his Men
to carry their *Tamahawks* along with them under their
*Match-coats,* which they did, and being acquainted when to
fall on, by the Word given, they all (upon this design) set
forward for the feast, and came to the *Coranine-town,* who
made them welcome, and had gotten Victuals, Fruit, and
such things as make an *Indian Entertainment;* having provided all things necessary to make their new Guests welcome, after Dinner towards the Evening (as it is customary
amongst them) they went to Dancing all-together; when the
*Machapunga* King saw the best opportunity offer, he gave
the Word, and immediately his Men pulled out their *Tamahawks,* or *Hatchets* from under their *Match-coats,* killed several, and took the rest of them Prisoners, except some few
that were not at the Feast, and about four or five that made
their escape; some of these they sold as Slaves to the *English.*
At the time this was done, these *Indians* had nothing but
Bows and Arrows, being intire strangers to Guns and their
uses; neither are any of the two former Nations to be met
with (at this Day) living near *Machapunga River,* which
place is well inhabited by *Christians.*

Their Dances are of different Natures, and for every sort
they have a different Song or Tune, which is allotted for each
Dance. Upon these occasions they will continue dancing
for several Nights together, with the greatest briskness imaginable, their Wind never failing them: In a *War-Dance*
they have *Warlike Songs,* wherein they express with all the
passion and vehemency imaginable what they intend to do
with their Enemies; how they will kill, roast, sculp, beat,

and

and make Captives such and such numbers of them, and how many they have destroyed already: Whatever Trophies they have gained in War are set up for all those present to behold, round which they Feast and Dance with the greatest extasie of Joy that can be exprest or shewn by them.

All the Songs are made new for every Feast, neither is one and the same Song sung at two several Festivals; some one of the Nation (who hath the best gift of expressing their Designs) is appointed by their King and *War Captains* to make these Songs; these Persons or Poets being in great request with the King, and Nation to whom they belongs.

Their Peace Dances are generally made at their Feasts, and are of another Nature; as when several Towns, and sometimes different Nations have made Peace with one another, then it suits both Nations, and relates how the bad Spirit made them go to War and destroy one another, that it shall never be so again, but that their Sons and Daughters shall marry together, and the two Nations love each other, and become as one united People.

They have a third sort of Feast and Dances which are when the Harvest of *Corn* is ended, and in the *Spring;* the one to return Thanks to the good Spirit for the Fruits of the Earth, the other to beg the same Blessings for the succeeding Year. They plant their *Maze* or *Indian Corn* twice a Year, *viz.* in *March* and *June,* all in the same Soil, for as soon as one Crop is ripe, which is in three Months, they immediately gather it and plant the same Grounds over again. Before the *Europeans* arrived in these Parts, they used to dig their Grounds with an Instrument made of Wood, which was fashioned like a broad *Matock,* but at present they have *Hoes* from the *Christians,* and commonly plant two or three Grains

together:

together: They never Dung their Land, but set Fire to the
Weeds, which makes very good Manure; when the Land is
to be planted, the King commands one of the Men to assemble his Subjects every Day to Labour, and when the *Maze* is
gathered, it is all carried into a common Store-House, where
it is distributed to every one as there is occasion; they seldom sow more than what will serve them for six Months,
and that very sparingly; for during the *Winter* they retire
into the Woods to hunt, or fish, where they have plenty of
various kinds of wild Beasts, Birds and Fishes. To encourage the young Men to labour in planting their *Maze* and
*Pulse,* they place a kind of *Idol* in the Field, dressed up
exactly like an *Indian,* with a great quantity of *Wampum,*
or *Money* that is made of *Conk-Shells,* hanging about his
Neck. This Image none of the young Men dare presume to
approach, the old ones will not suffer them, but tell them
that it is some famous Warrior that died many Ages ago,
and now is come among them, to see if they work well, which
if they do, he will go to the good Spirit, and speak to him
to send them plenty of Corn, and to make them expert Hunters, and mighty Wariors; and many other incredible Stories,
with which they amuse their Youth. All this while the
King and the old Men sit round the Image, and seemingly
pay the most profound Respect and Veneration imaginable
to the same. One great help to them in carrying on these
Cheats, and inducing their Youth to do what they please is,
the uninterrupted Silence which is ever kept and observed
amongst them.

At these Feasts, which are set out with all the Magnificence
imaginable, or that their Fare will allow of, the Masquerade
begins always at Night. There is a Fire commonly made in
the middle of the largest House in the Town, which frequently

happens

happens to be that of their King or *War Captain,* or a House
made for that purpose, where two Men are placed on a Mat
on the Ground, the one with a *Rattle* made of a *Gourd,*
with some *Indian Corn* or *Beans* in it; the other with a *Drum*
made of an *Earthen Pot,* covered with a dressed *Deer Skin,*
with one Stick in his Hand to beat thereon; thus they begin
the Song appointed for that purpose, at the same time the
one Drums, and the other Rattles; this is all the artificial
Musick of their own making that I ever saw amongst them.
To these two Instruments they sing, which may be supposed
to make but indifferent *Musick,* for *Europeans,* and yet the
Cadencies and raising of their Voices are formed with that
equality and exactness, that to us it seems very strange and
admirable how they should continue these Songs without
once missing to agree with each others Note and Tune.

As for their *Dancing,* were there Masters of that Profession amongst them, as there are in *Europe,* I am certain they
would dearly earn their Money; for these People take the
most Pains that Men are able to endure:  I have seen thirty
dancing together, and every one with the Sweat dropping
down, as if Water were powred on their Backs.

They bring up their Youth in many laborious Exercises,
to make them able to endure Fatigues, and improve their
Wind, which is indeed very long and durable, being a hard
matter in any Exercise to dispossess them of it, there being
several Games amongst them that is won by him that hath
the longest Breath.   In traveling and hunting they are most
indefatigable, being bred up after that manner from their
Youth, to which they have a double inducement, as it carries
both Pleasure and Profit with it.   I have known some of
them very strong, and particularly remarkable for their running and leaping: The agility of both Men and Women are

such,

such, that they will very readily swim over great Rivers, and sometimes carry their Children; they likewise very nimbly climb the highest Trees in the Country.

These People (as I said before) have solemn Feasts upon several occasions, such as for *War, Peace,* the Fruits of the Earth, and the like, at these Festivals they have great plenty of provisions, such as *Venison, Birds, Fishes,* and several sorts of *Fruits* and *Roots.* Their firing is made of Wood, which they kindle by strenuously rubbing one stick against another (the Sticks being of different kinds) and so roast their flesh Meat on wooden Spits, or Boyl it in Earthen Pots, of their own make, and sometimes broil it on the Embers.

They are for the most part very gentle, loving and faithful, void of Guile or Treachery (except they are highly injured) and live after the manner of the Golden Age, for they only take care how to defend themselves from the Cold in their short *Winters,* and to feed themselves with such Victuals as the Soil produceth. They sometimes have plenty of *Rum* at these Entertainments, which they purchase from the *Europeans,* but the common drink they make use of to quench their thirst is *Water,* and it is to be admired that they never yet found out the method of making *Wines* in these parts, where several sorts of *Grapes* are so plenty, and these People in general being extreamly fond of strong Liquors.

At Night their Revels begin, which is commonly in a House made for that purpose being the largest amongst their dwellings, this House is built in form of a Pyramid wherein are made handsome white Benches artificially of fine *Canes,* joining along the Walls, and the Door or entrance very low. In these *State-Houses* are transacted all publick and private

business

business relating to the Affairs of the Government, and the audience of Foreign Ambassadors from other *Indian* Kings; likewise their consultations for wageing and making of *War,* Proposals of Trade with their Neighbouring *Indians* or *Europeans,* who happen to come amongst them, and there determine what may be most convenient for them to act, and what to omit, old Age being always held in as great veneration amongst them, as any People you shall find in any part of the World.

It is to be observed, that during their consultations no manner of interruption is given to the Speaker, who gets up and declares to the Auditors what he thinks most advisable to be done in the Affair then depending; as soon as he has finish'd what he thinks proper to say on that Subject, he sits down and then the second proceeds after the same method, and so all the rest in their turns, and lastly their King, not one Word to be heard, or even a whisper during their whole conference but from him that stands up. The whole Assembly giving a great deal of attention to what each Person relates on that head, a profound silence and exact decorum being used during the Oration.

And it is even remarkable amongst them in their common Discourse, that they never interrupt each other, none offering to open his Mouth till the other has finished what he has to say on the Subject. This practice I am perswaded wou'd be of great use and advantage to the *Europeans,* who are so subject to interrupt each other, before they can utter their intentions, frequently judging from a few Words spoken, the whole Cause before they have heard the Merits of it.

These People are naturally very subtile and sharp witted, and ready to conceive our meaning by Signs, and to make answers to be understood again. If they have not seen the

thing

thing whereof you ask them, they will wink or cover their Eyes with their Hand to intimate thereby that it hath been hid from their sight, and if they understand not those things whereof you enquire, they will stop their Ears, and by many other such like signs, easie to be understood, they are apt to learn any thing of us, and are very willing to teach us the Names of each thing in their Language we demand of them.

All their dwelling Houses are covered with the Barks of Trees, But this *Senate-House* differs very much from them, being artificially Thatch'd with *Sedge* and *Rushes;* at the building whereof every one assists till it is finished, and as soon as it is compleatly finished, the King places some one of his chiefest Men to dwell therein, charging him with a diligent preservation thereof, in like manner as *European* Princes commit the charge and Government of Forts and Castles to some favorite subject they judge worthy of so great Honours and Trust.

They frequently send Ambassadors to each other, who make very odd and strange Figures at their Arrival, having their Faces and Hair painted all over as red as *Vermillion,* a *Fusee* or *Bow* and *Arrows* in their Hands, and a *Cutlash* or *Tamahawk* stuck in their *Girdle.* As soon as they arrive they are brought to the Kings House, from thence are conducted to the *State-House,* where they take the place that is assign'd them, and there treat of those important Affairs with which they are commission'd from their Kings and Nations to whom they belong.

I have frequently made use of the word Civilized *Indians,* and for the better information of my Readers they are those that assisted the *Christians* against the other *Savages* of that Country in the late *War* when the Hon. Colonel *Barnwell* intirely defeated them in *Bath* County, *Anno Dom.* 1712.

But

But to returne to their Feasts, in these *State-Houses,* the King being come, and seated invites the *Europeans,* if there be any amongst them at that time, who are always placed next the King, with his *War Captains* on each side; being thus seated, there is a circular Fire made of split *Canes* in the middle of the House, which otherwise would be as dark as a Dungeon, and is as hot as a *Dutch Stove.* One Man is constantly employed to supply split *Canes* as the others are consumed. The Guests being all seated on *Benches* or *Mats* on the Ground, they bring in several pieces of *Bears-flesh* and *Venison,* roasted and boiled; *Wild Turkeys* in great plenty, dressed after their manner; various kinds of other Wild Beasts and *Fowl, Fish,* and several kinds of Medlies made of *Maiz, stewed Peaches, dried Peaches,* and variety of other *Fruits.* Every one of the *Indians* bringing something with him, to enlarge their Banquet, according to their Degree and Quality.

When all their Dainties are brought in, the first Entertainment begins with kicking out the *Dogs,* which are like the *Wolves* in these parts; for it is supposed that they are a Species of them, made tame by beating and starving. They are the worst *Dog-masters* in the World, for you shall never see an *Indian Dog* that is fat amongst them; neither do I find that they make any use of them, for they never bring them to their *Hunting-matches.*

They are of a quite contrary Disposition to their *Horses,* to whom they are the best of Masters, for they are continually feeding them with *Maze,* or whatever he will eat, until he is as fat as a *Hog,* yet they never ride or make any manner of use of him, except only to carry a *Deer* home that they have killed near the Plantations; or Firewood for their Houses.

As

As soon as the Dogs are discharged, the Company are summoned by beat of Drum and the Rattle; which two Instruments I have already mentioned, and whilst the one rattled the other in Consort beat the Drum, others at the same time sung mournful Ditties, the burthen of their Songs being in remembrance of their former greatness and numbers of their Nation, the famous Exploits of their renowned Ancestors, and all Actions of moment that had been performed by their forefathers in former Days.

No sooner does this kind of Consort begin to play and sing, but presently come in some *Indians* finely dressed up with *Feathers,* their Faces covered with *Vizards* made of *Gourds;* round their Ancles and Knees are hung Bells of several sorts, having wooden Falcions in their Hands, such as our *Gladiators* commonly use upon the Stage; in this Dress they dance about an Hour or more, shewing many strange Gestures, brandishing their Weapons as if they were going to fight each other, oftentimes walking round the Room with so much dexterity and nimbleness, that you may not hear their Bells make the least noise, which is very strange to see them perform, turning their Bodies, Arms and Legs, into such strange and frightful Postures, that to an *European* they would seem like a parcel of *Bedlamites,* void of Sense or Reason; after they have cut two or three high Capers, they immediately leave the Room. As soon as they disappear, come in a parcel of Women and Girles, each taking place according to their degree in Stature, the tallest leading the Dance, and the least of all placed last. They then form themselves into a Ring, representing the Fire they dance about. Several of them having Bells about their Legs, dressed with Flowers and Feathers like the Men, others with small Bells about their Necks, though their way of Dancing is

nothing

nothing but a sort of stamping, which they continue for
several Hours together, till they are all of them in as great
a sweat as if they had been dipped in the River.

During these Dances the Spectators do not neglect to fill
their Bellies with the Provisions that are there, more or less
of them being continually eating: When the Dancing is
ended, every Youth that is so disposed, takes hold of the Girl
he fancies to be his Bedfellow for that Night, few Ceremonies
being used upon that head amongst them.

At these Festivals and publick Assemblies they give a traditional Relation of what happened amongst them for many
Years past, to their young Men; having no other Method to
record what their Ancestors have done, or known only by
Tradition from Father to Son, and their *Hierogliphicks,*
being entire Strangers to Letters or Learning.

They have another sort of Feast where their Priests or
Conjurers pretend to converse familiarly, and demand divers
strange things from Spirits by their Invocations, and the
Magical Charms which they make use of. This Feast they
celebrate in the open Fields, where a large Circle is made;
all the *Indians* that come to it are variously painted and
adorned with rich Feathers of divers Colours; they have
singing and dancing at this as at the others: After they have
sung and danced for a quarter of an Hour, and turned about
three times, they run like distracted Men into the Woods; then
the Women continue the rest of the Day in Tears, and as
melancholy as possible, then in a Rage they cut the Arms of
the young Girls with sharp *Shells* of *Fishes,* 'till the Blood
follows, which they cast into the Air, with loud Shreeks and
Cries.

Those

Those that begin this Feast (which is always in the Morning) are their Priests or Conjurers, to whom they give great credit and belief, not only because they are very subtile and crafty *Magicians,* and find out things lost, but likewise because they heal Diseases by their Charms and Knowledge in Plants. They first run to the Woods, from whence they return in two Days, and then begin to Sing and Dance in the middle of the Circle (which the Women sweep and make very clean against their return) and are very chearful and merry with the old *Indian* Fathers that stay'd behind, by reason of their natural Indispositions and feebleness: When all these Ceremonies are ended, they begin to eat with such greediness, that they seem rather to devour their Meat than eat it, because they neither eat nor drink during their two Days continuance in the Woods.

At these Feasts most of all the Nations that are in Peace with each other meet, though seventy or eighty Miles distant from each other, where they sell and buy several Commodities as we do at our Fairs and Markets.

They are very much given to Gaming at these publick Meetings, and often strip one another of all they have in the World; and what's more to be admired is, that they frequently play themselves away, and remain the Winners Servants 'till their Relations or themselves pay the Money to redeem them; and it is observable, that the Looser is never dejected or cast down at his misfortune, but seems contented and as chearful as if he had been the Winner. They never differ at Gaming, neither did I ever see a Dispute about the legality thereof so much as arise amongst them.

The chief Game is a kind of *Arithmetick,* which is managed or played with a parcel of small split *Reeds* about the thickness of a small *Bent;* these are made very nicely, that

they

they part and are tractable in their Hands. They are fifty one in Number, and their length about seven Inches; when they play they throw part to their Antagonist, the Art in this kind of Game is to discover upon sight how many you have, and what you throw to him that plays with you; some are so expert in guessing the Numbers they gave, and what they have remaining, that they will not miss once in ten times; they are so taken with this particular Game, that several of them have lost large *Indian Estates.* A good Set of these *Reeds* to play with, are generally valued and sold for a dressed *Doe-Skin.*

They have several other Games and Plays wherewith they frequently divert themselves, as with the *Kernels* or *Stones* of the Fruit of the *Persimon* Tree, which are in effect the same as our *Dice,* because winning or loosing depend on which side appears uppermost, and how they happen to fall together.

Their manner of playing *Ball* is after this manner, *viz.* they place a square *Mat* made of *Reeds* or *Bullrushes* at the top of a Tree eight or nine Fathom from the Ground, and whoever hitteth the *Mat* in playing thereat, winneth the Game.

They have another Game which is managed with a *Battoon,* and very much resembles our *Trap-Ball;* as the Nations differ so do their Games and Pastimes, having several peculiar to themselves which are not practiced by others; yet these I have mentioned are the chief that I have observed amongst them.

They are charitable and kind to each other, especially to those of their own Nation; for if any one of them has suffered loss by Fire or otherwise, they order him to make a Feast (their Victuals being in common) and to invite them all to

it:

it: On the Day appointed they all come, and after every Man's Victuals is dealt to him, one of their Speakers, or grave old Men makes an Harangue, to the Company to this effect, that *That Man's House hath been destroyed, together with all his Goods. That he and his Family very narrowly escaped. That he is every Man's Friend in that Company, and that it is all their Duties to help him, as he would do any of them, had the like Misfortune befallen them.*—— In such like Speeches he accosts all that are present, to a charitable compliance in behalf of the distressed Person. After this Oration is over, every Man according to his Quality and Ability, throws down upon the Ground some Present, which is commonly *Beads, Ronoak, Peak, Skins,* or *Furs,* which often amounts to treble the loss he has sustained. The same assistance they give to any Man that wants to build a Cabin or make a Canoe, or any other Convenience that he is not able to perform, and stands in need of: For, they say, it is every Man's Duty so to do, there being several Works that one Man cannot effect, therefore they must give him their help, otherwise the Society would soon fall, and they should be deprived of those urgent Necessaries which Life requires.

Their Charity is no less extensive towards Widows, for it often happens that a Woman is destitute of a Husband, either by Wars or otherwise, and hath a great many Children to maintain, such a Person they always help, and make their young Men Plant, Reap, and do every thing she is not capable of doing herself; yet they will not allow any one to be idle (especially in the Harvest time) but employ themselves in some Work or other. As they are unacquainted with the value of *Gold* or *Silver,* they prefer their *Indian-Money* before it, which is of different Sorts, but all made of *Shells,* that are found on the Coast of *Carolina,* and especially the

22 Uu *Conck-shells;*

*Conck-shells;* these are very large and hard and difficult to be cut, yet some *European Smiths* have tried to drill these *Shells,* thinking to get an advantage by them, but it proved so hard and tedious in the working, that nothing could be gained thereby, that they have intirely laid it aside for the *Indians* to manage, who never value their Time, so that they can make them according to their Fancy.

They frequently make of these *Shells* several sorts of Figures, in imitation of *Gorges, Crosses, Stars,* or any other odd kind of Figure that their imagination suggests, these they wear about their Necks and Arms tied with a String; there are some of these *Gorges* that will sell for three or four *Buck Skins* ready drest, whilst others are only valued and sold for one *Doe Skin.* But the general and currant Species amongst all the *Indians* of *Carolina,* and I believe all over the Continent as far as the Bay of *Mexico,* that which we call *Peak* and *Ronoak,* but *Peak* more especially. This is that which they call *Wampum* at *New York,* and has been made use of as current Coin for many Years amongst the *Europeans* settled in that Province. This is what many Writers call *Proclean* and was formerly made at *New York* in great quantities, and with us in some Measure. Four Cubits of this purchase a dressed *Doe Skin,* and six or seven are the purchases of a dressed *Buck Skin:* An *European* could not afford to make so much of this *Wampum* for five times the Value; for it is made out of a very large Shell of which that Country affords plenty.

This Shell they grind smaller than the small End of a *Tobacco Pipe,* or a large *Wheat Straw;* four or five of these are about an Inch in length, and every one drilled through, polished and made as smooth as Glass, yet they are as strong as *Beads.* A *Cubit* of the *Indian* Measure contains as much

in

in length as will reach from the Elbow to the end of the little
Finger. They never regard or stand to question whether he
is a tall or short Man that measures it; but if this *Wampum*
or *Peak* be of a black or purple Colour, as some part of the
Shell, then it is twice the Value.

They grind these Shells upon Stones and other things, 'till
they make them current, but the Drilling is the most difficult
to the *Europeans,* which the *Indians* do with a Nail stuck in
a Cane or Reed, but whether they have any Method in soft-
ning these Shells, is uncertain. They rowl it continually on
their Thighs with the right Hand, and hold the bit of Shell
with their left; thus by degrees they drill a hole through it,
which is a tedious Work, but especially in making their
*Ronoak,* four of which will scarce make one length of *Wampum.*

The *Indians* in general are a People (as I observed) that
set very little value on their Time, and need never be under
any apprehension or fear that the *Christians* will take the
Trade out of their hands. This is the Money with which
you may buy *Skins, Furs, Slaves,* or any thing they have except their Children, it being their *Mammon* (as our Money
is to us) that persuades and intices them to do any thing.
With this they will buy off Murders, or whatever a Man can
do that is Ill, and be his Crime of never so black a Nature,
this Money is sufficient to purge him of it, and have it buried
in Oblivion for ever, such an influence hath this Almighty
Gain over them, that the most inhuman practices shall appear innocent and laudable, and engage them in the most
scandalous and barbarous Actions, without once reflecting or
condemning themselves in the least for it.

Formerly in their hunting Matches they used to dress themselves very artfuelly in *Deer Skins,* by which counterfet they would come as near the *Deer* as they pleased, by mimicking each Gesture of that Beast as they approached, by which means they killed vast numbers of them, but some of themselves being shot in this disguise, it is now intirely laid aside and that practice disallowed of by the express Orders of their Kings.

They have particular Methods by which they can preserve the Eyes of Beasts as if they were still living, this they will by no means discover to the *Christians;* they have many other curious things that the *Europeans* are desirous to know and learn from them, but they will by no means discover or make known to them, being a People that are secret, crafty, and subtile in all their Affairs, though of ever so small a moment.

Although these *Indians,* in respect of us, are a poor People, and their want of Skill and Judgment in the Knowledge and use of the Sciences, generally esteem Trifles to things of real value, not having the advantages of improving themselves as the *Europeans;* yet in their own manner and way of Thinking, they seem to be ingenious, and shew excellency of Wit, notwithstanding the many inconveniencies they labour under, and their want of Tools and Instruments to assist them in any of their Undertakings, for I have, during my continuance amongst them, seén many useful Instruments made for several uses, with nothing but an indifferent Knife.

They commonly barbecu or dry their *Venison* on Mats or Hurdles in the Sun, first salting it with their Salt, which is made of the Ashes of the *Hickery Wood;* this Venison so cured, they keep and make use of in time of scarcity, and bad Weather, which they tear to pieces with their Hands and Teeth (for want of Knives) and then put it into a Morter

and

and pound it very fine, adding the Powder of the *Hickery Nuts* or *Wall-nuts* and other ingredients, whereof they make a savory Dish.

Their Kings, as they are most absolute, put to death any of their Subjects that have committed those Crimes that they think worthy of so great a Punishment; which is strictly observed, and put in execution by the War Captains after different and barbarous Methods, according to the King's Will and Pleasure.

Their Sculping and sticking them full of Splinters of *Light-wood,* and setting these Wretches on Fire, their fleaing and cutting their Feet at the Instep, I have already made mention of; during which time they never cease feasting, dancing, singing and playing a thousand antick Tricks, especially if it be one of their Enemies; at other times they rip open the Bellys of these wretches, fasten their Bowels to a Tree, and force them round 'till such time as their Intrails are out, or their Strength is intirely spent, that they can shew no more Diversion to the Spectators, who delight in such inhuman Actions: It is incredible to see with what Courage and Bravery these Wretches behave in the midst of these Tortures and agonies of Death, not once seeming to bemoan themselves, believing and imagining their Enemies will have the same Fate when they fall into the Hands of those belonging to their Nation.

There was an *Indian* put to death whilst I was in the Country by the Kings Order, for cleaving the Scull of one of his own Nation with a *Tamahawk,* of which Wound he instantly died. The Offender was immediately brought forth, and two other *Indians* were ordered to get a couple of Ropes tyed up in the nature of Nooses, with which they strangled the Offender, one pulling one way and the other the contrary,

'till

'till he was dead; the nearest Relations of the deceased striking him on the Head with great Clubs. These are the most
common Methods that are yet known amongst them, by which
they torture and put one another to death; but doubtless
there are many other barbarous Methods that they make use
of, which as yet we are strangers to.

The King most commonly gives orders to put the offender
to Death, yet the punishment due to the offender is very
often left to the nearest Relation of the deceas'd, who prose-
cutes him with all the rage and fury imaginable, being both
Judge and Executioner till he is fully satisfied; yet this revenge is oftentimes bought of with their *wampum, Beads,
Tobacco,* and such like commodities, whereof they are very
fond, and are useful amongst them, though the crimes were
of the highest Nature, Villany, or Barbarity that cou'd be
acted by Mankind, yet these trifles make a sufficient attone-
ment for all.

They have a strange custom or Ceremony amongst them,
to call to mind the persecutions and death of the Kings their
Ancestors slain by their Enemies, at certain Seasons, and
particularly when the *Savages* have been at War with any
Nation, and return from their Country without bringing
home some Prisoners of War, or the Heads of their Enemies.
The King causes as a perpetual remembrance of all his pred-
ecessors to beat and wound the best beloved of all his Children with the same Weapons wherewith they had been kill'd
in former times, to the end that by renewing the Wound, their
Death should be lamented a fresh.

The King and his Nation being assembled on these Occasions, a Feast is prepared, and the *Indian* who is authorized
to wound the Kings Son, runs about the House like a distracted Person crying and making a most hidious noise all
the time with the Weapon in his Hand, wherewith he wounds

the

the Kings Son, this he performs three several times, during which interval he presents the King with Victuals or *Cassena,* and it is very strange to see the *Indian* that is thus struck never offers to stir till he is wounded the third time, after which he falls down backwards streaching out his Arms and Legs as if he had been ready to expire, then the rest of the Kings Sons and Daughters, together with the Mother and vast Numbers of Women and Girls fall at his Feet and Lament and Cry most bitterly; during this time the King and his retinue are Feasting, yet with such profound silence for some Hours, that not one Word, or even a Whisper is to be heard amongst them, after this manner they continue till Night, which ends in Singing, Dancing, and the greatest joy imaginable.

The *Sapona Indians* live at the West branch of *Cape Fear,* or *Clarendon River,* which is very beautiful, and has good Land about it; it is five or six Days Journey over the Mountains to go to the *South-Sea.* These Mountains are very Barren, with abundance of Rocks and Marble, but no Fowl or Water are to be found in these Parts. The *Indians* residing here are very powerfull, but seldom make visits amongst us except it be their Traders who bring us *Skins* and *Furs.*

The *Toteras* are neighbouring *Indians* to the *Saponas,* and live *West-ward* in the Mountains; I have been informed by some of them that Trade amongst the *Europeans,* that they have *Bazoar-stone,* but I never saw any of it whilst I was in those parts.

The *Keyawees* live likewise on a Branch of *Cape Fear* River which lies to the *North-west.* The Lands here are very Fertile and in many places abounding with Rocks of several sorts of Stones, such as *Lime-stone, Marble,* and the like.

I have

I have frequently convers'd with their *Doctors,* who are in great request and esteem amongst them, they told me of many great cures that they have performed, but woud never discover any thing of what they knew, or by what Herbs or plants they perfected them, notwithstanding I importun'd them and even offered rewards.  These *Savages* in general being a very wary People, seldom or never revealing any of their secrets to the *Europeans,* yet are willing to assist them in any *Indian* disorder that should afflict them, as in the biting of *Snakes* or any other misfortune of that Nature wherein they have any Knowledge, but as to *European* Disorders they are entire Strangers, which most commonly prove fatal amongst them.

The *Indians* in *Carolina* have no Fences to part each others Lots in their *Corn-Fields,* but every Man knows his own proportion, and it scarce ever happens that they rob one another of so much as an *Ear* of *Corn;* which if any is found to do, he is sentenced by the Elders to Work and plant for him that was Robb'd, till he is fully recompenc'd for all the damage or loss he has sustained in his *Corn-Field;* this is very punctually performed, and the Thief held in disgrace that steals from any of his Friends or the Nation he belongs to.

When these *Savages* live near the Waters they frequent the Rivers in *Summer-time* very much where both Men and Women often in a Day go in naked to wash themselves, not both Sexes together, yet this is not out of any point of modesty that being a virtue or qualification that is very little regarded or make use of amongst these People.

These *Indians* generally are the best marks Men with *Guns* that are to be met with in most parts of the World, and commonly kill what they Shoot at with a single Ball; this is prin-

cipally

cipally owing to the steadiness in their Limbs and the sharp Sight with which they are endued. They take a great deal of pains when they buy a *Gun* first, to find out if it has any fault in the Barrel, which they generally take out of the stock and cut a Notch in a Tree where they make it streight, if there be occasion, and after shoot several times at markes, that they may be acquainted with its faults and perfections, this they do before they go to kill *Deer,* or any other kind of Game that is to be met with as they hunt in Woods. It is remarkable in them that they will seldom stir or go abroad into the Woods to Hunt before the *Sun* is an Hour or two heigh, and hath exhaled most part of the Dew from the Earth, then are they indefatigable in walking from Morning till Night in pursuit of their Game. When they are Traveling in the Woods together, they always keep a constant Pace, neither will they stride over a Tree that lyes across a path in their way, but always go round it, which is a quite contrary custom to the *Europeans,* but for what reason the *Indians* use this Ceremony I never cou'd learn, though I have frequently importuned them on that Head. And what is worthy of Observation is, that none of the *Indians* in *North-Carolina* are to be met with Left Handed; whether this be owing to their method of Nursing, or otherwise, I cannot account for. When ever they cut with a Knife, they always turn the Edge towards themselves, whereas the *Europeans* cut and Whittle from them.

Before the Arrival of the *Europeans* in these parts of *America,* these *Savages* not knowing the use of *Steel* and *Flints,* they got their fire from Sticks, which by vehement collision or rubbing together kindle and take fire. This method they will sometimes practice even now when it has happen'd through rainy Weather, or some other accident,

Xx that

that they have wet their *Spunk,* or *Touch-wood,* which is a sort of soft Corkey substance, generally of a *Cinamon* colour, and grows in the *Concave* or hollow part of an *Oak, Hickory,* and several other sorts of Wood, which they dig out with an *Ax* as they have occasion. It is in great plenty in *Carolina,* and is always kept by the *Europeans* and *Indians* instead of *Touch-wood* and *Tender,* both which it exceeds.

It is very surprizing to find so many different Languages amongst them as there are, there being few Nations that understand each other. But I believe the principal reason of this great difference and confusion of Languages as are to be met with amongst them, is owing to these People seldom or never conversing with any Nation but their own. And I have often observed several of the *Indians* with whom I have been acquainted and freely conversed with at *Bath* and *Edentown,* that when I chanc'd to meet them in the Woods, they wou'd not speak one Word of *English* (which they could do tolerably well) but would either answer me in their own Language or by signs; the reason whereof I coud never understand, though I made all the strict enquiry I could. These differences in their Languages cause Jealousies and fears amongst them, which often occasion Wars, wherein they destroy each other; otherwise the *Christians* had not in all probability settled themselves so easily as they have done, had these tribes of Savages united themselves into one People, or general interest, or were they so but every hundred Miles together. In short, they are a strange sort of People under their present Circumstances, and have such odd and uncouth ways in their management and course of living, that it seems a miracle to us how they bring about their designs as they do, when their ways are commonly quite contrary to ours. I am perswaded that were it not for the continual

Wars

Wars they have amongst themselves, they wou'd enjoy the happiest state in this World of all Mankind, being neither Slaves to Riches or Grandure, which bewitches the greatest part of the World, and occasions daily care and trouble in those that are thus in Love with it, which these *Savages* are entirely free from.

*Drunkeness* and several other Vices were intirely unknown to them before the Arrival of the *Christians* amongst them, and *Swearing,* their Language cannot express, yet those that learn *English* soon learn that fashionable vice of *Swearing,* and it is generally the first thing they can talk, hearing those vile and abominable expressions so often repeated by the *Europeans.* The many Vices they see and hear daily practiced by the *Christians,* have in a great measure perverted these miserable Creatures, that they never desire to be instructed in the light of the *Gospel,* but rather look upon us as a more unworthy race of People than themselves; that at this very Day they are no nearer *Christianity* (in all appearance) than they were at the first discovery made by the *Christians* of this part of the World. Yet it is most certain, that they have several abominable vices amongst them, which no doubt they might be brought off, if the *Europeans* woud show those good examples of Virtue, Piety, and Morality, which are essentially necessary for every *Christian* to do and practice. They have likewise several good Qualities amongst them, and are very Hospitable and fond of the *Europeans,* who generally look upon them with all the disdain immaginable, and very often return ill Offices for their gratitude.

They have a strange and odd Custom amongst them in making offerings of their first Fruits, and likewise throwing the first Bit or Spoonful of every Meal they sit down to, into

the Ashes near the Fire, and all the reason they give for so
doing is, that it is the same to them as the pulling of our
Hats and talking when we go to Victuals is to us.  The
*Indians* in *Carolina* call *Rum* and *Physick* by the same
Name, and the reason they give is, because *Rum* makes Peo-
ple sick, as if they had taken any Physical or Poysonous
Plant, notwithstanding they cannot forbear drinking it to
excess, when they can by any means purchase it or any other
Spiritous Liquor.

They are a craving People, and if you give them any
thing by way of Present, they imagine that it obliges you to
give them another, and so on, until you have given them all
you have; so insatiable and unreasonable are they in their
Demands, that they have no bounds to them.  If they give
any thing as a Present, it is with a View to receive twice the
Value, for they have no consideration that you shall want or
have any occasion for those things you give them; for their
way of Living is so contrary to ours, that neither we nor they
can fathom one anothers Designs or Methods.

They set the least value upon Time of any People in the
World, for if they are going out to Hunt, Fish, or any other
indifferent Business, you may keep them as long as you
please provided you entertain them in Discourse, and seem
pleased with their Company; yet no People are more expeditious and safer Messengers than they, when any extraordinary Business that they are sent about requires it.

The *Indian Women's* Work in this Province is generally
to dress their Victuals for the whole Family, and make
*Mats, Baskets, Girdles* of *Possum's Hair,* and such like
things, which they commonly sell to the *Europeans.*  The
*Mats* they make are of *Rushes,* about five Feet broad, and
two Fathom long, sowed double, whereby they become very

commodious

commodious to lay under our Beds, or to sleep upon in the *Summer* Season in the Day, and for our Slaves at Night. There are other *Mats* made of *Flags,* which the *Tuskeruro Indians* make and sell to the Planters. The *Baskets* our neighbouring *Indians* make are all of a very fine sort of *Bullrushes,* and sometimes of *Silk-grass,* which they work with the figures of *Beasts, Birds, Fishes,* and the like; in these they carry several sorts of *Fruits, Flowers,* and many other things of that nature, which they either sell or make Presents of to the *Christians.* The *Savage Indians* who live a great way from the *Christians,* make both their *Baskets* or *Mats* of split *Reeds,* which are exceedingly neat and handsome, being made only of the outward shining part of the *Cane;* with these I have seen *Mats, Baskets* and *Dressing Boxes,* very artificially done, they sell these to the Planters when they come down amongst them to dispose of their *Deer-Skins, Furs,* and other Commodities.

The *Indians* that live near the *Christians* frequently Buy or rather Barter *Deer-Skins* and other Commodities for *Rum,* which they carry to the *Indians* that live *Westward* on this and the other side of the Mountains, who never knew what it was 'till within these few Years: This Liquor they carry in *Rundlets* for many hundred Miles, but sometimes they cannot forbear breaking their Cargo in their Journies, and sit down in the Woods and drink it all up; then they begin to Hollow and Shout after such a manner, that the most distracted Persons can scarce be compared to them. When they happen to carry it safe (which they seldom do without drinking some part of it, which they supply by filling up the Vessel with Water) and come amongst the *Indian Towns;* those that buy the *Rum* of them have so many Mouthfulls for a *Deer-Skin,* they never use or have any other kind

of

of Measure at present: for this purpose the Buyer always makes choice of his Man who hath generally the widest Mouth, whom he brings with him to the Place where it is to be disposed of, with a Bowl to put it in.

The *Indian Merchant,* or Seller, looks very narrowly to the Man's Mouth that measures it, for fear he should swallow any down, either through wilfulness, or otherwise, which if he should happen to do, the *Merchant* or some of his Party do not scruple immediately to knock the fellow down, exclaiming at the same time against him for false Measure, so that the Buyer is obliged to get another Mouth Piece to measure it by; most certain it is, that the *Indians* have not such puny Palates (as many of the *Europeans* have) otherwise they would find out some decent Method or other to measure their Liquor. This way of Trading must not only seem strange but very diverting, to the *European* Spectators, to see so much Quarreling and Controversy, as frequently happens in this new and uncommon way of Dealing or measuring *Rum*.

The *Indian* King is the Ruler of the Nation he belongs to, and has others under him to assist him, as his *War Captains* and *Counsellors,* who are chosen out of the most ancient and wise Men of his Nation. These he consults in all general Debates, concerning *War* or *Peace, Trade, Hunting,* and all the Adventures and Accidents of human Affairs, that appear or come within their Jurisdiction, where all these Matters are discoursed of and argued *pro* and *con* very deliberately (without making any Parties or Divisions) with the greatest Conduct and Prudence immaginable, having nothing more at Heart than what may be intirely for the publick Good and safety of their Nation, always valuing that before their own private Interest. After every Man has given his

Opinion

Opinion freely as he thinks proper, yet he that has the most
Voices, or in summing up what hath been offered, and is
found to be the most reasonable, that they make use of without Jars or Wrangling, and put it in execution the first
Opporttunity that offers; these being People that discharge
their Duty with all the integrity and justice immaginable;
every town amongst them has a Ruler or Governor over it,
yet the King is absolute over his whole Nation.

The Succession falls not directly to the King's Son, but
to his Sisters, which is a sure way to prevent Impostures in
the Succession. They sometimes poyson the Heir that they
do not approve of, or judge incapable not to govern them.
The King himself is commonly the chief Person concerned
in this wicked and abominable Practice. The *Indians* are so
well acquainted with the Poysons that this Country produces,
that they have been known to poyson whole Families, and
most part of the Town; and it is certain, that they can poyson
a running Spring or Fountain of Water, that whoever drinks
thereof, will soon after infallibly dye. When the Offender
is discovered, his own Relations urge for his being put to
death, whom nothing will appease but the most cruel Tortures Imagination can invent, and these executed in the most
public manner that is possible for such a Tragical Scene to
be acted, so great is their abhorrence of such wicked Practices. All the Nations to whom the Offender belongs, and
the other Nations in Peace with them within a hundred
Miles or more (if it be possible to acquaint them) are summoned to come and appear at such a Time and Place, to see
and rejoyce at the Torments and Death of such a Person,
who is the common and professed Enemy to all the friendly
*Indians* thereabouts, who now lies under the Condemnation

of

of the whole Nation, and accordingly is to be put to Death at such a time as they prefix.

Upon this Summons or Notice, all that are able to appear from all the adjacent parts, with all the Joy imaginable, as if they were going to celebrate some Play or other Diversion for the Entertainment of the whole Company. At this Meeting they generally have a Feast prepared before they begin the Execution of the Criminal, which they perform in the manner following: They bring the Prisoner to the place appointed for his Execution, where he is set down upon the Ground, all the Company get about him, and there is not one sorrowful or dejected Countenance to be seen amongst them: Every thing being thus prepared, the Person appointed to be chief Executioner takes a Knife, and bids the Criminal hold out his Hands, which he does, then another cuts the Skin round the Wrist, which is drawn off like a Glove, and flead off at the Fingers end, break his Joints and Bones with great Clubs, and buffet and torment him, 'till some violent Blow puts an end to his wretched Life: They burn him to Ashes, which they carefully gather and throw down the Rivers, as unworthy that the Earth should contain them.

As soon as this tragical Scene is over, they begin their Feast, and eat and drink chearfully, repeating all the Actions of the Tormenters, with the Prisoners behaviour during his Tortures; thus they spend the Night in one continued Scene of Mirth and Jollity, in having put to Death the common Enemy of their Nation, and all the others in Friendship with them.

These Accusations are often wrongfully laid against *Indian Heroes,* or a great Man they have a mind to get rid of, that has more Courage and Conduct than his Neighbouring Kings, or *War Captains;* it is then they alledge the Practice

of

of Poysoning *Indians* against him, and make a rehearsal of every Person that died for a Year or two, and give out they were poysoned by such an *Indian;* this Report being once spread abroad, stirs up all the Relations of the deceased against the said Person; by such means they take an advantage against him, and he is presently put to death.

They are very reserved and politick in these Affairs, and will attend a long time with a great deal of Patience to bring about their designs, these People being never impatient or over hasty in executing any of their designs of revenge; yet they never forget injuries done by their Enemies, but always take a proper time to accomplish them, for they will endure a great many Misfortunes, Losses, and Disappointments without ever showing themselves vexed or uneasy at them.

If at any time they go by Water, and there happens a Head or contrary Wind, they never fret, or make themselves uneasy as the *Europeans* are most subject to do; and let what troubles or misfortunes so ever attend them they never seem to relent, but carry it off with as much resolution as any People upon Earth. Neither are they guilty of that vice so common amongst the *Europeans* of envying each others happiness, because their station is not equal or above their Neighbours: Of this Sin I never knew an example amongst them, though they are a People that set as great a value upon themselves as any sort of Men in the World, upon which account they find something valuable in themselves above Riches or Grandure.

Thus he that is a good Warriour is the proudest creature living, and he that is an expert Hunter is esteem'd very much by the People and himself; yet all these are natural virtues or Gifts and not Riches, which are as often in the possession of a Fool as a wise Man. Several of them are possess'd of great Quantities of *Deer,* and *Bever Skins, Wampum, Amunition,* and many other things which are esteemed Riches amongst them, yet such an *Indian* is no more esteemed or regarded by them than any ordinary Fellow, provided he has no Personal Endowments, which are the only Ornaments and Perfections that must gain him credit and esteem amongst these People, for a great dealer amongst them is no otherwise valued or respected, than a Man that strains his Wits, and fatigues himself to furnish others with necessaries of Life.

There is something surprizingly undaunted in their Behaviour when they are taken Captives, and expect to die after the most miserable and tormenting manner that *Savages* can invent against such unfortunate Creatures, as happen to be their Prisoners; for at the very approach of Death they are observ'd to sing, and shew the greatest resolution and bravery of any People in the World; having no dread or fear to die; for they know by instinct of Nature, and daily Experience, that all things living are subject to Death, wherefore they have that great and noble gift to submit to every thing that happens, with the greatest resignation imaginable, and value nothing that attacks them in this Life.

They are never fearful in the Night, neither do the thoughts or dread of Spirits ever give them the least trouble, such as the *Hobgoblins* and *Bug-bears,* the Apprehensions of which we suck in our infancy from Nurses and Servants, who sugest to us, strange and Idle Tales of *Fairies* and *Witches,* which make such impressions on us in our tender Years, that at maturity we are most commonly afraid of our own *Shaddows,* and carry *Pigmie-souls* in *Giant-bodies* ever after, by which means we are so much depriv'd of reason and

unman'd,

unman'd, that we are never afterwards able to be Masters of half the Courage and Bravery nature designed for us, whilst we remain in this World. Several instances whereof are daily to be met with amongst us, which I omit as being Foreign to what we treat of. Not but that the *Indians* have as many lying Stories of *Spirits* and *Conjurers* as any People; but they never tell them with that disadvantage, or after that frightful manner, that the *Europeans* are subject to inform their Children. The old Men amongst them bring themselves into very great esteem by making the others believe their familiarity with *Devils* and *Spirits,* and what great advantage they have thereby, which if it once gain credit amongst them, they are ever afterwards held in the greatest respect and veneration imaginable; and whatever they impose upon these People for the future is received as certain Truths.

Some of them are so very poor, that they have no manner of Cloaths, only a Belt and wad of Moss, to cover their Nakedness; these are such as are lazy, or will not Work or Hunt, and are given to Gaming and Drunkenness; yet these get Victuals as well as the rest, because that is in common amongst them all: If they are caught in Theft amongst themselves, the Offender is made a Slave until such time as he makes full satisfaction to the Injured Person; but to steal from the *Christians* they reckon no Crime, nor think any harm in so doing; notwithstanding they are seldom guilty of this Vice amongst themselves or the *Christians.*

The *Indians* (as I observ'd before) are indefatigable and expert Travellers in the Woods, and though they have not the use of our *artificial Compass* to guide them, yet they are never at a loss to find their way, and let them be in never so great a Wilderness, they understand the *North Point* perfectly well, the principle Guide they have to instruct them, being altogether Natural, which is a short *Moss* that grows on some Trees exactly on the *North side* thereof.

They have likewise Names for eight of the thirty two Points, and call the Winds by their several Names as we do, but indeed more properly; for the *North-West Wind* they call the *cold Wind,* the *North-East,* the *wet Wind,* the *South,* the *warm Wind,* and so agreeably of the rest, according to what Weather is produced by each of them.

It frequently happens that they have large Rivers or Lakes to pass over, and if the Weather be so foggy, as it sometimes happens, especially in the *Spring* and fall of the Leaf, that they cannot see what Course to steer, in this case they being on one side of the River or Lake, they know what course such a Place (which they intend for) bears from them: Their Method in such cases is this, they get a great many *Sticks* and *Chunks* of Wood in their *Canoe,* and set off directly for their intended Port, and as they proceed, they keep throwing over Board a piece of Wood, which directs them; for by seeing how the Stick bears from the Sterne of the *Canoe,* they observe to keep right aft; this is their *Compass,* by which they will go over a Water of ten or twenty Leagues abroad.

They know the Head of any River, though five, six, or seven hundred Miles off, although they were never there before, as is often proved by their appointing to meet on the Head of such or such a River, where perhaps not one of them ever had been, yet they shall rendezvous there exactly at the time prefixed. If they meet with any Obstructions in their Journey, they leave certain Marks in the way, that those who come after them will understand how many have passed before them, and which way they are gone. It is not

to

to be imagined how they will trace and find out each other in these solitary and desolate Woods and Desarts, where there are no Roads to guide, or any humane Creature to tell the way. They are also very expeditious in finding out the *Negroes* that frequently run away from their Masters into the Woods, where they commit many outrages against the *Christians,* as it happened in *Virginia* not long since, where above *three Hundred* joined together, and did a great deal of Mischief in that Province before they were suppressed. The *Indian* Kings are sent for on these Occasions, who soon find out their Haunts, and commonly kill many of them whenever they are sent in pursuit after them, for they never cease pursuing 'till they destroy or hunt them out of the Woods: this they will do in the tenth part of the Time that the *Europeans* could do. These *Negroes* whenever they find the *Indians* in pursuit of them, they return, and chuse rather to submit to the *Christians,* whom they have injured, than fall into the Hands of the others, who have a natural aversion to the *Negroes,* and take Pleasure in putting them to the most exquisite Torments, when ever they find them thus in the Woods, being allowed so to do by the *Christians.*

I saw four and twenty of these *Negroes* hanged in *Virginia,* for conspiring against their Masters, who had taken Sanctuary in the Woods for some time before they were discovered, or hunted out by the *Indians,* who are very serviceable to the *Christians* in those Parts, and many other Provinces in the hands of the *English.*

Another Instance of this Nature happened not many Years ago in this Province; some of our neighbouring *Indians* made their Complaint to the Governor, that two *Indians* from the Mountains came to their Town when they were abroad, and had taken one of their Wives by surprize, and

carried

carried her away; the Governor desired them immediately to pursue them, and if it were possible to recover the Woman, which two of them accordingly did: In travelling some Days, they brought back the Woman, and the Skins of the Heads of their Enemies; though they had been three Days gone off with the Woman before the others pursued them; how they could discover which way they went, in those Woods, and Desarts, is not a little surprizing, and few or none can account for but themselves.

In their War Expeditions they have certain *Hieroglyphicks,* whereby each Party inform the other of the success or losses they have met with; all of which is so exactly performed by their *Sylvan* Marks and Characters, that they are never at a loss to understand one another, yet there never were found any Letters among the People in this Province, and I am persuaded that there are neither Letters or Learning to be met with amongst any of the Natives in all *America.*

It is admirable to see how exactly they will draw Maps of all the Rivers, Towns, Mountains, and Roads, or what you shall enquire of them, which may be drawn by their Directions, and come to a small matter of Latitude, reckoning by the Days Journies. These Maps they will draw in the Ashes of the Fire, and sometimes on a *Mat* or piece of *Bark.*

I have likewise seen a Pen put into one of their Hands, wherewith he has not only drawn the Rivers, Bays, and other parts of this Country, but likewise has imitated the Hand Writing of those in Company very nicely, but whenever they make these Discoveries to us, we must be very much in their Favour, otherwise they will not show you any thing they do or know.

There

There are several sorts of rich Mines in this Country, some of which the *Indians* are well acquainted with, and particularly one, whereof they make *Bullets* for their Guns to shoot *Deer* and other Game: I have seen some of this Oar with them, which is *Lead,* and of the richest sort, but they will not discover to us where they get it, especially if it be near their hunting Quarters; for, they say, it is this *Metal* the *Europeans* so much covet (as they do their *Peak* and *Ronoak*) which if they should discover to the *Christians,* they would settle near them, and so deprive them of the best hunting Matches they have, as they have already done where they are settled or inhabited; so that by that Means they shall be driven out of their Country to some unknown parts to live, hunt, and get their Bread in.

These are the Reasons that they give for not discovering what they know of this Nature. But amongst the *Christians* there have been few or no Enquiries made at present, but what were discovered by Chance; yet I am satisfied that the Mines and Minerals that this Country produces are extraordinary good and valuable, several Pieces whereof are daily to be seen amongst them, who make no other use of it than what I have already mentioned.

The principal Reason of our want of Knowledge in the Mines and Minerals, and many other valuable Secrets in Nature that are produced in this part of the World (as the *Spaniards* are with theirs) is for want of Encouragement amongst us; for I am certain were such an Affair managed and carried on by a Company of Wealthy Members, they would not only find their Account in so advantageous an Undertaking, but likewise be a great Means to enrich the *British* Monarchy. This I testifie from the Knowledge and Dis-

covery

covery of some Mines that were made known to me during my stay in that Country, which I shall be ready to discover when ever there is just Encouragement given. Such a beneficial Undertaking might be carried on very cheap in this Country, where there is not only the benefit of a fine healthful Climate, and all manner of Necessaries for Life in great plenty, but likewise all other Conveniences proper for carrying on such an Affair, to be had in it. I coud say a great deal more on this Head, having travelled in several parts of this Province to make the best discoverys I possibly cou'd of the valuable produce of the Country.

As for *Iron-Mine,* it is no where better and in greater plenty, yet there is none of it Manufactured at present. I will just mention one thing more about the *Mines,* which I had like to have forgot: Not many Years ago an *Indian* came privately to some of the Planters in this Province, and told them he wou'd discover a *Mine* for some small gratuity, but at the same time conjured them to Secrecy, for if it were known to his Nation, they woud put him to Death, and likewise that he never durst come amongst them the Second time for fear of being discovered by his Country-men. Things being agreed upon, the *Indian* brings them to the *Mine,* and desired that they wou'd take particular care to remember and find out the place again, and immediately left them, and retired into the Woods; with transports of Joy they returne home, bringing some of the Oar with them, which was a very rich *Copper-Mine,* for I have seen both the Oar and some of it that was Smelted, but when they had prepared all things necessary to dig and search for it, yet they cou'd never find out the place again, or meet with the *Indian* afterwards.

When

When they are disposed to hunt in the Woods, they generally go out in great Numbers together, and several Days Journies from home. They always begin these Hunting matches at the approach of *Winter,* when the Leaves, are fallen from the Trees, and become dry, or when Skins and Furs are best in Season. It is then they burn the Woods, by setting fire to the wither'd Leaves, *Bent* and *dry Grass,* which they do with matches made of the Black *Moss* that hangs on the Trees, which is sometimes above six Feet long. This *Moss* when dead becomes black (though of an Ash colour before) and will then hold Fire as well as the best Match in *Europe.* In places where this *Moss* is not .to be found (as towards the Mountains and Heads of the Rivers) they make Lentels of the Bark of *Cypress,* which serves as well.

Thus they frequently leave their Houses and retire into the Woods for four or five Months together, *viz. November, December, January, February,* and *March,* at which time the Skins are in Season, and set Fire to the Woods for many Miles together to drive out the Deer and other Game into small Necks of Lands, and other places where they fix their Guards, by which means they kill and destroy what they please, especially such as strive to escape the Fire and get through the passes they have made for that purpose.

In these Hunting matches they bring their Wives and Mistresses along with them, where they eat several kinds of Fruits which that Country produces, and live in all the Mirth and Jolity that it is possible for such People to entertain themselves with. It is in these Hunting matches they get their complement of *Deer-Skins, Furs,* and many other commodities to trade with the *Christians,* the *Deer-Skins* being in Season here in *Winter,* which is contrary in *Eng-*

Zz                                                                      *land*

*land* and *Ireland;* most of all their small Game they kill with their Bows and Arrows, such as *Geese, Turkeys, Ducks,* and various kinds of wild Beasts, as *Raccoons, Possums, Squirrels,* and several other sorts of Vermine, judging it not worth throwing Powder and Shot after them.

The wild *Turkeys* being very plenty in *North-Carolina,* especially in the *Oak Lands,* as most of it is that lies any distance backwards; some of these they Roast or Boyl, others they Barbecue and eat with *Bears-grease,* this is accounted amongst them a good Dish, and indeed I do not doubt but it is, for the *Bears-grease* (as I said before) is the sweetest and least offensive to the Stomach of any Fat of Animals yet known in *America;* and I am very certain that the *Turkeys* are Fat, and exceeding good eating, if well dress'd.

The Men never beat their *Corn* to make *Bread,* that is the Women's Work, and especially the Girls, where you shall see four of them beating with long *Pestils* in a narrow wooden *Mortar,* and every one keeping her stroke so exactly, that it is worthy of admiration, and curious to behold them when they are thus at Work; for these *Indians* have no manner of *Mills,* or any other way to make their *Meal* but with *Mortars.*

Their *Cookery* continues from Morning till Night, dressing their *Venison* after different Methods, according to each one's Fancy, this being the Women's business: The Hunting makes them Hungry, and they are a People that eat very often, and frequently get up at Midnight, and other unseasonable Hours to eat and satisfie their craving Appetites, notwithstanding you shall never see any of them Corpulent or Fat.

They plant several sorts of *Pulse,* part of which they eat green in the *Summer,* keeping sufficient quantities for their *Winter* Provision; this they carry with them to eat in their

Hunting

Hunting Matches. The small *Red Pease* are very common with them, and several other sorts, which they boyle with their Meat, or with *Pigeon's* or *Bear's* Fat; this Food makes them break Wind backwards, which the Men frequently do, seem well pleased, and laugh heartily, being accounted no Ill Manners amongst them; but the Women are seldom known to be guilty of that indecent Custom.

At their setting out either for War or Peace, or upon any other extraordinary Expedition, there are several Formalities amongst them, and they whose Business it is to attend their hunting Camp, are generally those that are not good or expert Hunters, therefore are employed to carry Burthens, to get Bark for their Cabins, and all other servile Work, likewise to go too and fro to their Towns, and bring News to the old People (whom they leave behind) of their Success and Welfare.

The Women are likewise obliged to carry their Loads of Grain and other Provisions with them to these randezvous, and provide Firewood to dress Victuals; for a good Hunter or Warrior, in these Expeditions is employed in no other Business than the Affairs of Game or Battle. The great quantities of Fruit that they dry in the *Summer* over Fires and Hurdles, and in the Sun, are at these times brought into the Field; as are also the *Cakes* and *Quiddonies* of *Peaches;* with this Fruit and the *Bill-berries* dried, they stew and make fruit Bread and Cakes, and have variety of other sorts of Fruits preserved, which are brought out upon these occasions.

In some parts of this Province, especially near the Mountains, and amongst the *Indians* in those Places, they have several hundred Gallons of *Pigeon's Oil* or Fat, which they preserve for their *Winter* Stores, using it with their *Pulse, Roots,* and *Bread,* as we do Butter: These Fowl are so plenty, that Millions of them are seen in Flocks in a Day, they sometimes break large Boughs of the *Pine,* and other Trees whereon they perch or roost at Night, making the Ground as white as *Snow* with their Dung, and destroying every Herb or small Plant where it falls, being in some Places above half a Foot deep. The *Indians* take a Light of *Pitch-Pine* in one Hand, a long Pole in the other, and go into the Woods at Night where they are, and kill thousands of them by knocking them off the Trees; this is always done in the *Winter,* at which time they appear in Flocks.

Thus they remain in these hunting Camps all the *Winter,* and part of the *Spring,* 'till such time as the Season approaches for planting their *Maze, Pulse,* and other Fruits. In these Quarters at spare Hours, they make *Baskets* and *Mats* to lie upon, and those that are not extraordinary Hunters, make Bowls, Dishes and Spoons, of *Gum-Wood* and *Tulip-Tree.* Others where they find a Vein of *White* Clay fit for their Purpose, make *Tobacco Pipes,* and several other things, which are often transported and bartered with other *Indians* that have plenty of *Deer* Skins, or such Commodities as they have occasion for. They buy with these Manufactures, their Raw Skins with the Hair on, which our Neighbouring *Indians* bring to their Towns, and in the *Summer* make their Slaves and bad Hunters dress them; the *Winter* Sun being not strong enough to dry them; those that are dried in their Cabins are black with the *Lightwood* Smoak, which they commonly burn.

Their way of dressing their Skins is by soaking them in Water; they get the Hair off with an Instrument made of the Bone of a *Deer's Foot* (some use a sort of *Iron Drawing Knife,* which they purchase from the *Europeans*) after the Hair is take off, they dissolve *Deer's Brains* (which they

have

have made into Cakes and baked in the Embers) in a Bowl of Water, where they soak and rub the Skins 'till they have sucked up all the Water, then they dry them gently, and keep continually working them with an *Oyster-shell,* or some such thing to scrape withal 'till they are dry, by which means they become soft and pliable. The Skins dressed after this manner, will not endure Wet, but become hard; they therefore Cure them in the Smoak, or Tan them with the Bark of Trees: When they have not the Brains to dress their Skins, they use the young *Indian Corn* beaten to *Pulp,* which hath the same Effect as the former, for they are never at a loss for one or the other to Cure them, but whether they have any other Method is unknown to the *Christians,* which I am apt to believe they have; for I have seen abundance of them drest, which would endure the Water, and were as pliable as any in *Europe,* and would wash as well.

They are not only good and expert Hunters of the Wild Beasts and Game of the Forest, but likewise very dextrous in taking the Fish in the Rivers and Waters near which they inhabit, and are acquainted with. Thus they that live a great way up the Rivers practice striking *Sturgeon, Rock-fish* or *Bass,* and several other sorts of fish with lights, that come up the Rivers and Creeks to Spawn.

They have *Fish-gigs* that are made of the Reeds or *Hollow Canes,* these they cut and make very sharp, with two Beards, and taper at the Point like a *Harpoon;* being thus provided, they either wade into the Water, or go into their *Canoes,* and paddle about the Edges of the Rivers or Creeks, striking all the Fish they meet with in the depth of five or six Feet of Water, or as far as they can see them; this they commonly do in dark calm Nights, and whilst one attends

with

with a Light made of the *Pitch-pine,* the other with his *Fish-gig* strikes and kills the Fish: It is diverting to see them fish after this manner, which they sometimes do in the Day; how dexterous they are in striking, is admirable, and the great quantities they kill by this Method.

They likewise kill vast quantities of *Sturgeon,* which they take in Snares as we do *Pike* and *Trout* in *Europe.* The *Herrings* in *March* and *April* run a great way up the Rivers and fresh Streams to Spawn, where they make large Wears with Hedges of long *Poles* or *Hollow Canes,* that hinder their passage only in the middle, where an artificial pond is made to take them in, so that they cannot return. These Wears are common all over the Rivers, and fresh Water Streams in these parts, where they take vast quantities of *Herrings, Trouts, Pikes,* and several other sorts of Fish that are plentifully to be met with in them.

The taking of Craw Fish is likewise very pleasant and diverting, for when they are disposed to get these Shell Fish, they take a piece of *Venison* and half *Barbcue* or *Roast* it, then they cut it into thin *Slices,* which they stick through with Reeds about six Inches distance betwixt each piece, the Reeds are made sharp at one end, and they strike a great many of them down in the Bottom of the Water (thus baited) in small running Brooks where the Craw fish constantly frequent. Thus they sit by and attend those baited Sticks, every now and then taking them up to see how many are at the Bait, where they generally find abundance, so take them off and put them in Baskets provided for that purpose, and then stick down the Reeds again, by this method in a little time they will catch several Bushels full, which are as good as any in *Europe.*

Those

Those that live or frequent near the Salt Water take abundance of Fish of several sorts, some of them are very large, which to preserve, they first Barbecue, then pull them to pieces, and dry them in the Sun, and keep them for their Necessities; as for *Scate, Oysters, Cockles,* and several other sorts of Shell-fish, they open and dry upon Hurdles, keeping a constant Fire under them; these Hurdles are made of *Reeds* or *Hollow Canes,* in shape of a Gridiron. Thus they dry several Bushels of them, and keep for their Provision in time of scarcety.

At the time when they are on the Salts and Sea Coasts, they have another sort of Fishery for little *Shell-fish,* called in *England, Blackmoor's Teeth;* these they catch by tying bits of *Oysters* to a long String, and lay it in such places as they know these Fishes haunt; they get hold of the *Oysters* and suck them in, that they pull them up by the Strings in great Quantities; they carry these a great way into the Main Land to trade with the remote *Indians,* where they are of great value, but never near the Sea, being common, and therefore not much esteemed by them that live near the Salts.

It is an established Custom amongst all the Natives in these Parts, that the young Hunters never eat of that *Buck, Bear, Fish,* or any other sort of Game which happens to be the first they kill, because they believe if they should eat thereof, they never would be afterwards fortunate in Hunting. The like foolish Custom they hold when they make a Wear to take Fish in, if a Woman with Child eat of the first Dish caught therein, they say that Wear will never take much Fish in it afterwards.

The *Tobacco* is in such great Esteem amongst some Nations of the *Indians,* that they think their Gods are delighted

therewith,

therewith, whereupon they make Fires and cast some of the Powder thereof into it for a Sacrifice, and being in a Storm upon the Waters, to pacifie the *Bad Spirit,* they cast some up into the Air and the Water; likewise a Wear to take Fish, being newly made, they cast some thereon, and into the Air, as also for an escape from Danger. All this is performed with strange Ceremonies and Gestures, one while Stamping, Leaping, Dancing, clapping of Hands, and uttering of strange Words.

As for killing of *Snakes,* most *Indians* avoid it, and if they even lye in their way, they will not molest them, but pass by on the other side, because their Opinion is, that if they should kill them, the *Serpent's* kindred would destroy some of their Brethren, Friends, or Relations, in return. They have a thousand of these foolish Ceremonies and Customs amongst them, which they stedfastly believe, and are strict observers of, but are too tedious to mention, and would be of little or no advantage to the Readers.

There are some few of them that use the *Jewish* Custom of *Circumcision,* though this kind of Practice is but seldom used amongst them; I never knew but two Families in all the Nations of *Indians* I have conversed with, that were so; the Reason whereof I could never learn, notwithstanding I was very intimate with them, and have often urged them to give me an account on that Head, but could get no manner of Answer, which with them is as much as to say, *I will not tell you.* They have many other strange Customs amongst them, that they will render no Reason for, or give any Account of to the *Europeans.*

The *Savages* in these parts are never known to be guilty of that abominable Sin called SODOMY, as many in the *Philippian Islands* are said to be. Mr. *Candish* in his Travels

reporteth,

reporteth, ' That the *Savages* in *Capul,* an Island near *Ma-*
' *nila* in the *West Indies,* have a very strange Custom amongst
' them, which is this, every Man and Male Child hath a
' Nail of Tin thrust through the Head of his Private Mem-
' ber, being split and rivited at the lower End, this is done
' whilst they are young, and the place groweth up again
' without any great pain to the Child, this Nail they can
' take out and in as there is occasion,' And the same Author,
as a Confirmation of the Truth hereof, says, ' We ourselves
' have taken one of these Nails out of the Private Member
' of a King's Son, who was ten Years old.' This Custom
he likewise says, was granted at the Request of the Women
in that Country, who finding their Men to be given to
SODOMY, desired some Remedy against that Mischief, and
obtained this of the Magistrates.

They are very great *Conjurers,* of whom there are several
strange Stories related who perform their *Exorcism,* after
the following Manner. The *Sorcerer* apparells himself in
a clean dres'd *Deer Skin;* they make a large Fire in the
middle of the Plantation, the *Indians* all sitting round it;
the *Conjurer* is blindfolded very secure, and surrounds the
Fire three times; leaving the Company at the Fire, he went
some distance into the Woods, where he stayed a short time,
at his Return he surrounded the Fire as before, and leaving
them a second time, he went into the Woods, where he remained about half an Hour, he performed this *Exorcism*
the third time, after this he made a very strange and frightful Howling, which being finished, an *Indian* immediately
caught hold of him, and led him to the Fire; by this time
he was so feeble and weak that he could not stand alone,
being all over in a Sweat, and as wet as if he had fallen into

the River, after some little time he recovers his Strength, and gives them an Account of what they demand.

It is reported by several Planters in those parts, that they raise great Storms of Wind, and that there are many frightful Apparitions that appear above the Fires during the time of their *Conjuration,* that large Swarms of very strange and uncommon sorts of *Flies* have been seen to hover over the Fire for some time and then to fall into it, where they were all visibly consum'd, and likewise the Appearance of several frightful sorts of Birds, and lastly a strong smell of *Brimstone,* whilst they are performing these Charms.

I shall mention some of their practices, and so leave them to the Judgment of every Reader; these *Conjurers* are the *Priests* and *Doctors* of every Nation amongst the *Indians,* to whom the common People give great Credit and Respect, because they believe them to be great *Magicians,* that they frequently converse with the *good* and *bad Spirit.* They likewise make the Orations at every Feast or publick Meeting.

These *Conjurers* likewise serve them instead of *Physitians* and *Surgeons,* who constantly attend the sick, and always carry about them a bag full of Herbs to cure their disorders, these make Harangues about the deceas'd, let his Death be occasioned after ever so different a manner, for if it shou'd be occasion'd by Sickness, then he tells the People that it is the *bad Spirit* that occasion'd his Death. But if it shoud happen that an *Indian* comes to an untimely Death by any accident, then the *Doctor* makes an Oration suitable to the Occasion.

For it happen'd not many Years ago, that an *Indian* was kill'd by *Lightning,* and before the Interment, according to their Custom, every one had some hot Victuals or *Yaupan-Tea* given him, which he did with what he pleased. Then

the

the *Doctor* began to talk, and told the People what *Lightning* was, that it kill'd every thing upon the Earth, that the very Fishes did not escape, for it often reach'd the *Whales, Porpoises,* and other Fishes, and destroyed them; that everything strove to shun it, except the *Mice,* who he said were the busiest in eating their *Corn* in the *Fields* when it *Lightned* and *Thunderd* the most. He likewise added, that no Wood or Tree cou'd withstand it, except the *Black-Gum,* and that it wou'd run round that Tree a great many times to enter therein, but cou'd not effect it. Now you must understand that sort of *Gum* will not split or rive; therefore I suppose the Story might arise from thence. Lastly he began to tell ridiculous absurd lyes about *Lightning,* that cou'd be invented; as that an *Indian* of their Nation had once got *Lightning* in the likeness of a *Partrige,* that no other *Lightning* cou'd hurt him whilst he had that about him, that after he had kept it for several Years it got away from him, and that then he became as liable to be struck with *Lightning* as any other Man; thus they amuse the People with a Thousand such like ridiculous stories, which they receive for the most infallible Truths.

They likewise deliver the hearers several traditional stories of great Battles that were fought by their Ancestors, of strange Beasts and Birds that were to be met with many Years ago, and that a great *Rattle Snake* that lived in a Creek in *North-Carolina* kill'd abundance of *Indians,* but at last a *Bald Eagle* kill'd it, and they were rid of a *Serpent* that us'd to devour whole *Canoes* full of *Indians* at a time. So that you may see how easie these Wretches are to be impos'd upon by these old *Cunting Knaves,* who I am perswaded understand a little better than to give credit to any such Fooleries.

Aaa²

I

I will in the next place give some account of their *Physick* and *Surgery*. These *Doctors* or *Conjurors* are those (as I said before) that visit and attend the sick, who use many charms of *Witchcraft,* and to gain a greater esteem and credit amongst these People, they tell them that all their Destempers are the effects of the *bad* or *evil Spirit,* who has struck them with this or that malady. Therefore none of these *Doctors* undertake any distemper, but that he first comes to an *Exorcism* to effect the Cure, and acquaints the sick parties Friends or Relations, that he must converse with the *good Spirit,* to know whether the Patient will recover or not; if so, then he will drive out the *bad Spirit,* and then the sick Person will recover and become well.

When an *Indian* is sick, if they think there is much danger of Life, and that he is a great Man, or hath good Friends, their method or behaviour in curing is as follows. The *Doctor* is immediately sent for, and as soon as he comes into their *Cabin,* the sick Person is placed on a *Mat* or *Skin* stark naked, lying on his Back all uncover'd, except some small trifle that covers their nakedness when ripe, otherwise in Children, or young People there is nothing about them. In this manner the *Patient* lies when the *Conjurer* or *Doctor* appears, and generally the King of that Nation comes to attend him with a Rattle made of a *Gourd* with Pease or *Indian-Corn* in it, which the King delivers into the *Doctors* Hands, whilst another brings a Bowl of Water and sets it down.

Things being thus prepared, the *Doctor* then begins and utters some few Words softly; afterwards he smells to the Patients *Navel,* and sometimes Scarifies him a little with a *Flint,* or an Instrument made of *Rattle-Snake's Teeth* for that purpose, then he Sucks the part, and gets out a Mouth-

ful

ful of *Blood* and *Serum,* but *Serum,* chiefly, which he spits into the Bowl of Water, by which means he pretends to Suck out what occasions the Distemper.

Then he begins to mutter and talk apace; and at last to cut Capers and clap his Hands on his Britch and sides till he is all over in a Sweat, which to an *European* woud not only seem a very odd and strange Sight, but likewise that he was running Mad, every now and then Sucking the *Patient,* till such time as he gets great quantities of Blood and ill colour'd Matter, out of the *Belly, Armes, Breast, Forehead, Temples, Neck,* and most other parts of the Body, still continuing his Grimaces and Antick Postures, which to *Europeans* woud seem more like the Actions of Men in *Bedlam* than *Doctors* attending the Sick.

At last you will see the *Doctor* all over in a Sweat, and so feeble, that he is scarce able to stand or utter one Word, having quite spent himself, then he will cease for a while to recruit his Spirits, and begin again, 'till he comes to the same pitch of raving and seeming Madness as before; during all this time and these performances of the *Doctor,* the sick Person never so much as moves, although doubtless the Scarifying and Sucking must be a great punishment to him.

But they are the most patient under the Misfortunes of Life, of any People I ever saw in all my Travels: Lastly, the *Doctor* makes an end, and tells the Patient's Friends whether the sick Person will Live or Dye, and then some one that waits at this Ceremony takes the Blood away (which remains in a Lump in the middle of the Water) and immediately Buries it very secretly in the Ground, the Place being unknown to any but he that inters it.

These

These People are great Inchanters, and use many Charms of *Witchcraft,* for when they are troubled with the Head-ach, they tye a great Stone with a String to a Stick or Pole, and with certain Prayers, or bewitching expressions, they lift up the Stone from the Ground to the top of the Pole, which sometimes with all a Man's strength they cannot stir from the place; and at other times they lift as easy as a Feather; by this *Spell* and certain Ceremonious Words, they expect to have immediate ease and help for the Patient.   I am thoroughly satisfied that these *Conjurors* are very great Impostures, yet I have seldom or never known their Judgment fail in regard of the Patients living or dying, though I have seen them give their opinion after this manner several times:   Some affirm that there is a smell of *Brimstone* in the *Cabins* whilst they are thus *Conjuring,* which I cannot contradict, nor will I take upon me to argue how it came there, but shall proceed to another relation of one of their *Indian Kings* being sick, and the method us'd by the *Doctor* for the recovery of his health, which is something like the former, *viz.*

One of their Kings being sick, the *Doctor* was immediately sent for, and as soon as he arriv'd, he orderd a Bowl of Water to be brought him and placed before the King, on whom he sprinkled some part out of his Mouth, then he took a string of *Ronoak* about too Feet long (which is like a string of small Beads) this he held at one end between his Fingers, and the other touched the Kings Stomach; he began to mutter many expressions or Words, and to use many grimaces for sometime, at length the string of Beads that hung thus perpendicular, turn'd up as an *Eel* woud do, and without any motion of his Hand came all up in a Lump under his Hand, and remain'd so for a considerable time, he never

closing

closing his Hand all the while; at last they returned to their former shape and length; at which the *European* Spectators were much surprized, some of them confidently affirmed, that they heard something answer him whilst he muttered some Words, though there was nothing to be seen. The *Doctor* told the Company that the King would recover, and that his Disorder would remove into his Leg, that it would be much inflam'd and swell'd, which happened exactly as he foretold.

They also conjure for stollen Goods, though Robbery and Theft are not common Vices amongst them, yet they are sometimes guilty of these Crimes; and steal *Ronoak* and *Deer Skins* from each other; when they cannot discover the Thief, they immediately send for the *Conjurer* to find him out, and as soon as he appears, he begins after the following manner. First he orders three Fires to be made after a triangular Form, which is accordingly done; he is then hood-winked very securly with a *Deer Skin,* doubled two or three times, over his Face; when this is done, he is placed in the center of the three Fires: after he has made some Motions (as always these *Conjurers* do) he went directly out of one of the three gaps of the Fire, as directly as if he could see, muttering to himself, having a Stick in his Hand, with which, after some time, he gives two strokes very hard upon the Ground, and made thereon a kind of Cross, after which he told them the Name of the Person that had stolen the Goods, and said he would have a Mark like a Cross on his Back, which proved accordingly, for when he was taken and search'd, there appeared two great Wheals on his Back one cross the other.

There are several other Stories of this Nature, which the most substantial and credible Planters in these parts affirm for Truth, and that they have been Eye-witnesses to. They

also

also report that they have seen one of these *Conjurers* take a *Hollow Cane* about two Feet long, in his Mouth, and stand by a Creek side, where he called with the Reed two or three times, at last opened his Arms, and flew over a Creek about a quarter of a Mile broad, as if he had been running upon *Terra Firma.* I shall urge no Man's belief in this, having never seen it done by any of them, and only give it as reported above; but some of the former I have been a Witness to, therefore dare boldly assert as Fact.

As to their *Religion,* it is impossible to give any true Description of it, for as they can neither read nor write, whatever they have of this kind is founded meerly upon Tradition. There are a great many Customs, or rather Absurdities amongst them, which they keep as the most profound Secret; that they never will acquaint any of the *Christians* with the Knowledge thereof, notwithstanding the many Methods used, such as making them Drunk, the promise of Rewards, &c. but to no purpose, for so subtile and cunning are they, that it is next to an impossibility to make them discover it, or to fathom out their secret Designs, whether they do this because they are sensible of their own Weakness in practicing them, or any other Motive they may have to induce them so to do, is known to none but themselves, let other Writers pretend what they will to give a true Notion of their Worship; you shall see them amongst their *Idols* and dead Kings in their *Quiogoson* or *Charnel House,* where the Bones of the deceased are laid (a Custom like this we read of practiced by the *Indians* in the Kingdom of *Pegu* in the *East Indies*) into which place the King, with the *Conjurers* and some few old Men are admitted to go, but as for the young Men, and the chiefest Number of the *Indians,* they are kept as ignorant of what the Elders are as any

*European,*

*European,* let him be in ever so great Esteem and Friendship with the King or great Men; he is not admitted to enter the House at those times, or to have Knowledge of their Secrets or what they are doing.

They are generally very ignorant of the first Creation of Man, or from whence they came, for some say they are descended from an old Man who came thither in a Boat, which they call a *Canoe;* but whether this was before or after the Flood, they can give little or no satisfactory Account. Others (with whom I have frequently conversed on that Head) believe that they are made out of the fine white Mould or Earth, and that the *Blacks* or *Negroes* are formed out of the black Dirt and swampy Earth; this was all that I could ever learn from them on that subject. They all believe that the World is round; and that there are two Spirits, the one Good and the other Bad. The Good one they reckon to be the Author and Maker of all Things, and say that it is he that gives them the first Fruits of the Earth, and teaches them to Hunt, Fish, and be wise enough to overcome the Beasts of the Wilderness, and all other Creatures, that they may be assistant unto Man. To which they add, that the *Quera,* or *Good Spirit* has been very kind to the *Europeans,* in teaching them how to make *Guns* and *Amunition,* besides a great many other Necessaries that are helpful to Man, all which they say will be delivered to them when the Good Spirit shall think fit: They also believe the Good Spirit does not punish any one in this World or that to come, but that he delights in doing good to Mankind, in giving them plenty of the Fruits of the Earth, instructing them to make many useful Things, and all the Advantages and Pleasures they enjoy. But as for the Bad Spirit (who lives separate from the Good one) they say it is he that torments them

Bbb                                                    with

with Sickness, Disappointments, Losses, Hunger, Cold, Travel, and all other Misfortunes that are incident to human Life, whom they worship to appease his Wrath. As to what concerns their Treatment in the other World, I shall treat of it hereafter, when I come to make mention of their Notions concerning *Heaven* and *Hell.*

Though the *Indians* are very resolute, and die with a great deal of Courage and Bravery, in the Hands of their Enemies; yet I have known them tremble, and be in the greatest fear and agony imaginable, when they had sentence of Death pronounced against them by the *English,* for Capital Crimes, whereof they have been sometimes guilty. Whether this Fear was owing to their not being put to death by their common Enemies, or being delivered up to the *English* by their own Nation, I cannot determine. I am certain they meet with more Favour from the *Christians,* than they do amongst themselves, who only hang them on Trees for their Offences. These *Savages* sometimes shew the greatest Reluctance and Concern imaginable to deliver up these Offenders to the *Europeans,* especially if he was a great Warrior or Hunter amongst them; yet for their own safety they will comply, and put the Offender into their Hands, to be dealt with according to their Laws.

These Kings have been known to make offers to the *Christians* by way of Exchange for an Innocent Person to die in the room of the Guilty: so fond are they to preserve their own Men if possibly they can; but these being Requests contrary to the *Christian* Principles, are never granted or complied with.

When a Criminal is hanged, the King with the Relations of the deceased come and pull him by the Hand and say Words to this purpose: *Thou wilt never play any more*

*roguish*

*roguish Tricks in this World, and whether art thou gone now to play thy Tricks.* When the Criminal is dead and taken down, they are perfectly easy, and free from all manner of Concern about him, though a few Days before so unwilling to deliver him up; they generally end these Tragedies in Feasting and a fit of Laughter, which puts an end to their Mourning for the loss of their Friend, and never think of the deceas'd more.

Their Burials are different from each other, every Nation having peculiar Methods of their own; some of which I shall here give an account of, *viz.* They raise a Mole of Earth, the Mould whereof they take great pains to make smooth, and is higher or lower according to the Dignity of the Person deceas'd, whose Monument it is, over which there is a Shade or Umbrella, made Ridge-ways, like the Roof of a House, this is supported by nine Stakes or small Posts driven into the Ground, the Grave being about six or eight Feet in length, and near four Feet in breadth, about which they hang *Gourds, Feathers,* and such like Trophies placed by the dead Man's Relations, in respect to him in the Grave. The other parts of the Funeral Rights are thus: As soon as the Party is dead, they lay the Corps upon a piece of the Bark of a Tree in the Sun, seasoning or embalming it with a small Root beaten to Powder, which they have in plenty, but will never discover to the *Europeans* where it grows, it looks as red as *Vermillion,* which they mix with *Bear's-oil,* to beautifie and preserve their Hair. After the Carcase has lain a Day or two in the Sun, they remove and lay it upon Crotches made for that purpose to support it from the Earth; they anoint it all over with the above-mentioned Oyntment made of the *Red Root* and *Bear's-grease;* when this is done, they cover it all over very exactly with the Barks of the

*Pine.*

*Pine,* or *Cypress* Tree, to prevent the Rain falling upon it, and other injuries of the Weather; frequently sweeping the Ground very clean about it. Some of his nearest Relations bring all the Temporal Estate he was possest of at his Death, such as *Guns, Bows* and *Arrows, Beads, Feathers, Deer Skins, Matchcoats,* and the like, wherewith they adorn the Grave. The nearest Relation is the principal Mourner, being clad in Moss (that grows upon Trees) after a very odd and strange manner, with a Stick in his Hand, keeping a mournful Ditty for three or four Days, his Face being made as black as a *Negroe* with the Smoak and Soot of the *Pitch Pine,* mingled with *Bear's-grease;* during this time he tells all the Spectators that approach near him, or pass by, who the deceased was, and what great Feats he performed in his life time, all tending to the Praise of the defunct.

When the Flesh grows Mellow, and cleaves from the Bones, they take it off and burn it, making the Bones very clean, and anoint them with Ointment, wrapping the Scull up very carefully in a Cloth artificially woven of *Possum's Hair* or a dressed *Deer Skin,* which they every Year or oftner, cleanse and anoint with the *Red Oyntment,* by these Means they preserve them for many Ages; they likewise carry them from place to place as they remove their Dwellings; that it is common to see an *Indian* in the Possession of the Bones of his Grandfather, Father, or some Relation of longer Antiquity.

They have other sorts of Monuments or Tombs for the dead, as where one was slain, in that very Place they raise a heap of Stones, if any are to be met with in the Place, if not, with Sticks, to his Memory; that every one that passeth by that place augments the Heap in respect of the deceas'd. Some Nations of these *Indians* have great rejoycing and Feasts at their Burials.

There

There are other Nations who differ from the former in burying their Dead: When one of them dies, the greater he was in Dignity, the more Expensive is his Funeral, and performed with the greater Ceremony: When a King dies, they bury him with a great deal of Solemnity; (according to their Method) upon his Grave they set the Cup wherein he used to drink out of, about the Grave they stick many Arrows, weep and fast three Days successively without ceasing; all the Kings who were his Friends make the like Mourning, in token of the Love they had for him; they cut off more than the one half of their Hair, the Women as well as the Men: During the space of six Moons (so some Nations reckon their months) there are certain Women appointed which lament the death of the King, crying with a loud Voice three time a Day, *viz.* Morning, Noon, and in the Evening. All the goods of the King are put into his House, and then they set it on Fire wherein they consume all. They likewise bury the Body of the *Priests* or *Conjurers* in their Houses, which they set on Fire with all the Goods.

For it is to be observ'd, notwithstanding these People are so very illiterate and bred after such a Savage manner: Yet they have as great regard and respect for their Kings and great Men, as any People to be met with. When any of these great Men dye, their methods in their Burials are different from the former, for the first thing that is done is to place the nearest Relations nigh the Corps, who Mourn and Weep very much, having their Hair hanging down their Shoulders in a very Forlorn manner. After the dead Person has lain a Day and a Night upon their Hurdles made of Canes, commonly in some out House prepared for that purpose. Those that Officiate about the Funeral go into the Town, and the first young Men they meet with that have

*Blankets*

*Blankets* or *Match-coats* on, which they think fit for their turn, they strip them from their Backs, who suffer them so to do without any manner of resistance; this being common amongst several of their Nations; these they wrap the dead Bodies in, and cover them with two or three Mats, which the *Indians* make of *Rushes,* and last of all they have a long Web of woven *Reeds* or *Hollow Canes,* which is their *Coffin,* and is brought round the Corps several times and tyed at both ends, which indeed looks very decent, and well amongst these Savages.

Then the Corps is brought out of the House into their Orchard of Peach Trees, where another Hurdle is made to receive it, about which come all the Relations and Nation that the dead Person belong'd to, besides several other Nations in alliance with them, they all sit down upon Mats on the Ground, spread for that purpose, every one seemingly dejected for the loss of their deceas'd Friend and Countryman, but more especially the Relations.

Things being thus accomodated, their Priests or Conjurers appear, and after having commanded their Attention, and every one is silent, he pauses for some short time, then begins to give an Account who the deceased Person was, how stout a Man he approved himself, how many Enemies and Captives he had kill'd and taken, how strong, tall, and nimble he was, that he was a great Hunter, a lover of his Country, and possessed of a great many beautiful Wives and Children; which is esteemed the greatest of Blessings amongst them, in which they have a very true Notion. Thus this Orator runs on highly extolling the dead Man for his Valour, Conduct, Strength, Riches, good Humour, and even enumerating his Guns, Slaves, and all he was possest of when living. After

this

this he addresses himself to the People of that Town or Nation to whom the deceased belonged, and bids them supply his Place by following his Steps, who he assures them is gone into a Country (which lies a great way off in this World, that the Sun visits in his ordinary Course) where he shall meet with all his Relations and Friends who are gone there before him, that he shall have the enjoyment of handsome Women, great store of *Deer* to hunt, and never meet with Hunger, Cold or Fatigue, but every thing to answer his Expectation and Desire.

This is the Heaven which they propose to themselves, but on the contrary, for those *Indians* that are Lazy and Thievish amongst them, bad Hunters, and no Warriors, nor of much use to the Nation, to such they allot in the other World, or the Country that they are to go to, Hunger, Cold, Fatigue, Trouble, old Ugly Women for their Companions, *Snakes,* and all sorts of Nastiness for them constantly to feed upon; after this manner they describe their *Heaven* and *Hell.*

After all this Harangue, he amuses the People with some of their traditions, as when there was a violent hot *Summer,* or very hard *Winter,* when any notable distemper rag'd amongst them, when they were at War with such and such Nations, how victorious they were, what were the Names of the *War Captains,* and many other things of Antiquity; and to prove the times more exactly, he produces the Records of the Country, which are a parcel of *Reeds* of different lengths, with variety of distinct markes, and Notches, known to none but themselves, (by which they seem to guess very exactly at accidents that happen'd many Years ago, nay two or three Ages or more).

They

They likewise give an Account that in the Year 1608, there was such a hard *Winter* in *North-Carolina,* that the great Sound was so Frozen, that the *Wild Geese* and other Fowl came into the Woods to eat *Acorns,* that they were so tame (I suppose through want) that they kill'd abundance in the Woods by knocking them on the Head with Sticks, and it is very strange how exactly one Nation will agree with another as to the time when these things happen'd, having no manner of Records to guide them but these bits of Sticks.

But to returne to the dead Man, when this long Tale is ended by the *Conjuror* that spoke first; perhaps a second begins another long story, a third, and fourth, if there be so many of these *Priests* or *Doctors* present, which all tell partly one and the same thing, at last the Corps is brought away from the *Hurdle* to the *Grave* by four young Men, attended by the Relations, the King, old Men and most part of the Nation.

When they come to the *Sepulchre* which is about six Feet deep, and eight Feet long, having at each end (that is at Head and Feet) a *Light-wood* or *Pitch Pine-fork* driven close to the sides of the *Grave,* firmly into the Ground (these two *Forks* are to contain a *Ridge Pole,* as I shall presently describe) before they lay the Corps into the *Grave,* the bottom is covered two or three times over with the Barks of Trees, then they let down the Corps (with two *Belts,* that the *Indians* carry their Burthens with) very leisurely on the said Bark, then they lay over a Pole of the same Wood into the two *Forks,* having a great many Pieces of *Pitch-Pine-logs* about two Feet and a half long, they stick down one End of them in the sides of the *Grave,* and the other End lies on the *Ridge-Pole,* that they decline like the Roof of a House, being thus placed, they cover them (many double) with

Barks

Barks of Trees, and throw the Earth thereon that was taken out of the *Grave,* and beat it down very firm: By this means the dead Body lies as in a *Vault,* nothing touching it, which I esteem a very decent way amongst them, having seen several *Christians* buried without the tenth part of that Ceremony and Decency.

As soon as the Flesh begins to cleave from the Bones, they take up the Carcasses and scrape them clean, which they joint in the nature of a *Skeleton;* afterwards they dress them up in pure white *Deer Skins,* and deposite them amongst their Kings and Grandees in their *Quiogozon,* which is their Royal Tomb, or Burial Place of their Kings and *War Captains.* This is a large and magnificent Cabin amongst them (according to their way or method of Building) raised at the publick Charge of the Nation, and maintained in due form and neatness. About seven Feet high is a Floor or Loft, whereon lye the Bones of all the Princes and Great Men that have died for several hundred Years past, attired in the *Dressed Deer Skins,* as I have before Remarked. No Person is allowed to have his Bones lie in this *Quiogozon* or *Charnel House,* and to be thus dress'd, unless he gives a good Sum of their Money to the Rulers for Admittance.

It is to be observed, that if they remove to any part of the Continent, they seldom fail to carry these Bones along with them, though the tediousness of their short daily Marches keep them never so long on their Journies. They reverence and adore this *Quiogozon,* with all the Veneration and Respect that is possible for such a People to discharge; they had rather loose all they are possessed of than have any Violence or Injury offered thereto; by this we may see what a Respect they have for their deceas'd Ancestors.

They differ some small matter in their Burials from each other, some burying right upwards, and some otherwise, as I have before intimated; yet for the most part they all agree in their Method of Mourning, which is to appear every Night, or oftner, at the Sepulchre, and weep and howl after a dismal manner, having their Faces daubed over with *Light-wood-Soot,* and *Bear's-oil,* which makes the Face as black as *Oil* and *Lamp-black* could do. In this black Figure they remain for a Year or longer, according to the Dignity of the deceas'd.

If the deceas'd Person was a Grandee, such as a *King* or *War Captain,* and the like, to carry on the Funeral Ceremonies with greater Formality and Pomp, they hire People to cry and lament over the deceas'd: There are several Persons of both Sexes that practice this for a livelyhood, and are expert at shedding abundance of Tears, and howling like a Parcel of *Wolves,* or distracted People in *Bedlam;* by this means they discharge their Office with abundance of Art, and great Applause from the *Indians.* These People regarding those kind of Performances or Ceremonies very respectfully, looking upon them as Rights justly due to the deceas'd.

Their Women are never accompanied with these Pomps or Ceremonies after Death; and to what World they allot that Sex, I could never learn, unless it be to wait on their deceas'd Husbands, or to be metamorphosed into those pretty and ugly Women in the other World or Country where the *Indian* Men expect to go after death, which I have before made mention of. Yet these Women have more Wit than some of the *Eastern* Nations (as we are informed) who sacrifice themselves to accompany their Husbands in the other World, which the former never do. It is the deceased Person's Relations by Blood, as his Sons, Daughters, Brothers,

Sisters,

Sisters, Uncles, Cousins, that mourn in earnest; the Wives thinking their Duty discharged, and that they are become free when their Husbands are Dead, all their Care being to look out as fast as they can for another to supply his Place.

Thus I have given the most exact Account of the *Indians* of *Carolina* Conjuring over the *Sick, stolen Goods,* and the Nature and Manner of burying their dead. I shall therefore make a small Degression, to inform my Readers with the manner of our Travelling up to the *Charokee Mountains,* having already set forth the many and different Observations we made in this spacious Country, and then proceed to the *Indian Distempers;* some of which I have been Eye-witness to.

The latter end of *February, Anno. Dom.* 1730, we set out on our intended Journey, being in Number Ten *White Men,* and Two *Indians,* who served for our Huntsmen and Interpreters. Having provided a sufficient quantity of *Fire-Arms, Amunition, Horses,* two *Mariners Compasses, Rum, Salt, Pepper, Indian Corn,* and other Necessaries, we began our Journey; and after we had past the *Christian Plantations,* our Accommodations were as follows: All the Day we were diverted with variety of beautiful and strange Objects; in the Evening we encamped an Hour before Sunset, tyed our Horses to Trees near us, which we made the *Indians* climb up to procure a sufficient quantity of *Moss* for their Food, and to make Beds for us to lie upon, which was generally under the shade of some large Tree: Our next Business was to send the *Indians* to Hunt; our Care in the meantime was to make a large Fire of the broken pieces of Timber which we found in plenty lying dispersed up and down the Woods;

this

this we piled up in order to continue burning all Night, which prevented all manner of Wild Beasts and pernicious *Insects* being troublesome, or approaching us or our Horses.

As soon as our *Indians* had discharged one or two shots, and given us a signal of their Success by *Hollowing,* we immediately dispatched some of our Party to their assistance, to bring home the Game they had killed; for they seldom return'd without more than a sufficient quantity of *Venison, wild Turkies,* and other Game for the support of all our Company, during our whole Journey. Being thus provided with Provisions, our next business was to perform our *Cookery,* which consisted chiefly in *Roasting* and *Broiling,* according as each Person was disposed. When Supper was ready, and a sufficient quantity of *Indian* Corn roasted, which we made use of instead of Bread, we sat down upon the Ground, and generally eat with a good Appetite, the Air being no where better or purer than near the Mountains. In this manner we supped each Night, our Kitchen Furniture being a *Wooden Spit,* and our *Table, Dishes* and *Trenchers* the Barks of Trees. Supper being ended, we made our *Punch* (the Bowl being a large *Gourd*) which we distributed equally to each Person a good Harmony being observed amongst us during the whole Journey. At Night when our Company were disposed to rest, we made our Beds of *Moss* near the fire, where we slept comfortably, keeping a constant Watch by turns every four Hours. Thus we enjoyed ourselves 'till our arrival at the Mountains, and what continually rendered our Journey more agreeable. was the beautiful Prospect of the Country, being adorned with Woods, Savannas, spacious Rivers, together with various kinds of *Beasts, Birds, Fishes,* &c.

It would not be proper to trouble the Reader with the Adventures of each Day, and the many Observations we made

therein,

therein, these being sufficiently set forth already: Let it suffice to inform them, that after fifteen Days Journey, we arrived at the foot of the Mountains, having met with no Human Specie all the way. It seems upon our first arival we were discovered by a Party of the *Iroquois Indians,* who, as I said before, are very powerful, and continually at War, wandering all over the Continent betwixt the two Bays of *Mexico* and *St. Lawrence.* As soon as they had discovered us they disappeared, (as we were afterwards informed) and gave Notice thereof to their King, who sent immediately an Ambassador, or one of his Attendants, painted as red as *Vermillion,* together with a strong Party of his Men, armed with Bows and Arrows.

When they appeared the second time, the Retinue halted at about half a Mile distant from us and the Ambassador attended with one Person, came to the place where we were (which was in a large *Savanna*) with a green Bough in his Hand, and gave us to understand that he was sent to us by Order of his King, who desired to know whether we came for Peace or War, or what other Business had brought us to those Parts; In such like Speeches he accosted us. We assured him by our *Indian* Interpreters, that we were come in a friendly manner, with no other Design than a Curiosity of viewing the Mountains. When we had thus satisfied him he sat down with us, and dispatched the other Person that attended him, to acquaint the King with the Reasons of our coming.

During his Absence, we entertained the Ambassador with *Punch,* and made him a Present of some few Toys, which he accepted of, and was highly pleased therewith. About four Hours after the Messenger returned, whom the Ambassador received at a little distance from us, where they discoursed for

some

some time, and at his return told us, that the Message from the King was, to desire us to make him a Visit, assuring us at the same time of his Friendship. This Message occasioned several Debates to arise amongst us, concerning the consequence that might attend it; we seemed unwilling to go, which he perceiving, assured us in the strongest Terms of our safety, and the Sincerity and Friendship of the King. At length, rather than incur his Displeasure (notwithstanding we were determined to sell our Lives at the dearest rate, if we met with any opposition) we complied, and arrived about six o'Clock at the *Indian* Town (attended with the Guards that came with the Ambassador, who marched at some distance from us) and were conducted to the State House, where the King was seated with his *War Captains* and *Councellors,* who got up and placed us next to him; after we had paid our due acknowledgements to him, and made him some Presents, he then began to enquire the Reasons of our coming thither, and among other things, *How his Brother did,* meaning the Governor; and many other such like Speeches passed between us. After we had satisfied him in each particular that he demanded, he bid us welcome, shaking Hands with each of us; assuring us of his Friendship, and the great Regard he had for those of our Nation. The few Presents we gave (which were *Knives, Glass Beads, Punch,* and the like) had made so favourable an Impression in the Breast of his Majesty, and all his Councellors, in our behalf, that the King's Orders were issued out immediately, strictly charging all his Subjects to treat us in the most friendly manner, and supply us with whatever we had occasion for during our Pleasure to stay amongst them. After all these Speeches were ended, towards Night we were dismissed, and conducted to one of the King's Houses (being an Apartment prepared

for

for us) where we lay upon Benches, with the Skins of Beasts for our Covering; and this was the best Lodging we met with since our departure from the *Christians.* They took particular Care of our Horses, and treated us with all the good Nature possibly to be expected from them, supplying us with sufficient quantities of Provision, such as *Venison, Wildfowl, Fish,* and various Kinds of dried *Fruits, Pulse,* and *Water,* no stronger Liquors are to be met with amongst these People.

The King's Houses are partley in the Center of the Town, the rest of the Buildings being erected in a confused Order, no regular Streets, Shops, or even Handy-craft Trades, are to be met with amongst them.

The news of our arrival brought prodigious Numbers of Men and Women to us, as also Boys and Girls, who were stark Naked; these would come and touch our Cloaths, and view us with admiration, having I am satisfied, never had an opportunity to behold any thing of this Nature before. The King diverted us every Day with Men and Women Dancing, shooting with Bows and Arrows, their Warlik Exercise, and several other kinds of Diversions, wherein he imagined we took any Pleasure. Finding our selves thus in favour with the King, the first request we made was, that we might have leave to see the *Quiogozon,* or *Charnel House,* which was the largest of that Nature we had ever beheld: He easily complied with our Request, but with a strict Charge, that we should do no hurt, either to the Bones, or any other thing that we should observe there.

Two Days after our Arrival, we requested the King to have Liberty to depart, in order to view the Mountains, which he seemed very unwilling to comply with, pressing us to continue longer with him, urging many Arguments to persuade

us;

us; and that we had not as yet sufficiently refreshed ourselves after our late Fatigue. But we assured him that our Governor had given us strict Orders at our Departure, to be as expeditious as possibly we could in our return home. These Considerations at length moved him to a compliance sooner than he intended. But the chief Reason of our departing so soon was, that if we had remained there much longer, we should be deprived of all our *Rum,* which was a great support to us in this long and tedious Journey. The King then offered us a Party of his Men to guard us in the Mountains, least we should be molested by any *Indians* that might be Hunting in them, during our stay there. We most gratefully returned him our due Acknowledgments for his kind offer, and the many Favours he had already conferred upon us, and most humbly beg'd to be excused, which he readily granted us.

Having thus obtained our License of Departure, we made him a Present of a Bottle of *Rum,* in lieu whereof he gave us *Indian Corn, Venison,* and some dried *Fruits,* for our support in the Mountains, where Provisions are scarce. All things being prepared as usual, we set out the next Morning about six o'Clock, continuing our Journey still *Westward:* The King and his Guards conducted us about half a Mile, wishing us Health, and intreating us at the same time, to make him a Visit at our Return, which we did not, taking a Tour another way.

About the Evening we approached to the top of one of these Mountains, where we refreshed, being all in perfect Health. Here we had the greatest difficulty to be supplied with Moss for Provision for our Horses, but after some time searching, we found what was sufficient for them; then making a great Fire, and our Beds for that Night of the withered

Leaves

Leaves of the Trees, which we gathered for that Purpose. The next Morning very early having refreshed ourselves, we set forward, and in the Evening got on the other side of the first Ridge of Mountains into a most beautiful Valley, adorned with *Woods, Savannas,* and a very rich Soil, here we encamped this Night, being the longest Days Journey we made from our first setting out, by reason that we were destitute of Water in these barren places, for our selves and Horses, only what we met with by chance in the hollow parts of the Rocks, which our Horses would hardly drink.

The next Morning we set forward with a great deal of Chearfulness, having plenty of Water, and all manner of Provisions. In this Days Journey we discovered an *Indian* in the solitary parts of the Woods, but as soon as he espyed us, he fled, notwithstanding we made signs to him to come to us, but in vain, for he quickly vanished out of our sight, that we could not learn what Nation he belonged to, or whether there were any more with him in those Parts. After two Days Journey we arrived at another Ridge of rocky Mountains, with large Trees in several Places, but little or no Pasture like the former, but much higher, having a beautiful Prospect of large Woods and Forrests, as far as our sight would permit. From this Mountain we returned, making our Journey Eastward; meeting with nothing worthy of Observation, but what we have already made mention of; and in thirty two Days, to our great Satisfaction, arrived amongst the *Christians,* our Company being all in perfect Health, having had no Misfortune all the way, but the loss of one of our Compasses.

As there are in this Country many poysonous Herbs and Creatures, so the *Indian* People have excellent Skill in ap-

plying

plying effectual Antidotes to them; for *Medicinal Herbs* are
here found in great Plenty, the *Woods* and *Savannas* being
their *Apothecary's Shops,* from whence they fetch *Herbs,
Leaves, Barks of Trees,* with which they make all their
Medicines, and perform notable Cures; of which it may not
be amiss to give some Instances, because they seem strange,
if compared with our Method of curing Distempers. They
have a certain Method in poysoning their Arrows, and they
will temper them so as to work slow or swift as they please;
they can make it so strong, that no Art can save the Person
or Beast that is wounded with them, except it be by their
Kings and Conjurers, their young Men being ignorant of it.

They use Sweating very much, especially if violent Pains
seize the Limbs, or any other part of the Body, which is
performed by certain Vegetables which they are well acquainted with; for as soon as they are afflicted with these
kind of Disorders, they take Reeds or small Wands and bend
them, with these they make little Huts, covering them with
*Deer Skins, Blankets,* or their *Matchcoats,* and the like; they
have other Sweating Houses built in shape like large Ovens;
they have Fires made not far from these Sweating Houses,
wherein they heat Stones, or (where these are wanting) the
Bark of Trees, putting them into these Stones, which occasion an extraordinary Heat, by the help of which, and the
Herbs which are boiled in a Pot, they sweat very plentifully.
They likewise use Bathing often in the Waters for the like
Disorders.

They never miss curing most kinds of *Cutaneous Eruptions* by the Plants that are produced in this Country: They
infallibly cure *Scald Heads,* which they chiefly perform with
Oil of *Acorns,* but from which *Oak* I never could be rightly
informed, they being very secret in what they know. They

cure

cure Burns beyond Credit; I have seen of these Wretches burnt in their Drunkenness after such a miserable manner, that in all Appearance they could not live; yet I have seen them cured in a very short time, contrary to all expectation; that they have been capable of going abroad in ten or twelve Days. I have known others to be miserably burnt with Gun Powder, which they have cured in a short time; but by what Ingredients they perform these speedy and wonderful Cures is known to none but themselves. They seldom or never make known any Secrets of this Nature to the *Europeans,* but are very ready to serve them upon such Occasions, if required, for a small Gratuity.

What is worthy of Observation is, that amongst all these *Indians* there are no running inveterate *Ulcers* to be met with, neither do their Wounds turn to a *Gangrene,* and they are very expert in healing all manner of *green Wounds* and *Dislocations,* which they perform so speedily, that I dare boldly say, that they are the greatest Artists in these kind of Performances of any People in the known World.

There was a Planter in *North Carolina* who had a grievous *Ulcer* in his Leg for many Years, which was deemed incurable by all those that beheld it; and many attempts were made by the best *Christian* Artists in that Country to perfect the Cure, but all to no purpose, for his Leg still grew worse and worse; at last he was prevailed upon to apply himself to one of those *Indian* Doctors, who performed the Cure in a very short time for the value of three Shillings *Sterling,* though it had cost him above one hundred Pounds before to little or no Purpose.

The *Indian* Doctor performed this Cure after the following manner; first he made a strong Decoction of the Bark of

the Root of *Sassafras,* in which he bathed the Patients Leg
very well, then he took the rotten Grains of the *Maiz,* or
*Indian Corn,* well dried and beaten to Powder, and the soft
Down that grows upon the *Turkeys* Rump, with this he
quickly dried up the filthy *Ulcer,* and made a perfect Cure,
of what was thought incurable, to the great Joy and satisfaction of the Planter, who had so long laboured under it.
This I had affirmed to me by the Planter himself, and several
others that were Eye-witnesses to the whole Affair.

The *Pox* is to be met with amongst some Nations of these
*Indians,* being as it is Reported communicated to them by
the *Europeans,* it being a Distemper intirely unknown to
them before their Arrival. By this Disorder, some of them
have lost their Noses, and particularly one of their greatest *Conjurers,* whom I have seen and conversed with; but
whether or no this Distemper was known to them before the
*Christians* came amongst them, I will not take upon me to
decide it, being in no way material to my present Design,
which is only to satisfie my Readers with the Advantages
and Disadvantages that are to be met with in this Spacious
part of the World.

These *Savages* of late cure this Distemper with certain
*Berries* (that grow in this Province) which Salivate like
*Mercury,* notwithstanding they use Sweating and strong Decoctions with it, as they do almost upon every Occasion, and
when they are in the greatest Extreamity of Heat, leap into
the Rivers or Ponds of Water, by which Practice many have
lost their Lives, yet at present it is not sufficient to deter
them from this kind of Practice.

The *Yaws,* is a Venerial Disorder (as I said before) in
all respects like the *Pox,* only it is not attended with a *Gonor-*

*rhœa*

*rhœa* in the beginning, but having all the other Symptoms that attend that Disorder, such as *Cutaneous Eruptions, Nocturnal Pains,* &c. This Distemper of late has been communicated to the *Indians* by the *Christian* Traders, and though it is not very common amongst them, yet some few have lost their Noses by it, and others are become most miserable Spectacles by neglecting it's Cure; at last they make a shift to cure or patch themselves up, and live for many Years after; such Men commonly turn *Doctors* amongst them, and some of these *No-Nose Doctors* are in very great Esteem amongst them. The Juice of the *Tulip* Tree is used by the *Indians* as a proper Remedy for this Distemper.

The *Small Pox* proved very fatal amongst them in the late War with the *Christians,* few or none ever escaping Death that were seized with it. This Distemper was intirely unknown to them before the arrival of the *Europeans* amongst them. Their Method in this, as in all other Fevers, is to run directly into the Water in the extremity of the Disease, which strikes it in and kills most that use that Method.

They use *Scarification* in most Distempers; their chief Instruments are the Teeth of the *Rattle-Snake,* which they poyson with upon occasion. They take out the Teeth of the *Snake,* and suck out the Venome with their Mouth, which they spit on the Ground, and receive no damage thereby; it is of a greenish Colour, as I have frequently observed. These Teeth they keep for the uses above-mentioned, having no Notion of *Lancets,* or other Instrument proper in those Operations.

The *Spleen* is a common Distemper with the *Indians* in this Province, which they cure by burning on the Belly with a *Reed* or *Hollow Cane,* after the following manner: They take the *Cane* and put the End into the Fire where they burn

it

it 'till it is red hot, then they lay the Patient on his Back, and place a piece of thin Leather on his Belly, between the Pit of the Stomach and the Navel, so press the hot *Reed* on the *Leather,* which burns the Patient to that degree, that they ever after have the Impression of the *Reed* wherever it was laid: This Method is sometimes used amongst them for the Belly Ach.

The *Plague* was never known amongst the *Indians* that I could ever learn; yet the *Small Pox,* their continual Wars with each other, their poysoning, and several other Distempers and Methods amongst them, and particularly their drinking *Rum* to excess, have made such great destruction amongst them, that I am well informed, that there is not the tenth *Indian* in number, to what there was sixty Years ago.

They have a kind of *Rheumatism,* which generally afflicts their Legs with grievous Pains, and violent Heats; whilst they are thus tortured, they employ the young People continually to power cold Water upon the part aggrived, 'till such time as the Pains are abated, and they become perfectly easy, using no other Method for this kind of Disorder.

They are never troubled with the *Scurvy,* neither are they afflicted with the *Dropsy, Diabetes, Gout, Stone, Pthisick, Consumption, Asthma,* or *Palsie,* which Distempers are too well known amongst us, and frequently attended with most fatal Consequences. Neither is the *Struma* to be met with amongst them, and many other *European* Distempers too tedious to name.

They have several Remedies which they use for the *Toothach,* which frequently carries off the Pain; but if all their Endeavours should fail, they have recourse to punching out the Tooth, which is done with a small *Cane* placed against it,

on

on a bit of Leather, then they strike the *Reed* and push out the Tooth, this they perform with a great deal of Dexterity, and never endanger the Jaw, which other Instruments are apt to do.

They seldom make use of *Amputation,* except it be to the Captives that they take in War, when they cut off the Feet, which I have mentioned in another Place. But in any immoderate defluctions of Blood, or any other Humour from any part of the Body, they are never at a loss for a speedy Cure.

I never observed any of them to practice *Anatomy,* neither do I believe that they have any Knowledge therein, unless as I observed before, that they make *Skelitons* of their Kings and great Men's Bones. They can colour the Hair Black, though of a Reddish Colour, or any other Colour, which they do with a certain Seed or a Plant that grows in their Plantations. They make use of no Minerals in *Physick,* and very little of Animals, but chiefly depend on *Vegetables,* for all Disorders amongst them. They are well acquainted with the *Spontaneous Plants* that are produced in these Parts of the World; and a Flux of Blood seldom or never follows any of their Operations.

They are scarce ever known to make use of any *Gums* or *Rosins* in their Physick; as for *Catharticks* and *Emeticks,* so much in fashion in *Europe,* they do not esteem or make use of, unless it be immoderate Drinking such vast quantities of their *Yaupan Tea,* and vomiting it up again, this they continue every Morning, or oftner, where they can have this Plant, from which they receive great Benefit, not only in discharging and cleansing the Stomach from the *peccant Humours* there lodged, but likewise by its great *Diuretick* quality which carries off those Humours by the *Ureters,* that

might

might be prejudicial to their Health, and occasion Fevers, Agues, and many other Distempers, which they are not so subject to as the *Europeans;* which I am satisfied is owing in a great measure to their constant use of this Plant, which takes away both Hunger and Thirst for four and twenty Hours.

There is no Plant in these Parts in greater Veneration and Esteem amongst them than this is, and they frequently carry it to the *Westward Indians,* who give *Deer Skins,* and other Necessaries they want for it. They take the Leaves and small Twigs, bruise them in Wooden Mortars, 'till they become of a blackish Colour, and wholly defaced: Then they take and put them into Earthen Pots, over the Fire, till they Smoak, stirring them all the time 'till they are cured: Others take them thus bruised, and put them into Earthen Bowls, under which they put live Coals and cover them with *Youpan* Leaves, 'till they have done Smoaking, often turning them over, then they spread them on Mats and dry them in the Sun or Shade for use.

They commonly in most of their Disorders make use of the Juices of Plants, not out of any Foppery or Fashion, as many *Europeans* and other Nations are often fond of, but purely to relieve and free Nature of the Oppression and Burthen that she labours under.

They neither use *Unguents* or *Fats* in any external Application for Wounds or Ulcers, but they sometimes use the Fat of Animals to render their Limbs more pliable, and when they are weary to relieve the Joints.

The Bark of the Root of the *Sassafrass* Tree is very much used by them, which they generally *Torrefy* in the Embers, and strip off the Bark from the Root, beating it into a Paste, or a Consistance fit to spread, so apply it to the grieved

parts,

parts, which not only cleanses a fowl Ulcer, but after Scarification, being applied to the Contusion or Swelling, carries off the Pain, and asswages the Tumor. Yet these People in general are very careless and negligent of their Health.

In some Places these *Savages* Boyl and Roast their Meat extraordinary well, and eat abundance of *Broath* except those *Savages* whom we call the Naked *Indians,* who never make use of any Soup. These travel from the Banks of the *Messisippi* to War against the *Sinagars* or *Iroquois Indians,* and are commonly too hard for them except they are over power'd by unequal Numbers. These naked *Indians* will lye and sleep in the Woods without any Fire or covering, being inur'd thereto from their Infancy. They are the most hardy of all *Indians* that are known, and run so fast that they are never taken by any other *Indians* that pursue them. Their Enemies say that their Nimbleness and long Wind proceeds from their never making use of any *Broath.*

The Salts that the *Indians* in these parts make use of in their Meat, Bread, and Soup, to give them a grateful relish are *Alkalies, viz,* Ashes made of the Wood of *Hickery* and calcin'd Bones of *Deers* and other Animals. They never eat any *Sallads,* and as for *Pepper,* and *Mustard,* they imagine us to be no better than Madmen to make use of them at our Victuals.

The Vessels that our Neighbouring *Indians* make use of and most other Nations are, Earthen-Pots of several sizes. Their Dishes and Wooden Platters are made of the sweet *Gum Tree, Poplar, Sycomore,* and the like.

Thus I have releated their manner in curing several Distempers; I shall now only mention one strange Account more, which was attested by the Planter himself, and several other credible Persons in those Parts.

There was an honest and substantial Planter in those Parts who was afflicted with a strange and lingering distemper, not usual amongst the *Christians,* under which he emaciated and grew every Month worse and worse; this Disorder continued for some Years, during which time he had made use of the best and ablest *Doctors* and *Surgeons* in those parts, but all to no purpose, for the Disorder still persever'd. In the beginning of this Distemper the Patient was very wealthy, and had several Slaves which he was obliged to sell to satisfie the *Doctors.* But one Day it happen'd, as he and his Wife were comiserating his miserable Condition, and that in all appearance he could not expect to recover, and that Death must speedily put a period to his Days, and then in what misery he should leave his poor Wife and Family, since all his *Negroes* were already gone and dispos'd off. Whilst he and his Wife were thus debating the Misfortunes that in all probability might attend the Family after his Death. An *Indian* happen'd to come into the House, who was well acquainted in the Family, and hearing their Discourse (and having a very great regard and value for the Sick-man from whom he received many Favours) made this Reply to what he had heard them talk off, *Brother,* you have had a long fit of sickness, you have given away your Slaves to the *English Doctors,* what made you do so, and now become Poor? They do not know how to cure you, for it is an *Indian* Distemper that troubles you, and they know not the Nature of it. If it had been a Distemper known in their Country, probably they cou'd have cured you. But had you employ'd me at first, I coud have cur'd you for a small matter without taking your Slaves from you that provided *Corn* and other Necessaries for you, and your Family's support. And yet if you will give me a *Blanket* to keep me warm and

some

some *Powder* and *Shot,* to kill *Deer* with, I will do my best still to recover your Health.

The Poor-man being very much dejected with the Misfortunes that he had already met with, made the *Indian* this reply. I know my Distemper is now past the power of Man to cure, and if our *English Doctor's* cou'd not cure it, I am throughly perswaded that the *Indians* cannot.

But his Wife accosted him in the most endearing and mild terms and told him, he did not know but God might be pleas'd to give a greater blessing to the *Indians* undertaking than he had done to the *English,* and likewise said, if it shou'd please God that you shou'd dye, I cannot be much more miserable by giving that small trifle to the *Indian* which he demands. Therefore I beg of you to take my advice and try him.

At length by the many perswasions and Importunities of his Wife and Family he consented. And when the bargain was concluded, the *Indian* went into the Woods and brought with him several kinds of Roots and Herbs, whereof he made a strong Decoction and gave it to the Patient to drink, and immediately orderd him to go to Bed, adding that it would not be long before he wou'd return again to visit him. The Patient punctually perform'd every thing as he was ordered by the *Indian,* and had not been long in Bed before the Potion that was administer'd made him Sweat after the most violent manner that could be, and during its operation he smell'd so offensively to himself and all those that were near him, that scarce any one cou'd bear to go into the House or Room where he lay.

Late in the Evening the *Indian* comes to visit the Patient with a great *Rattle-Snake* alive (which terrified the Family almost out of their Senses) and told the Sick-man that he

must

must take it to Bed with him, at which the Patient was in
the greatest consternation in the World, and told the *Indian*
that he might as well dye of the Distemper he had, as to be
kill'd with the Bite of the *Rattle-Snake.* To which the
*Indian* reply'd he cou'd not bite him nor do him any harm,
for he had already taken our his Poyson and Teeth, and
shewed him by opening and putting his Finger into the
*Snakes* Mouth, that they all were gone.   At last by many
perswasions and Intreaties of all that were present, he admitted of the *Snakes* company, which the *Indian* put about
the Patients middle and order'd no Body to take it away, or
even to meddle with it upon any account, which was strictly
observ'd, altho' the Snake girded him as hard for a great
while as if he had been drawn in by a *Belt.*   At last he
found the pressure grow weaker and weaker, till by degrees
he felt it not; and opening the Bed the Snake was found
dead, and the Patient thought himself grown much better.
The Indian returned the next Morning to visit his Patient,
and finding the Snake dead, was very much transported, and
told the Sick-man the distemper was dead along with the
Snake, which proved as he said, for the Man very speedily afterwards recover'd his Health, and became perfect well,
and lived for many years after this strange and wonderful
Cure.

And what is remarkable in many parts of this Province
as you travel up towards the Mountains and through the
Woods, when ever you come to any places where the *Indians*
formerly dwelt and had Towns, you shall find abundance of
Flowers with variety of beautiful Colours, of several sorts,
and divers Qualities, and Use; some being Physical others
Poysonous, others for Ornament and sweet *Odor,* which at a
distance have a fine prospect, and look like a beautiful
Flower Garden, the uses whereof the *Indians* are well ac-

quainted

quainted with. I am perswaded that the reason why they took all these pains in planting these Simples was owing to their *Doctor's* Care, that upon all Occasions they might be provided with those Vegetables that were proper for the *Indian* Distempers, or any other use they might have occasion to make of them.

These *Savages* have one of the most diabolical Customs amongst them, that is to be met with in any part of the known World, which they call *Husquenawing* their young Men and Girls. Once a Year, or at farthest, once in two years, these *Savages* take up so many of them as they think are able to undergo this rigid Discipline, and *Husquenaugh* them, which they say is make them obedient and respective to their Superours and inures them to all manner of Fatigues and Hardships, and without it they never wou'd be fit to be their *War-Captains,* or Capable to act in their Councils; by this Method they say their Children have the same benefit as the *European* Children have at their Schools, where they are taught good breeding and Letters. Besides it carries off those Weak and Infirm Bodies that wou'd have been a Burthen and disgrace to their Nation.

This House of Correction, or where they undergo this rigid Discipline, is a large strong *Cabin,* made on purpose for the reception of these young Men and Girles that have not already pass'd these Graduations. The Season of the Year wherein they *Husquenaugh* their youth is always about *Christmas,* at this time they are brought into this House, which is made as dark as any Dungeon, and almost starved during the time they remain there. Besides they give them *Pellitory,* and several intoxicating Plants that make them go raving Mad, they make the most dismal and hidious cries and howlings that human Creatures are capable of expressing, all which continues about five or six Weeks, and the

little

little Meat they are allowed to eat is the nastiest loathsome stuff imaginable. After the time is expired they are brought out of the *Cabin,* which is not in the Town, but at some distance from it, and is guarded by an *Indian* or two, nominated for that purpose, who Watch by turns. When they appear or first come abroad, they are as poor and Meager as it is possible for any Creatures to be, resembling rather Skeletons than living Men; several of them dying under this Diabolical discipline. Moreover they either really are or pretend to be Dumb, and do not spake for a Month after they are out of their Confinement. It is likewise said that after this Discipline is over, they have intirely forgot all the Actions of their past Lives.

These *Savages* are described in their proper Colours but by very few, for those that generally write Histories of this *New World* are such as Interest, Preferment, or Merchandize draw thither, who know no more of the People or Country, than I do of the *Laplanders.* If we will make just Remarks, how near such Relations approach Truth, we shall find few worthy of Entertainment, and many parts of their Works stuft with Invectives against the Government they liv'd under, on which Stage is commonly acted greater Barbarities in murdering worthy Men's Reputations, than all the *Savages* of the *New World* are capable of equalizing, or even imitating. These Authors likewise pretend to various and strange accounts, about them, but their Relations seem much fitter to fill a Novel than a History. I must therefore beg leave of the *Gay Part* of the World, who seem infinitely pleased with such Relations in not gratifying them with the Particulars, which they themselves will give less Credit to every Day as their Judgment ripens.

*Lastly,*

*Lastly,* I shall mention some few Words of the *Indian* Language, together with the *English,* and so conclude this Treatise.

| English. | Tuskeruro Indians. | Pamticoe Indians. | Woccon Indians. |
|---|---|---|---|
| One. | *Unche.* | *Weembot.* | *Tone.* |
| Two. | *Necte.* | *Neshin-nauh.* | *Numperre.* |
| Three. | *Ohs-sah.* | *Nish-woner.* | *Nam-mee.* |
| Four. | *Untoc.* | *Yau Ooner.* | *Punnum-punne.* |
| Five. | *Ouch-whe.* | *Umperren.* | *Webstau.* |
| Six. | *Hone-yoc.* | *Whoyeoc.* | *Is-sto.* |
| Seven. | *Chauh-noc.* | *Top-po-osh.* | *Nominis-sau.* |
| Eight. | *Nec-kara.* | *Nau-haush-shoo.* | *Nupsau.* |
| Nine. | *Wearah.* | *Pack-ic-conk.* | *Weihere.* |
| Ten. | *Wartsauh.* | *Cosh.* | *Soone-noponne.* |
| A Blanket. | *Oorewa.* | *Mattosh.* | *Rooiune.* |
| A Coat. | *Kawhitchra* | *Taus-won.* | *Rummissau.* |
| Englishman. | *Nickrerurouh.* | *Tosh-shonte.* | *Wintsohore.* |
| The Fire. | *Utchar.* | *Tinda.* | *Yau.* |
| A Gun. | *Auk-noc.* | *Gau-hooptop.* | *Wittape.* |
| A Hat. | *Trossa.* | *Mottau-quahun.* | *Intome-posswa.* |
| Indians. | *Unqua.* | *Nuppin.* | *Yau-he.* |
| A Knife. | *Oosocke-nauh.* | *Rig-cosque.* | *Wee.* |
| Rum. | *Onaquod* | *Weesaccon.* | *Yup-se.* |
| Shot. | *Cauna.* | *Ar-rounser.* | *Week.* |
| Tobacco. | *Charho.* | *Hooh-pau.* | *Vu-coone.* |
| A Wife. | *Kateoca.* | *Squaba.* | *Yecau-au.* |

To

To enlarge any more upon this *Indian Jargon,* would be altogether needless, and troublesome to the Reader; they have such a strange way of abbreviating their Speech when they are Debating in their grand Councils, that the young Men do not understand what they say or treat of. It is to be admir'd, what hath occasioned so many different Speeches as they have; for the three Nations whose Languages I have now mentioned, are but a small distance from each other. These Differences in their Speech frequently occasion Jealousies and Fears amongst them, and are often the Motives of their continual Wars with each other; and were it not for these continual Feuds and Animosities amongst themselves, they would be as happy a People, as to this Life, as any upon the Earth.

FINIS

# INDEX.

[The author of this Index is not known. It was not printed with the book, but is a manuscript inserted in the copy of the history from which this reprint is made.]

## ANIMALS.

Bat, 132, 197.
Bear, 110.
Beaver, 121.
Buffalo, 107.
Cat, mountain, 116.
    wild, 117.
Deer, 109.
Elk, 108.
Foxes, 124.
Goat, 55.
Hare, 126.
Hogs, 55.
Horses, 53.
Jackall, 110.
Lion, 110.
Mice, 131.

Minx, 118.
Mole, 130.
Opossum, 124, 125.
Otters, 122.
Panther, 115.
Polecat, 118.
Rabit, 127.
Racoon, 123.
Rat, 129.
Sheep, 54.
Squirrel, 127.
Stags, 109.
Tiger, 114.
Weesel, 129.
Wolf, 119.

## REPTILES.

Alligator, 133.
Frog, 140.
Lizard, 141.
Tortoise, 137.

Tarapin, 138.
Snakes, 142, 151, 397.
Vipers, 149.

## INSECTS.

Ant, 158.
Bees, 154.
Beetle, Horned, 163.
Bots, 109, 127.
Bugs, 161.
Butterflies, 155.
Cantharides, 158.
Caterpillar, 167.
Cockroach, 161.
Crickets, 157.
Earwigs, 159.
Flea, 165.
Flies, 160.
    fire, 157.
    gad, 160.
    sand, 164.

Grasshoppers, 155.
Hornets, 164.
Lice, beetle, 162.
    hog or sow, 156.
Lice, 165.
Ladybird, 158.
Locust, 166.
Moth, 160.
Musquetos, 162.
Scolopenda or gally worm, 167.
Snail, 169.
Sows or hog lice, 156.
Spider, 159.
Teredines or water woodworms, 169.
Tick, 165.

## FISHES.

## VEGETABLES.

## NORTH CAROLINA.

The medicinal qualities of Vegetables and Animals are stated under each individual.

### PECULIARITIES.

## INDIANS.

## INDIAN TRIBES.

## WORDS DEFINED.

# CONTENTS.